MODERN
BONSAI
PRACTICE

MODERN **BONSAI** PRACTICE

501 PRINCIPLES
of Good Bonsai
Horticulture

LARRY MORTON   Featuring Walter Pall bonsai

Foreword and bonsai photography ©Walter Pall, 2016
Images © Shutterstock, pages 22, 37, 39, 40, 42, 48, 52, 55, 57, 59, 61, 65, 67, 73, 74, 91, 98, 99, 101, 103, 106, 107, 108, 125, 136, 143, 161, 175, 196, 202, 203, 204, 207
All other illustrations © Philip Morton, 2016

Printed and bound in the United States by IngramSpark. All rights reserved. Number of pages: 346.

First Printing 2016

ISBN 978-0-692-52139-7

CONTENTS

FOREWORD

Way too many good bonsai artists do not have the success they should have because they never felt the need to thoroughly study horticulture. They think it isn't necessary because there is already a huge body of knowledge available on bonsai. This knowledge was amassed by generations of mostly Asian gardeners over centuries—at least that's the underlying belief.

And we better trust them. Or should we?

In almost every field, a textbook that is more than fifty years old is considered valuable for historical reasons only. To take it literally would mean to not be taken seriously by one's peers. Today, many textbooks that are only five years old are dated already. In bonsai, unfortunately, fifty-year-old textbooks are considered to be the primary source of information and "wisdom."

If one tries to find out about the "truth" in bonsai horticulture, one has to wade through an enormous sea of information and often misinformation. Whatever someone claims to be true will be answered by someone who claims the opposite. So to whom do you listen? Well, most will listen to whomever they think are the experts. Unfortunately, way too often, the assumed experts are just repeating what they know from hearsay. Too often the experts have used the wrong, or at least questionable, practices for too long. Many have been doing bonsai for twenty years or more. Who wants to admit that he did the wrong thing for twenty years? What's wrong anyway? Is it not true that all the experts have had some success?

Yes, it is true. Somehow they all have success, and therefore they all can claim to be right. That's not because they are so smart, but it's because our trees, most of the time, are so tough and so flexible that they can stand all sorts of treatment—even the wrong one—for quite a while.

So how does one figure out who to listen to? I think there are two clear indicators:

1. *Scientific proof.* While it is fashionable in some groups and cultures to doubt the value of science, it really is the basis of our body of knowledge. Some of us likely slept in school during biology class and somehow got away

with it. But if you do serious bonsai, you must have a good understanding of how things work together horticulturally with our trees. There often is an underlying distrust toward scientists, especially if they "know nothing about bonsai." I ask you to sincerely forget about this and finally listen.

2. *Practitioners*. In addition to the scientists, there are the practitioners. So whom do we trust here? Basically it is simple: trust the one who has the best results over the longest period of time; the one who has the healthiest, best-growing trees over many years can not be wrong. If, in addition, his successes can be proven scientifically, then we should stop doubting.

I sincerely hope that the findings in this book will lead to better bonsai everywhere.

WALTER PALL

Walter Pall, a walking bonsai encyclopedia, is the renowned bonsai artist/photographer of all the bonsai images in Modern Bonsai Practice. *You can see more of his pictures at the end of this book and at http://walter-pall-bonsai.blogspot.com.*

ACKNOWLEDGEMENTS

Acknowledgements go to all who read and improved on all or portions of the manuscript, including Dr. Eugene Hill, PhD, plant and soil science; Dr. Brian Jackson, PhD, horticulture (substrate guru at NCSU); Dr. Jeff Gillman, PhD, horticulture; Dr. Larry Mellichamp, PhD, botany; Ken McLaurin, former editor of *Southern Poetry Review*; Jim Doyle, BS, horticulture (bonsai guru at Nature's Way Bonsai); Bob Hampel, White Bear Bonsai; Martin Sweeney, Bonsai Society of the Carolinas; and my beloved wife, Deborah.

Bougainvillea.

FROM THE PLANT'S POINT OF VIEW

Bonsai is horticulture, first and foremost. No matter how beautifully formed, a dead stick in a glob of mud is not bonsai. After the requirements for the living organism have been set, it is time to look to expression.
—Cheever, "The Tableau of Bonsai,"
Bonsai Journal of the American Bonsai Society *(Summer 1992)*

Modern Bonsai Practice is an easy, systematic approach to good bonsai care based on sound horticultural principles. The next ten chapters of *Modern Bonsai Practice* are about good, current, basic bonsai horticulture. Although all subjects are interrelated, any chapter can stand alone and be read out of order.

The last decade or so has brought out a tremendous interest in bonsai. If you are starting out, what information would be more valuable than knowing how your first bonsai respond from their point of view?

Bonsai enthusiasts use living material to pay tribute to nature by expressing the essence of a particular scene or past experience in nature. Before we were introduced to bonsai, we were already appreciating the special beauty of trees, nature, and art. Can you think of a better way than bonsai to satisfy the innate urge we have to represent a tree as living art? The way Arthur Joura, bonsai curator at the North Carolina Arboretum, puts it,

"The world of bonsai is miniature, but the natural world that it evokes is boundless."

Most likely, we would rather be known as good bonsai artists than as good bonsai horticulturists. But both talents add to the success and value of a bonsai.

Design elements include shape, line, color, texture, and space. The design principles include unity, dominance, balance, contrast, and scale. Design principles do not change. As we look at the line of a tree trunk, for example, we instinctively know whether that line follows and communicates the proven principles of good design.

Bonsai emerged as a skill and a craft. Adding proven facts of solid science (principles) to the culture of bonsai created the modern practice of bonsai. The horticulture involved is simply a combination of container growing and plant manipulation.

Knowledge of basic horticulture principles makes for healthy bonsai. You can use proven principles to develop and fine tunc your own practice. Modern horticultural principles are proven scientific truths and cannot change. Principles are supposed to work every time. We'll adapt and modify our horticultural practices according to a proven horticultural principle. Applying someone else's technique or practice to our own bonsai may inadvertently result in an unhealthy plant. Some techniques might work up to a point but may not end up the way they were intended.

No particularly right or wrong practices exist in art or in horticulture. Possible advantages or disadvantages, pros or cons, indications or contraindications, mark the differences of opinions concerning the best bonsai culture. Your practice of bonsai depends on you and where you live. When your bonsai stay happy and healthy, your practices are up to date.

Exceptions do exist for both principles and practices. The advantages and disadvantages in common practices are emphasized here more than any empirical right or wrong answers to growing bonsai.

I wish someone had given me this book when I started in bonsai. Do I follow all the practices in *Modern Bonsai Practice* and do they all apply to you? Not necessarily. Do I follow all 501 horticultural principles? Yes. Do my plants thrive? Yes.

Modern Bonsai Practice uses a few basic horticultural principles I've picked up at the University of Maryland for Ornamental Horticulture, along with over fifty years of horticultural study. Most of that time was in professional horticultural practice. I need to clarify that my own location is in between climatic zones 7 and 8. Use the specific tips given in this book and my location as a foundation to apply or modify that information to where you personally live and grow your own trees.

Growing practices seem somewhat different for bonsai, but basic horticultural principles are the exact same as they apply to gardening or landscaping. While growing bonsai, gardening, or maintaining our landscapes, we follow basic horticultural principles. The process of manipulating a plant to appear older, but on a smaller scale, includes horticultural practices such as branch and root pruning. The science of horticulture has already established proven basic principles for how to prune correctly from the plant's point of view. The science of horticulture also has well-established, proven principles of nursery container production, including proven substrates and fertilizers.

These 501 principles of good bonsai horticulture are not some mysterious secret; rather, they're simple to learn and simple to do. Simpler than you might think.

Most of *Modern Bonsai Practice* contains common knowledge. ***The more you know about the principles of how plants work, the better you can work on bonsai and the healthier they become*** (#1).

The constraints we work with are the size of the container and the size and quality of the plant grown in a relatively controlled environment. We're taking a plant out of its natural environment, but we can't change the plant's basic requirements. Our main challenge is to know what the plant needs and how that particular plant responds to its controlled environment.

When starting out, use small, inexpensive, hardy plants. Growing becomes easier with each bonsai, then intuitive, and, finally, becomes a part of you. Horticulture is doing bonsai not collecting bonsai. From its beginning, and for the life of your miniature tree, you'll be doing bonsai. Horticulture does seem a bit daunting at first. Doing bonsai, as well as any growing of plants, is never finished and seldom perfect. Persistence and patience are the secrets. Enjoy and understand the process and the outcome!

Our domesticated miniaturized trees seem to look better and live longer than their wild cousins. Why is that true? Perhaps we are more attentive to their needs and treat them better. Sometimes we continue doing good bonsai horticulture without knowing what our bonsai need from the plant's point of view. It doesn't require luck. Experienced aficionados of bonsai do good bonsai. Either we're consciously practicing good horticultural principles or our container tree art is tolerating the extreme ranges of the environment we offer them. Most plants shape themselves according to their circumstances. Our bonsai change and survive despite our lack of knowledge, attesting to the plant's considerable tolerance and adaptability.

What if our bonsai do not grow well? Where do we turn in order to get some help? Where does the best information come from—the Internet, a bonsai book, or a bonsai guru? How do we tell the difference between what works and what doesn't? What is right and what is wrong. What is debatable. How many people adhere to tradition? How many follow the tradition of flying in the face of tradition? Tradition and change are not necessarily antagonistically opposite in art or in horticulture.

Start making a list of questions. Ask the why and why not behind every recommendation you find. Are they playing by the rules of science? Is that advice still effective now? Ask Nature why. Be persistent in asking, and eventually you end up with an unanswerable question. We finally realize we don't know everything.

Every once in a while, some useful stuff does break through all the Internet noise. Sometimes we can't find the correct answer to our specific question online. For advice on growing your particular plant, go instead to the horticulture books written by someone in the horticulture industry for plants in your area. The horticulture industry has made tremendous strides in the last fifty years (and even in the last five years). How times have changed!

Sadly, conflicting printed misinformation still abounds. Many published books and magazines do not show positive evidence of the whys or the why nots for good bonsai horticulture. Trying to figure out the practical bottom line out of some published, peer-reviewed scientific research is also difficult. Even .edu sites spread myths.

In *Modern Bonsai Practice*, **key facts are highlighted in semibold italics and numbered from** #1 **to** #501, **noted in parentheses after the stated fact**. The key facts are emphasized and presented in an effort to address a "misunderstanding." A couple facts may be repeated in another chapter to underscore an important point.

"Misunderstandings" are tagged by quotes and highlighted in brown. You can recognize the existing horticultural misunderstandings in *Modern Bonsai Practice* by the 499 "quotations" rephrased in my own words. These quotes are not someone else's exact words. Any phrase you find in quotes is my gentle "Warning, you could have been misled by previous misinformation."

Quotations used in *Modern Bonsai Practice* are not intended to reinforce the quoted misunderstanding or practice. Rather, they are an effort to identify misleading or downright wrong advice or practices. Remember the principles and the correct answers but please forget the misconceptions. The emphasis here is only to identify the false or debatable horticultural practices by tagging them in quotes. Then, facts and explanations follow so you can draw your own conclusions.

Often, the method used here backfires and inadvertently reinforces the existing misinformation. Some previous, highly recommended bonsai practices are highly debatable. Let's not dwell on past issues. Let's discuss a few common practices and then go on to more productive subjects.

I can see the eyebrows raising already! New counter-arguments occasionally strengthen existing views. This is quite all right. There is plenty of room for everyone. The hope here is to produce more light than heat and clear up some ancient misconceptions.

Modern Bonsai Practice is an effort to show more recent accumulated scientific knowledge on good horticulture, validate it as accurate information, and apply it to growing bonsai. The good, basic horticultural information presented here is directed toward the undecided majority. Those enthusiasts struggling to learn and sort out conflicting bonsai information will be more confident and comfortable in enjoying that process. You'll be reminded of why a certain practice works or doesn't work as you tend to your trees.

The challenge in trying to separate the many existing bonsai myths from horticultural facts is difficult. Myths start from a false premise. Confusion is the result.

Horticultural folklore repeats itself as it's rediscovered and presented in a different way at different times. If you discard one way of practicing bonsai, be certain you don't replace it with something worse.

With today's modern science, we can better predict how our bonsai will grow and how they respond to what we do to them. Today's growing practices have shifted significantly since someone started growing plants in pots centuries ago. Gradually, we see bonsai standards becoming more scientifically based. Any of the definitions or principles offered here are horticulture industry standards.

Specific information, along with differing terminology written on bonsai culture, tends to be unnecessarily confusing. We relate to someone's personal approach or practice if his own specific microclimate is similar to ours. Usually, inaccurate information or a misconception needs to be cleared up and corrected before we can understand the correct information. Misunderstandings seem easier to clear up than misconceptions.

No matter where the authority comes from or where the information comes from, keep an open mind. What works in my area of the country might not work in your particular area or for all your particular plants. What is a misunderstanding for me might work in your practice. Sometimes you'll discover several different answers to your bonsai care questions depending on the particular plant species and where you live. The beauty is that the information is here, and you can apply it to your bonsai practice in the way that works best for you.

Man knows more about man than he knows about plants—because man can communicate with man. Can we communicate with our bonsai? Yes, if we can read their language.

Plants are so different from people. Woody plants and their environment are much more complex than man likely will ever know. Still, the process of learning how to keep a bonsai alive is intricate but not a complete mystery. So many plant species and so many growing variables make it seem complicated. Plants do what they do, and they rarely hide secrets.

We can't treat bonsai the same way we treat our houseplants. We do not need to kill forty bonsai in order to learn from our mistakes before we're certified green thumbs. Good cultural practices come not only from other hobbyists but also from professional growers and scientific researchers.

Some seasoned growers' claims may include a sliver of truth, even if those claims seem ludicrous at first glance. This claim, paraphrased from a bonsai book, could be partially true: "You can increase the thickness of the nebari flare by whacking it gently with a hammer." Try it!

Scientific experiments made in a controlled environment at a university don't always work outside the lab. Sadly, some plant labs turn out impractical information when applied to the real world of cultivating bonsai. And some people still propagate the right answers to the wrong questions. Science seems to be driven by big hearts or big pocketbooks. Scientists seem to look for the biggest problems economically and then study those.

How do we decipher and decode the good information from the misinformation, the good products from the useless products? All the many product claims will not be addressed here. Those products come and go faster than the universities can possibly test them all. Products you buy for the care and keeping of your bonsai may not have even been tested to prove any of their claims. I have no vested interest in any bonsai product.

Anyone with a product to sell is an expert for his side of the story and has testimonials (advertisements) that claim to work. New products coming along seem to be merely tweaks on a previous great-selling product. No magic bullet is available to give you the "secret of growing super bonsai." Be especially skeptical of undocumented product claims. Separate products from principles. Separate pseudoscience from science.

The main difference between expertise and technical knowledge is attitude. When you find advice conflicting with your otherwise good experiences and knowledge, err on the side of common sense. Absolutes almost absolutely do not exist in nature—or in knowing how to keep your bonsai thriving. The sole bonsai-ology rule set in stone is: observe how your bonsai respond and adjust for their health.

Recent studies show that we can clear our minds from stress and frustration from taking a walk through nature. Horticultural therapy seems to work well for juvenile delinquents, hardened criminals, and recent retirees, among others. As bonsai aficionados, we get to be involved with nature everyday. Doing bonsai (the verb: to bonsai) helps us feel better about ourselves and do more of the things we enjoy. And we also enjoy the ultimate result of doing bonsai: the bonsai. Warning: learning about and working with bonsai can become addictive.

Excuse me while I go back outside and get my bonsai fix…

Boxwood.

SOIL AND SUBSTRATE QUESTIONS

The next couple chapters are about the two most often misunderstood subjects: soils and fertilizers. Choosing good soils and good fertilizers is not such a complex, mysterious, and expensive process. Let's get those two subjects addressed right away.

Current advice on bonsai soils and fertilizers seems to be based more on spurious wisdom than on science. Factual references to a few guiding horticultural principles can help us learn the plant's side of thriving or surviving. Over the past fifty years, I've had to revise many of my own practices and assumptions when science proved me wrong.

Whether hobbyists or professional horticulturalists, we tend to consider the most important part of a tree to be what we see above the soil line. In this chapter, we look differently at our cultural practices. Consider healthy soil (or growing media) to be the most important part of healthy roots.

OUT OF SIGHT IS NOT OUT OF MIND

Is soil alive or dead? Can I put some of my good garden soil (field soil) in the pot to grow bonsai?

Both is the answer to the first question. In other words, part of the soil does include life but part of it is not living. Beneficial microorganisms feeding on dead roots and other organic matter make soil a living organism.

No is the best answer to the second question. Clay soil in a bonsai pot soon leaves the roots gasping for breath.

Most basic bonsai culture questions eventually use the word "soil." This book refers to soil as field soil in its natural state used for gardening purposes in the ground.

Field soil is the mineral-based top layer of earth found in nature. Soil is composed of approximately 50 percent solids, 25 percent water, and 25 percent air by volume when at its maximum water-holding capacity. Water-holding capacity is when the soil cannot hold any more water against gravity.

When that same volume of field soil is placed in a solid container the percentages change. *A container filled with field soil has no air because the side walls compress and compact all the contents* (#2). When field soil is placed in a bonsai pot and the plant is watered, roots can't breathe. That plant slowly declines and dies from too much moisture.

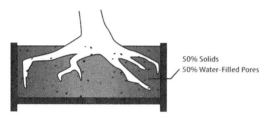

50% Solids
50% Water-Filled Pores

Field soil in the confinements of a pot.

Too much water and not enough air is why we don't use field soil to grow plants in containers. Even the most fertile field soil will not allow enough aeration or water drainage in a pot.

> *Tip*: You can place clayish field soil around the perimeter of a slab planting instead of buying special "muck." In that situation, the field soil has air without the compaction from container walls in a bonsai pot.

Roots require oxygen for respiration (breathing) (#3). It's not so much that substrate has to drain well but that the roots need to have air space.

Many authorities will say the main cause of plant death in a container results from overwatering. Lack of air is the real culprit. Bonsai roots thrive in modern, well-aerated substrate with adequate pore spaces.

Even good garden soil is variable in the quality of its physical, chemical, and biological properties. Field soil can also include a variety of insect and disease pathogens, nematodes, and heavy metals— and, of course, weed seeds. That's why we use an artificial substrate for our potted bonsai with little or no field soil included in the mix.

> *Tip*: If we collect a plant for bonsai that has been growing out in field soil, we can gradually replace some of the compacted field soil consisting of inadequate air spaces with substrate during each consecutive repotting. In the meantime, the temporary substrate requires a short drying-out period between each watering to ensure adequate air spaces for the root system.

■ What Is Substrate?

What are the basic properties necessary for roots to live in optimum condition in a bonsai pot? (Notice we didn't say the "What's the best bonsai soil?" That is entirely your decision.)

The term *substrate* is used in most parts of the world to describe the physical soilless components in a container where the roots grow.

No two fertilizer programs are alike, no two watering regimes are the same, and no two soilless substrates are alike. Most bonsai cultural problems seem to be substrate related. Substrate is the material in a container serving as a reservoir and as the source for root uptake of water and essential elements. Substrate should drain well yet hold some water, as well as keep the pH and salts in a tolerable range.

Try realigning your thinking about the material in which your bonsai grow.

Forget for a bit about ingredients or components. Think more about the physical properties that roots grow in. Focus more on the physical and chemical properties in a substrate that allow the bonsai to grow optimally.

Bonsai roots will adapt to almost any material that provides water, oxygen, and essential elements and is nontoxic to the plant. *Any workable component meeting the roots' cyclical needs of moisture, aeration, and essential elements will be "the ideal substrate"* (#4).

Any substrate also needs to buffer extreme temperatures, chemicals, and other environmental stresses the plant happens to encounter (#5).

Roots do not care about the physical appearance of the substrate (#6). The following substrate qualities allow the roots to function (adapted from the handout "Greenhouse Substrates and Fertilization" by D. Bailey et al. at the Department of Horticultural Science at NC State):

- Substrate should be porous. Air deserves its rank as the most critically important part of every substrate. Roots don't grow in soil or substrate. Roots grow in air spaces. *Air spaces are more for letting air in than allowing water out* (#7). Substrate should not hinder air from drawing in from the top.
- *Roots require a steady supply of oxygen to continually exchange carbon dioxide for oxygen* (#8).
- *Roots require a substrate with a high water-holding capacity* (#9). Water is held in both the small pores between the particles and also inside any porous substrate component. Pots have drain holes so the plant won't drown if sufficient water doesn't drain out through the substrate soon after watering. With common high-density, gravelly substrates, we will flush out anything smaller in size than the gravel. Anything that mixes with water, such as most fertilizers, can flush out of the pot with the next watering.

- *Roots require essential (chemical) elements and photosynthate* (#10). The word *essential* here means essential to plant life. Those essential elements are chemicals or minerals, as in the Periodic Table of Elements. We can interchange the word elements with minerals. Essential elements equals essential minerals. The word *photosynthate* means the product of photosynthesis.
- Roots require a substrate with the capacity to store a reservoir of these essential elements until the roots are able to use them.

Four factors affect the air and water in a bonsai pot:

- The substrate. Field soils may consist of 50 percent pore spaces for the air and water. The smaller-sized components, common in field soils, hold less air and water and compact easily. Modern substrates show potential for more than 70 percent porosity because of larger-sized components.
- The height and shape of the pot. Smaller and shorter pots are subject to overwatering or underwatering because of the perched water table effect (explained later). The height of the pot determines the available pore space after all the water drains out. *Taller pots hold proportionally more air and less water than shorter pots with the same substrate and the same volume* (#11). More undrained water is found in shallow pots than in deeper nursery containers. Square or rectangular pots hold more water than round pots of the same width, height, and length.

Taller pots hold proportionally more air and less water than shallow pots with the same volume.

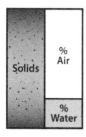
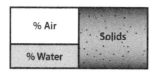

- The handling of substrate before and during potting. *Depending on the material, air space within the walls of the pot could be eliminated due to substrate compaction with tools during potting* (#12).

> *Tip:* Pots can be lightly filled and the excess substrate brushed away from the top after repotting. The substrate should not be packed around the roots because of the risk of eliminating valuable air spaces and smashing the roots. Water is added to the substrate before potting to swell dry components and to reduce the tendency for those components to fill the pore spaces after potting.

- *The watering of the substrate after potting. Both too often and too much watering influence the air and water content even more than the substrate components* (#13).

ORGANIC AND INORGANIC MATERIALS

What are the functions of any organic components we might use as part of bonsai substrate?

Organic materials are composed of dead carbon-based forms. Made with the carbon element, they can compose a large proportion of the small air pores in a substrate. *Organic materials help influence both a high water-holding capacity and a high nutrient-exchange capacity when part of modern substrates* (#14).

Those organic components have the potential to hold on to essential elements already present, such as nitrogen, phosphorus, sulfur, and calcium. Frequent watering of gravelly type substrate with no organic matter will leach most fertilizers right out of the pot. We do a disservice to the roots when our substrate contains no organic matter.

Organic materials were once alive and will attract good, living bacteria, fungi, and nematodes. Yes, 99 percent of the nematodes are beneficial to plant growth. Other microorganisms such as protozoa eat bacteria and help release essential elements in a mineral form available to the plant and essential for its growth.

Organic matter helps resist substrate compaction and probable pH changes (#15). Up to half organic matter by volume in any substrate would be quite beneficial to plants. I am fully aware that within our bonsai community, we may find a few differences of opinions.

"Organic matter inhibits the drainage in bonsai soil."
Fact: **Particle size and pore size determine drainage in a substrate** (#16). Larger textured particle sizes, whether inorganic material or organic material, equals more aeration and

good drainage. Finer particle sizes, whether inorganic material or organic material, equals poor aeration and inhibited drainage.

A substrate of coarse-textured inorganic material mixed with coarse-textured organic material combines to make larger secondary particles called aggregates. An aggregate mix is composed of larger-sized pore spaces. Larger pore size is the key to drainage.

If the substrate mixture contains more than 50 percent organic matter, the total pore spaces will decrease (#17).

Most "potting soil" we buy is way too high in organic matter. The organic matter in some materials such as compost will decompose and shrink in less than six months. "Potting soil" may also have an intolerably low pH.

> *Tip*: Amend any organic material with larger coarse inorganic materials to increase the pore spaces and add to the useful life.

■ What are the functions of the inorganic components we choose to use as bonsai substrate?

Inorganic materials are basically gravel, except for perlite and pumice and its kin. Some gravelly materials have a low nutrient-exchange capacity but can provide good physical properties for the substrate. Those components can help make up a large proportion of the air pockets necessary in a substrate.

Larger-textured inorganic materials help improve aeration and drainage but decrease the water-holding capacity in modern substrates (#18).

A totally sandy or gravelly type of material is not ideal as a bonsai substrate because a large proportion of the water and fertilizer drains out and is wasted (#19).

> *Tip*: Don't add any sand to bonsai substrate. If up to 15% sand is added to a substrate the total volume does not increase. Sand fills the available air spaces at the expense of healthy root growth. If sand is added to compacted clay field soil it makes it more compacted. Sand is for concrete or the kid's sand pile.

■ What can we learn from modern commercial container-growing nurseries and apply to growing our bonsai?

Successful commercial nurseries all over the world produce container plants by the billions. Research scientists grow millions more. We don't need to waste a great deal of time or effort in creating something that already exists. The modern trend is to consider that healthy substrate grows healthy roots, and healthy roots grow healthy plants—in that order of importance.

Professional growers and scientists confirm that an organic/inorganic substrate mix, amended with a synthetic, controlled release fertilizer (CRF) is the simplest, least expensive, and most successful system for optimum growth of plants in pots (#20).

Notice the substrate of the next nursery plant you buy that you want to turn into bonsai. It's practically all organic material. Woody plant growers typically tend to use local sources for their container substrate due to availability and transportation costs. In the western half of the United States, nurseries use fir bark or a commercial potting mix. The eastern half mostly use pine bark or a commercial potting mix.

Professional growers also agree that the person on the end of that water hose controls the profits. The person watering must know the plants and what to expect out of the substrate. Container growers have shifted from thinking about ingredients and products to analyzing substrate properties and parameters.

We think of our bonsai substrate as loose and well draining. Most professional nurserymen would find our typical substrate heavy and high-density. And terribly expensive.

■ Why do modern container nurseries commonly use bark as a substrate component?

Bark, or other cheaper wood substrate (as whole tree chips), is usually readily available and costs less than half as much as sphagnum peat moss. Bark has excellent drainage; can hold on to some essential elements; is relatively slow to decay; retains water; retains its original size under compression; has substantial amount of internal porosity to increase the total air pores when mixed with inorganic materials; is naturally acidic; has low initial fertility; is not phytotoxic if aged and handled properly; has shown to suppress the activity of bad, pathogenic fungi; and is long lasting.

Bark drains well at first; then it eventually starts to break down and hold more water. Roots readily colonize it at about the optimum time when the plant's water demands increase. Fresh bark typically has less than 20 to 30 percent fine particles and may not hold water as well as aged bark with different-sized particles.

Any bark, no matter how fresh, can be processed to have any water-holding capacity or air porosity properties (#21). The process of hammer milling makes fresh bark the same quality as particles that have aged for several months.

"Always use professionally prepared special bonsai mix."
Deciding to purchase a commercial potting mix or to make your own substrate depends on many factors. *Compare the physical, chemical, and biological properties of a commercial product to what properties your bonsai requires to live. (#22).* Think about your cultural practices and local availability of materials.

A specific plant, the local microclimate, and local sources of basic materials will determine what you end up using as a bonsai substrate (#23).

Many brands of substrate products won't have uniform quality and properties from one batch to the next (#24). Many of the components break down in texture size over time, and the physical properties may vary each time you buy a new batch.

For the most part, the bagged all-purpose potting mixes you find at the chain stores were originally formulated to use with vegetable plants or for herbaceous annual or perennial crops to be cultivated inside a controlled greenhouse environment. Those mixes hold far too much water, dry out far too quickly, and hold a pH far too low for us to use on our outdoor woody bonsai.

■ How do plants respond to different potting mixes?

They adapt. Plants care more about what the mix provides to their roots than what product is in a bag of "professionally mixed soil specifically processed for your bonsai." Plants respond to the air and water not included in the bag. If you measure the total

volume in a bag of proper bonsai mix, the largest component is space. Roots respond to pore spaces, not to products.

Why do experts offer different recommendations, such as garden soil, potting mix, pine bark, perlite, vermiculite, expanded clays, crushed lava (scoria), et cetera?

One reason could be that bonsai enthusiasts seem to have been programmed to buy certain products for their bonsai instead of looking at the properties of those products. Plants survived in spite of what product they were growing in. The substrate materials some people provide for their particular plants in their particular parts of the world may work best for them because of their unique climates. Once you've found the substrate that works for you, stick with it.

What other alternatives have been successfully used for substrates?

Pine and other whole wood chips, rice hulls, biochar, growstones (recycled glass), and dairy fiber compost have been thoroughly tested and successfully used as substrate material. Jim Doyle with Nature's Way Bonsai, www.natureswaybonsai.com, adds coconut fiber to his substrate, and reports it is inexpensive and works well.

What about calcined (heat-expanded) clays?

Those industrial clay aggregate products look granular and pottery-like but can increase the water and nutrient efficiency of a substrate without sacrificing plant growth.

Porous and lightweight, they make a durable substrate. It can be reused again and again when repotting because it does not crumble and break down over time. Other clay aggregates, such as Japanese subsoil, have a short useful life and cannot be reused.

The different manufacturers of calcined clays make it easy to compare the different properties of granules, textural sizes, water-holding, and nutrient-holding capabilities.

As an amendment to pine bark, calcined clays have the potential to reduce water usage, create a superior environment in the root zone, improve fertilizer efficacy, improve plant performance and improve the physical and chemical properties of pine bark substrate (#25).[*]

Another report indicated that calcined materials help retain phosphate from leaching out by 60 percent. Water savings were as much as 18 percent overall.[†]

Calcined clays act as a buffer against excess fertilization.[‡] A mix of half commercial pine bark blended with half commercially expanded, calcined clay has been lab tested over several years. Data from those tests confirms optimal percentage water-holding capacity, optimal percentage nutrient-exchange capacity, and optimal total percentage pore spaces and substrate consistency over time. Bonsai roots thrive in those substrate properties during both development and refined stages.

Processed bark easily captures moisture; is not hydrophobic, as you'd expect; and

---

[*] S. Warren and T. Bilderback, "Arcillite: Effect on Chemical and Physical Properties of a Pine Bark Substrate and Plant Growth," *Journal of Environmental Horticulture* 10, no. 2 (1992): 63–69; J.S. Owen et al., 'Finding the Balance: Calcined Clay Rates in Pine Bark Substrates," SNA Research Conference 49 (2004): 73–76.

[†] R. Oguta and K Williams, "Phosphate Sorption of Calcined Materials Used as Components of Soils Root Media Characterized in Laboratory sStudies," *HortScience* 44, no. 2 (2009): 431.

[‡] C. Catanzaro and S. Bhetti, "Use of Arcillite to Buffer Nutrient Loss from Container-Grown Chrysanthemum," *SNA Research Conference* 47 (2002).

also provides excellent root aeration for a few years. Calcined clays, although more expensive, can both hold water and remain stable. Add water, and some of it's still held and available the next day. Add controlled-release fertilizer pellets, and those used pellets are still found in the substrate several years later. The good stuff coated on the pellets might get used up and dumped in a few months' time. At least the plant had several months' benefit from those essential elements coated on the pellets. Chemicals were held on the pellets, the bark, and the calcined clay.

■ Does calcined clay or builder sand add any "nutrients" to a modern substrate?

No, it cannot contribute any essential elements. If locally available, industrial-fired clay aggregate products can increase both water and nutrient efficiency in a bonsai substrate. Adding sand merely adds weight, fills air spaces, and reduces the water-holding capacity.

"The more amendments you can add to your soil, the better it'll grow."

Better practices and easier-to-grow plants contribute more to successful growing than better substrate amendments.

You'll keep discovering several favorite, new, different-colored, and secret recipes for a bonsai substrate. You'll find almost endless materials or mixes to use.

Fact: ***Mixing more ingredients into the substrate is not going to stimulate any more plant growth. Manage the recipe for the properties of a substrate not for its ingredients*** (#26).

You can use one single material, or a mix of ingredients, depending on how much you need to regulate the substrate's water-holding capacity and nutrient-exchange capacity for a specific plant (#27).

Recipes for one-size-fits-all substrate won't work. The recipe varies according to the species grown, temperature, moisture, pot size, and light intensity.

Using both organic and inorganic materials in a mix can have a positive synergistic effect. For growing narrowleaf evergreen bonsai on the drier side, we might use a larger percentage of inorganic components.

Blended with organic components, the inorganic components increase the longevity and stability of the initial substrate mix. In a small bonsai pot, unstable organic substrates and clay aggregates break down relatively quickly over time. Eventually, the roots have too little air or too much or too little water. The finer particles can wash out through the drain holes along with the fertilizer.

■ Is adding humus or peat ever desirable in the modern substrate mix?

Humus includes organic material in an advanced stage of decomposition. Humus may contain foreign material such as fine silt and clay, along with other unwanted material. Considered by researchers to be undesirable in substrates, peat or humus can, however, improve the structure of field soil when planting stock in the ground.

Horticultural-grade sphagnum peat moss has been successfully used for greenhouse plant production but holds too much moisture to be used for cultivating bonsai. Sphagnum peat moss has no oxygen (anaerobic) and no beneficial organisms. Pure peat is organic. Recent studies on clay soils show that peat moss will absorb moisture away from clay particles.

■ When is perlite and vermiculite most appropriately used?

Peat, perlite, and vermiculite are commonly used by greenhouse growers in potting mix.

Their properties make those materials useful in plant propagation.

Perlite and vermiculite are both better than sand in nursery container production. Sand is not added to change physical properties but to add weight to nursery pots in hopes that the pots won't blow over in a high wind.

Perlite can increase aeration and does not easily compress but cannot absorb moisture. Lightweight perlite will float to the top of a coarse bonsai substrate, and the white color might be disagreeable to some people.

Vermiculite has a high nutrient-exchange capacity and is also used in propagation. It compresses and breaks down easily over time.

Both perlite and vermiculite are less appropriate for modern bonsai substrate and more appropriate for propagation or for a greenhouse potting mix (#28).

■ Why can't most plants live on salty (saline) soils?

All water inside the plant contains chemical salts (fertilizers), sugars, and other dissolved substances. Water in the soil or substrate is usually able to diffuse easily into the roots.

If the pure water in a plant was as pure as the water in soil, no water would move into the plant. Water goes where water isn't. With salty soils or overfertilization (too much salts), water pulls out of the roots back into the soil. The plant dehydrates and dies.

■ Are some substrate components hydrophobic (hard to wet)?

Practically all inorganic and most organic materials are hydrophobic when completely dry. Any part of any substrate mix can become hydrophobic when that section, usually the middle core, completely dries out.

■ Should substrate components be pre-wetted or remain dry before blending together or potting?

Any mix with organic matter should be moistened prior to potting to improve its wettability (#29).

That will reduce the tendency of water to stay on a highly compacted surface that was dry when first blended. Avoid overly wet components and most clay particles since they compact easily.

> *Tip*: Moisture improves fresh substrate aeration by slightly swelling the organic components, thus reducing the compaction. Add a little water for the hydration process and then wait a couple hours before potting with organic components.

"Prevent drying out by changing the soil every spring and repotting the plant."
Fact: **There's no need to repot if the roots haven't yet colonized the existing pot** (#30).

> *Tip*: If you notice the foliage wilting on one otherwise healthy bonsai more than on the other plants nearby, try moving that bonsai into a shadier spot. If the substrate still seems to dry out too quickly, make a mental note to add more organic matter to the new substrate for that particular bonsai next time it gets repotted.

■ How do I get my soil and substrate tested?

County extension educators can assist you. Your samples can be sent to a state department of agriculture, a state agricultural university, or a private lab to test your substrate for pH and soluble salts, among many other possible tests. You usually test substrate only if you have unhealthy plants.

The optimal condition for the roots in a bonsai pot is approximately 15 percent solids, 70 percent water, and 15 percent percent air by volume when the substrate is at container capacity (the amount of water held against gravity after drainage) (#31).

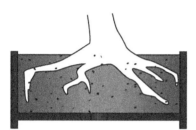

15% SOLIDS
70% WATER
15% AIR SPACE

Roots thrive in modern well-draining substrate.

The recommended physical characteristic range of values for nursery container substrates after irrigation and drainage is: available air space, 10 to 30 percent, and available water content, 25 to 35 percent.*

> *Tip*: Inexpensive all-in-one probe meters are available to monitor the ever changing salt levels, pH, and moisture in the substrate and to check the light levels at the substrate surface or at the top of the plant. Measuring moisture is not always simple or accurate with some garden center-type probe meters.

---

* Southern Nurserymen's Association (SNA), *Best Management Practices: Guide for Producing Nursery Crops*, 3rd ed. (n.p., 2013).

PHYSICAL PROPERTIES

■ What are the optimal physical properties for a bonsai substrate?

The quality of our substrates is the most important part of bonsai culture. Our bonsai industry will probably never get universally accepted standards for the best substrate or the best-quality plant. We can easily improve the physical properties of our mix when we understand where roots like to live.

Physical structure is how substrate holds together, and physical texture is the particle size. They both affect the water and air in the pot. Potted plants care more about the physical texture. Plants grown in the ground are more concerned about the physical structure of the soil.

We have two main concerns about the textural properties of any substrate: 1) ensuring the roots are growing in the right amount of porosity, or pore spaces, and 2) ensuring the same physical texture maintains adequate porosity over a few growing seasons.

Roots grow in pore spaces between and within substrate particles. Pore space is determined not only by the size of particles but also by the amount of substrate compaction. Root hairs only infiltrate pore spaces where they can find water and air.

Root hairs and fine mineral particles are invisible to the naked eye and completely lost in gravel-sized substrates (#32).

The average diameter of the aggregate pore size should not be larger than the average root diameter.

The optimal physical properties for a substrate are an adjustment between the available air and the resistance to compaction. Pore space keeps the air. Finer particles keep the water. Stable particles keep the substrate long-lived.

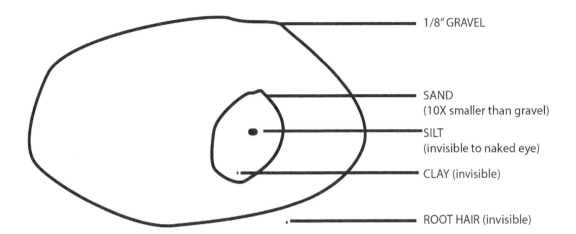

1/8″ GRAVEL

SAND
(10X smaller than gravel)

SILT
(invisible to naked eye)

CLAY (invisible)

ROOT HAIR (invisible)

Substrate components should be fairly stable so the plant won't require constant repotting as the substrate breaks down (#33). The substrate is constantly changing as any organic material decomposes, and most inorganic material eventually breaks down.[†]

Too many small mineral particles hold too much water and not enough air. Small particles can pack together, and compaction makes even smaller pore spaces.

As the substrate particle size increases, the water-holding capacity decreases, and the aeration capacity increases (#34).

Our objective is to include large air spaces for aeration and drainage and smaller air spaces for water-holding ability and for the new tiny microscopic roots.

Fresh bonsai substrate could start out with optimal physical properties. Physical changes in the substrate characteristics over time can gradually affect the bonsai's health. Settling, compaction, decomposition, and shrinkage of any organic matter will lower the porosity. The roots eventually will be suffocated in too little air and too much water. The ideal substrate must continue to retain air, water,

and essential elements to be available to the plant after the substrate has been fully wetted consistently over a few growing seasons.

Roots are healthiest with the potential for 50 to 85 percent substrate porosity after watering. One "professional bonsai mix" I initially tested showed 30 percent porosity and ended up testing less than 10 percent porosity over a period of six months.

■ Why not use all gritty, coarse-textured (small gravel–sized) materials for bonsai substrate?

You can, but you'll be wasting water and fertilizer. Smaller, microscopic root hairs cannot grow successfully in extremely large pore spaces (unless in 100 percent humidity of greenhouse or hydroponic conditions).

Fresh roots easily dehydrate in a substrate consisting of mostly sand or small gravel particles (#35).

Those components are too coarse textured to hold on to water or essential elements long enough to keep your bonsai alive without continually watering them. Microscopic-sized organic material or clay particles are small enough to attract and hold on to water and elements until required by the plant.

---

† SNA, *Best Management Practices.*

"Sieve out all the fines less than one-eighth inch. Dust is detrimental to new root growth."

It took some research to find where a one-eighth-inch standard originated. That figure was evidently pulled out of thin air! What starts out as one-eighth of an inch may soon end up as mush soon after those big pores start filling up with dead roots and dust.

The practice of sieving substrate material came from a period more than fifty years ago when people used field soil with clay aggregates for growing bonsai. They traditionally had to "sieve out the dust." Now, some people screen simply because of tradition or because we're told "fines will accumulate at the bottom of the pot and clog up screen holes."

> *Tip*: Wash or rinse substrate materials, if you must, instead of sieving. Or simply leave a few "fines" in the mix for better water- and nutrient-holding properties.

Screening, sieving, or sifting is already a huge part of how today's nursery substrates are being engineered and designed. They're screened for the purpose of reducing the total weight of the plant and container.

Fines in a substrate do not appear to hinder or decrease the growth of woody nursery plants (#36).[*]

Practically all modern nursery substrate materials we can buy today are already sieved and ready to use (#37).

---

[*] J. Robbin, "Effect of Media Type on the Growth of Container-Grown Woody Ornamentals," *SNA Research Conference* 47 (2002).

■ **Why does the bottom wet zone of the bonsai pot seem to stay soaked for such a long time, especially in shallow pots?**

All the water we pour into our substrate is not going to automatically drain out of the holes at the bottom of the pot (#38).

Shallow bonsai pots or trays easily get waterlogged from limited air space and a higher perched (undrained) water table. The total percentage of air decreases as the substrate depth decreases and as the percentage of water increases.

The mix in a shallow pot requires more air space than the mix in a tall pot (#39).

Capillary action is the main reason why fine-textured substrate holds more water than the gravelly textured substrate commonly used by some bonsai growers. Water goes up and down in a pot. By capillary action, the smaller pore spaces, with a greater total surface area, hold a greater force against gravity. Capillary action wicks water into the smaller pore spaces, where it can stick to substrate particles.

Capillary water doesn't clog the pores because it sticks better to the substrate particles. Free water clogs pores and stays at the bottom wet zone (#40).

The bottom zone of gravel in the pot collects water and resists gravity's effect of draining out the holes because of capillary action and because the hydrogen in water is bonding to the substrate (#41).

A perched water table, which is the zone of fully wet substrate at the bottom of every planted pot, continues to hold water after each watering (#42).

Water perches at the bottom of the bonsai pot, unused and undrained. No actively growing roots will be found in a constantly waterlogged perched water table. No "inverted air exchange" can take place in the perched water table of a pot even if the substrate consists of coarse gravel.

A common problem seen with a bottom gravel layer is the deeper perched water table and less root space. Water is held at the bottom by surface tension, capillary action, and gravity. Then it's drawn upward against gravity to a higher level.

Adding a gravel layer decreases root space and increases standing water.

This water-logging problem becomes worse in the winter and springtime in shallow bonsai pots. A substrate with a shallower "drainage layer" makes the pot even more shallow.

The so-called drainage layer works against drainage. Our objective for our substrate should be to always ensure good aeration.

Water's cohesion (sticking to other things) and adhesion (holding the water together) keeps it sticking and holding to the substrate in any bonsai pot. If the substrate mix is not homogenous throughout the entire pot, the upper layer requires full wetting before a different-textured lower layer gets any water (#43).

Why? Water always goes to an area where water isn't. If you use the same homogenous substrate for all your bonsai, regardless of the pot height, then the perched water table will be the same height for all your pots.

For instance, the perched water table in a tall twelve-inch cascade-type pot may be one-half-inch deep at the bottom. In a shallow two-inch tray, the perched water table with the same substrate is also one-half-inch deep.

The tall pot requires more watering than the shallow tray with the same volume and same type of substrate because the tall pot dries out quicker (#44). A sponge

filled with water drains slower horizontally than when placed vertically.

"Water the bonsai three times in a single watering, once for the layer of smaller particles at the top, once for the intermediate particle sizes in the middle, and the third time for the larger particles that are placed in a drain layer at the bottom of the pot."
A "drain layer" or "air exchange layer" in itself does not help either substrate or field soil to drain any better or to exchange air (#45). Keep in mind that if a substrate has different layers, water must fully wet a layer of fine-textured particles before it is finally forced down by gravity into a bottom layer of larger-textured particles.
Fact: **Different-sized particle layers in a bonsai pot do more harm than good. A bottom layer of coarse gravel with large pore spaces creates an effective barrier to downward water movement** (#46).
Explanation: Water tends to move from an area of large pore size to an area of small pore size in the pot (#47).

Water goes where water isn't. This occurs from capillary action. Capillary action wicks the water upward from the bottom layer until the top layer is fully wetted.

Layering also tends to promote a buildup of chemical salts at the top of the substrate after each application of fertilizer. Root rot is a common result of the roots trying to live in a waterlogged environment.

■ What happens to the roots of a pot-bound tree when trying to grow in a slow-draining substrate?

The root system can become less healthy due to increased carbon dioxide, increased growth of fungi, and decreased pore spaces. Photosynthesis is helpful to the roots in another sense by decreasing substrate carbon dioxide as substrate moisture increases

Many bonsai growers fail to appreciate that the small amount of pore spaces in a small bonsai pot quickly becomes filled with roots. Plants dry out quicker in those conditions.

In a substrate composed of too large particle sizes, the finer new roots also dry out before they can occupy the pore spaces. Plant growth is compromised in either too large or too small pore spaces (#48).

■ Once the substrate is fully wetted and no further drainage occurs through the drainage holes of the bonsai pot, how can any excess water be removed?

Tilt the pot up slightly and hold it up with a wedge or stick under one edge of the pot. Hang a wick over the rim extending from the inside bottom of the pot. Move it to a sunnier spot. The sun will evaporate some of the water from the substrate surface.

Established plants draw out excess water through foliage transpiration. *Recently root-pruned, repotted, or transplanted trees are going to have much lower rates of evapotranspiration (evaporation and transpiration). Having no fresh roots makes it more difficult to pull up and remove excess water from a pot* (#49).

The fresh roots can establish new root hairs in as little as two weeks after root pruning or shaving. Ease up on the heavy watering for a couple weeks after potting unless you are going into a dry heat spell.

■ Can bonsai be overwatered in modern substrate?

Bonsai are so easy to overwater. In theory, anyone should not be able to overwater plants in coarse-textured substrate. In actual practice, you can overwater any bonsai.

Usually the problems from overwatering result from a rigid watering schedule instead of watering when the plant requires water.

Some plants are going to require much drier condition, while other plants tolerate wetter conditions. Smaller pots require more irrigation frequency and less water volume.

The amount of water and air in a substrate is influenced more by watering practice than by the substrate itself, especially if the plant is pot-bound or drainage is impeded. No roots can grow in a waterlogged container.

Watering is a product of how many times you water multiplied by the amount of water applied (#50).

"Upsizing to a larger pot keeps the roots from getting too waterlogged and drowning."

Usually the opposite happens when small root systems are transplanted to a much larger pot. When you have plants in bigger containers, you may feel you don't have to water as frequently. Overwatering is easy to do with large pots. In a pot size consistent with an adequate root system and a substrate with free air spaces, excess water is usually taken care of with bottom drainage, surface evaporation, and top evapotranspiration.

■ How can I check and monitor the water-holding capacity of my substrate?

The roots require a well-aerated substrate for two big reasons: to get enough oxygen promoting healthy growth and to prevent disease (#51).

■ Why does the free air space change so much even in one year?

There are two big reasons for this: root expansion and substrate decomposition. What starts out as 30 percent air space can decline to less than 10 percent in one growing season (one full year). Not allowing the pot to dry down after a good soaking means the substrate has less time with the minimum 10 to 30 percent air required to support healthy roots.

> *Tip*: Here's one quick and easy method to check your favorite substrate for water-holding capacity and percent porosity. Check when freshly potted and recheck after one year. You'll learn the difference between what works and what only seems to work.
> - Choose a few potted bonsai with an almost dried-out substrate and tape the drain holes.
> - Slowly add water to each pot until the water starts to overflow the top.
> - Without tipping out any water, lift the pot, remove the tape, and catch the draining water for a minute or so.
> - Measure the volume in cubic centimeters (cc) using a small cc measuring cup.
> - Use the centimeter scale on your tape measure to calculate the cc volume of the pot (length times width times height).
> - Divide collected cc's of water by total substrate cc volume.
> - Multiply decimal result by 100 to get percent porosity. Aim for over 50 percent total porosity.
> - Air replaces all the water you collected. If you measure 20 percent or less, consider adding more coarse-textured gravelly material to the substrate mix for next repotting. You'll be glad you did.

■ **How does watering a bonsai also aerate the substrate?**

Watering not only provides water for the roots, but also, as it drains through the holes in the bottom of the pot, it draws air down after it into the substrate's empty pore spaces (#52).

■ **Why does the substrate seem to shrink over a period of time?**

Substrate physical properties will quickly change (#53). Shrinking can occur from compaction of the organic matter resulting after constant wetting and drying. It can occur from the decomposition of organic materials. After a couple years in the same pot, organic components change from firm to spongy.

Small particles will fill the voids between larger particles. Many times, little or no substrate volume loss is observed because, as roots grow, they quickly fill the voids created by decomposing particles. Sometimes we notice the substrate seems to be expanding as the confined roots expand in the pot.

Shrinkage is more noticeable in shallow containers. The greater the difference in particle sizes of a substrate mix, the more the shrinkage. Finer-textured particles could be washing out over the top of the container or leaching out through the drain holes.

Roots don't "eat the soil." *Growing roots can fill any available pore spaces and even lift the entire root ball up from the bottom of the pot* (#54). This is another good sign that you should repot—and a good reason not to habitually wire the top of the roots down to the bottom of the pot if unnecessary.

■ **How well should I mix substrate components?**

Overmixing and compaction are big problems because we're breaking down the physical structure of the components. Organic materials are especially easily broken when handled repeatedly. We tend to overmix when blending small batches of substrate. A blend that appears powdery is probably already damaged from overmixing.

"Use different soils for training bonsai than for maintaining bonsai. Use different mixes for imported bonsai than for native bonsai."
Three or four different mixed particles are no better than merely one or two ingredients as a bonsai substrate. Container plants don't need different substrates at various stages of development. Even so, some plants with more fibrous root systems require finer-textured particles but adequate pore spaces for their roots.

"Grit will drain the water and won't freeze. Fines and organic matter hold water and will freeze. Ice will break down the soil."
Don't be too concerned about ice breaking down fines and organic matter. Interestingly, loose aggregates of finer-textured clay particles and organic matter remain stable even when frozen.*

"Root tips hitting sharp-edged sand or gravel will get irritated and divide and multiply, which produces an echoing division in the top growth of the tree."
Roots don't know the difference between coarse gravel and smooth gravel (#55).

"Sharp sand" is also a myth. Sand is sand by definition of its size. The root cap can make its own way through the open pores of the substrate without the help of sharp-edged, rough, angular sand or gravel.

---

* G. Lehrch et al., "Freezing Effects on Aggregate Stability Affected by Texture, Mineralogy and Organic matter," *Journal of Soil Science* 55 (1991): 1,401–06.

Branches don't know or care which direction the roots are growing (#56).

"Rake the surface of the soil once a month to ensure adequate water penetration in the soil."
There's no need to rake the soil. Modern substrate drains and aerates well. If water flows off the top of a compacted substrate, it could be one of the indications that you need to repot.

"Adding hydrogels will reduce the need for watering."
Fact: *Hydrogels have not been scientifically proven to reduce watering needs or frequency* (#57).

Also called hydrophilic polymer amendments, among other fancy terms, hydrogels look similar to clear gelatin and have about the same potential as gelatin for helping out with the watering needs of a plant. They have proven somewhat effective when used as a slurry on the bare roots of liners in shipping.

CHEMICAL PROPERTIES

■ *Why should we be concerned with substrate chemical properties?*
Chemical reactions influence the supply and storage of essential elements that all plants require in various amounts. Essential elements are able to be stored on certain substrate particles until they're taken up by the root system or drained out the bottom of the pot. All of the essential elements except carbon get into the plant by being dissolved in water (in solution).

The capacity to reserve and obtain certain essential elements, the cation exchange capacity, and the anion exchange capacity vary widely between organic and inorganic materials. *A high cation exchange capacity holds on to certain elements after fertilizer is applied* (#58).

The pore spaces of bonsai substrates composed entirely of sand or gravel-sized particles are too large to hold on to the essential elements dissolved in water (#59).

> *Tip*: Check the amount of fertilizer salts with a simple meter after you apply liquid fertilizer to your substrate. Then water the next day and recheck the availability of fertilizer salts. What does that tell you? Water drains and carries some fertilizer with it.

Clay aggregates hold on to the water and chemicals. Eventually those aggregates break down and hinder the roots from growing well in the confinements and compaction of a pot. Activated carbons (charcoal) hold onto ions too well and won't release them.

Bonsai require fertilizer applications more often in a gravelly, nonorganic substrate with a low cation-exchange capacity than stock grown out in the field (#60). *The roots' uptake of essential elements is a totally different process than their uptake of water from a substrate. Some essential elements must change chemically and exchange ions before they can enter the roots they contact* (#61).

Cation exchange capacity (sometimes wrongly referred to as "nutrient exchange") indicates how well the substrate holds some chemicals from leaching out (draining away) between fertilizer applications.

Contrary to some opinions, a substrate's high cation-exchange capacity does not "lead to leaf burn." Leaf burn can usually be traced to a recent foliar spray of the urea component in some water-soluble fertilizers.

This drawing shows two tiny root hairs on one lateral root. They are trading one small hydrogen from the root hair for one larger nitrogen from those three tiny clay particles (or tiny organic matter particles).

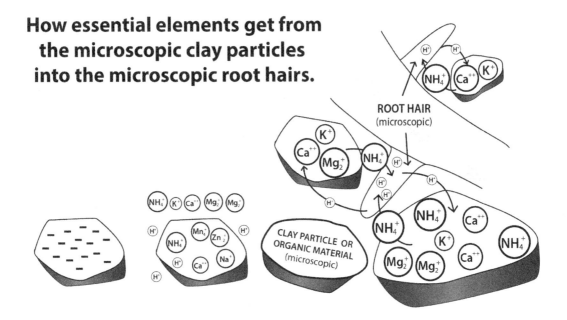

How essential elements get from the microscopic clay particles into the microscopic root hairs.

ROOT HAIR (microscopic)

CLAY PARTICLE OR ORGANIC MATERIAL (microscopic)

In either field soil or substrate, this natural barter system (cation exchange) exists where the roots of the plant can get their essential elements. The capacity to reserve elements until they're needed varies between organic and inorganic materials.

The elements put in fertilizers are simple salt crystals (similar to table salt crystals) that release their chemical bonds in water. Both organic matter and clay particles are tiny but with large amounts of negative spots to attract any tiny positive cations in the vicinity.

Opposites attract. Those negative-charged anions sticking to the surface of organic matter or clay will attract positive-charged cations from fertilizer crystals dissolved in water. Cations stick to the surface of organic materials or clays.

Positive-charged elements in sticky water will free up those elements so they can trade for negative-charged elements on those tiny colloid surfaces to make them available to the roots.

A microscopic-sized clay particle is covered with negative charges. A few positive-charged ions (cations) floating around in sticky water stick to those tiny particles (#62).

Some minute substrate particles (fines) are tiny enough for negative-charged ions to cover their surface. Those fines attract a few cations from the sticky water that latch onto those particles until the plant needs any particular essential element.

Dissolved fertilizer salts are also sticky. A root hair near a charged particle (again, not a sand or gravel particle alone as in most modern substrates) will exchange one cation for another cation. *When one cation enters a root hair, then another cation must exit. That replaced essential element is then transported up the plant by proteins* (#63).

Organic matter (not akadama) has the highest cation-holding capacity of any substrate ingredient. Next in line would be clay particles and calcined (baked) clays.

Organic pine bark will hold on to those essential elements twenty times better than the inorganic gravel most commonly used in bonsai substrate (#64).

The inside of those bark particles also holds the water that will later be beneficial to roots.[*]

"Always use akadama, never any clay soil."

Explanation: Akadama is mined as a volcanic-origin subsoil and dried in hot air. It is an unstable aggregate composed of ultra-small, fine clay particles. Minute traces of silicon and iron are said to be present. The red color comes from the iron oxidation (unstable loss of electrons).

Being high in finer clay particles, akadama and its kind have a high cation exchange capacity, which is good. Unfortunately, all clay aggregates (except for the oven-fired calcined clays), degrade into mushy mud over time. Waterlogged, it soon creates unhealthy conditions for the roots.

Being subsoil, it contains no trace of organic material or living organisms. But it is not "sterile," as claimed. Organic "bonsai food" cannot be utilized by solid mineral subsoil.

Local, low-cost clay aggregates are perfect for Far Eastern climates. Akadama is important for its aggregate structure, not for the texture (clay) and not for any nutrients. Dr. Ross Clark, botanist, puts it in practical terms. Since so many soil mixes work and since there is a very wide variety of rock and soil in North America, there is no need to import special soil mixes or ingredients from other continents. [†]

---

[*] T. Bilderback, "Managing Container Substrates," 2002 handout, Nursery Crop Sciences, NC State University.

[†] R. Clark, *Native North American Plants for Bonsai* (n.p.: American Bonsai Society, 2012), 258.

Tip: Be more concerned about substrate properties than names or types of products. Locally sourced materials are the most cost effective and worthy components for growing your own bonsai.

"Adding charcoal to the potting soil prevents the roots from rotting."
Sorry, charcoal won't make a bit of difference to the roots or rot. Some forms of charcoal are unhealthy for the roots.

"Mix some starter fertilizer or lime in the substrate before potting bonsai."
This outdated practice cannot be recommended for bonsai. Plants do not require and can't use any fertilizer until after they start pushing out fresh new roots (#65). That usually doesn't happen until at least a couple weeks after being pruned. New roots don't appreciate rubbing up against raw chunks of salty fertilizer. Research has also concluded that uneven mixing of fertilizer incorporated into the substrate container production causes uneven growth. Seedlings and cuttings can't even use fertilizer.

We can control the availability of essential elements later on in the growing season with a slow-release granular or liquid fertilizer application to the infertile substrate. **Premixing fertilizers, wetting agents, or lime into bonsai substrates is unnecessary** (#66). In the olden days, lime was used to raise soil pH for vegetable gardening in the field. Modern bonsai substrates already stay close to the "ideal pH range" of 5.0 to 6.0. Much above 7.0 is a bit high for woody plants. Watering and fertilizer practices over time may raise the pH.

"Watering the plant more frequently makes a higher risk the soil will be saturated with too much fertilizer salts."
Frequent watering usually drains out excess fertilizer in solution. Test your water for alkalinity to be sure.

BIOLOGICAL PROPERTIES

■ **What's that nice, fresh earthy smell in garden soil?**
Actinorhizae, when it's fixing nitrogen. Mycorrhizae is not a nitrogen fixing bacteria (#67).

"All roots benefit by soil that has been inoculated with mycorrhizae."
Fact: **No good benefit exists for adding any type of microorganisms to any bonsai substrate** (#68). Dying roots make mycorrhizae available by providing organic matter. Beneficial microorganisms already exist or will eventually come to any organic matter, depending on the plant species.

Mycorrhizae are organs composed of both tree tissues and fungi. You can save some of the old soil clinging to the roots when transplanting from the field if you observe some evidence of the mycorrhizae. Otherwise, don't waste time, money, and trouble on any mycorrhizae product.

We tend to repot too frequently and use too much fertilizer and water. Those good microorganisms flourishing in field soil can't colonize most bonsai substrates. High fertility and high moisture conditions promote pathogenic or bad organisms at the expense of the most beneficial mycorrhizal fungi. Good microorganisms won't survive in inert grit, gravel, and subsoil.

■ **You notice some white-looking mycorrhizae on some pine needle mulch. Will it help a spruce bonsai if I add those pine needles in its substrate?**

Several different varieties of mycorrhizae exist, each specific to a plant or groups of plants. The mycorrhizae for spruce needs to be of the same exact mycorrhizal variety that will benefit spruce. Pine and spruce each have different species of mycorrhizae, and one species probably will not benefit the other species.

■ **Water barely penetrates the substrate on one of your bonsai. A white-looking substance is growing on both the substrate bark and the root system. What could it be?**

That stuff could be a fungal growth binding the particles of bark together and causing the substrate to repel water. Omit the fertilizer and fungicide for a season. Maybe repot.

■ **My developing trees planted in the ground look better than my developing bonsai planted in a pot. Is it the microbes?**

Soil microorganisms are much healthier and more useful out in the field soil with organic matter than in a pot. When planted out in garden soil, plants are better able to fight off pathogens by themselves. The good microorganisms outnumber all the bad microorganisms by ninety-nine to one.

Plants growing in the ground are more self sufficient than when growing in a pot (#69).

We don't tend to fuss so much with field-grown plants as we do with our plants in a pot. *Compact trees grown in the ground, even over a couple good growing seasons, will produce noticeably larger trunks and thicker branches than those kept in a pot* (#70).

■ **Why should I remove the field soil eventually and replace it with a substrate mix when moving a collected tree from the field to a pot? Can the good soil microorganisms survive inside a pot?**

Normally, field soil conditions can't be duplicated or maintained in a pot. The physical texture and the living microorganisms found in the ground of field soil will eventually deteriorate or diminish over time in container conditions. The soil texture becomes finer and less able to allow the passage of air and water throughout the container. The clay aggregates left on a collected plant's roots can extract moisture from the other parts of the bonsai substrate.

Some larger collected plants cannot tolerate a bare rooting operation all at one time. The growth of fibrous fine roots closer to the trunk may be hindered until the soil can eventually be replaced with a coarser particle substrate over time.

"Make sure you buy only sterilized soil." *Fact*: **Sterilized, inert substrate would be impossible to keep sterile** (#71). **Live bonsai roots require both living microorganisms and dead chemicals** (#72).

Explanation: Sterile means free from living microorganisms. Inert means chemically inactive. Soil sterilization kills beneficial bacteria and desirable good microorganisms. Sterile substrate is sometimes used for propagating seeds, seedlings, or cuttings. If weeds later appear in our bonsai pots, they were most likely from weed seeds blown in by the wind. No need to bother with sterilizing inert substrate

So how many times a year do you "feed your bonsai"?

UNDERSTANDING FERTILIZERS

You'll be able to save some time, money, and bonsai with this basic fertilizer information. Fertilization is a rather simple practice made much more complex than it needs to be because of the increasingly more abundant amounts of products available.

It's time to take the fear out of chemistry. Water, fertilizers, and pesticides are all chemicals (elements). Every time you prune a tree, chemicals are released. ***The day-to-day defense and survival in bonsai is chemistry*** (#73). ***Both natural organic and synthetic inorganic fertilizers are chemicals*** (#74). Plants, not being politically correct, don't care where their chemicals come from. As they say, nitrogen is nitrogen is nitrogen. If someone suggests all chemicals are bad, tell her not to eat or drink!

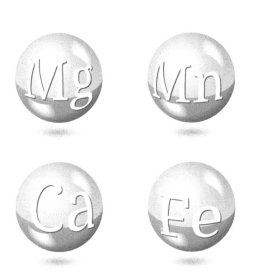

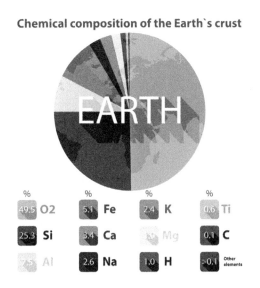

Chemical composition of the Earth's crust

%		%		%		%	
49.5	O2	5.1	Fe	2.4	K	0.6	Ti
25.3	Si	3.4	Ca		Mg	0.1	C
7.5	Al	2.6	Na	1.0	H	>0.1	Other elements

We are bags of chemicals, feeding on recycled chemicals of plants and animals. We are mostly proteins. Bonsai are mostly carbohydrates. We wiggle and wobble around, unlike plants. As long as we're wiggling and wobbling, we are considered alive and doing well. Both plants and animals eventually return their bag of chemicals (elements) back to the earth's crust.

ESSENTIAL ELEMENTS

■ From the plant's point of view, what chemicals (elements or minerals) are essential?

At least nineteen elements are essential to a plant. *These elements, from boron to zinc, are necessary or beneficial for bonsai to grow, live, or reproduce* (#75).

All naturally occurring elements found on the earth's crust are found in plant tissue, but only nineteen are essential. Nothing else can be substituted for those nineteen essential elements. If you add or take away any one of those essential elements, everything changes in that plant.

These elements, or minerals, in alphabetical order include boron, calcium, carbon, chlorine, cobalt, copper, hydrogen, iron, magnesium, manganese, molybdenum, nickel, nitrogen, oxygen, phosphorus, potassium, silicon, sulfur, and zinc. From the plant's point of view, the order is a little different.

In the amount of concentration, plants consist of carbon, oxygen, hydrogen, nitrogen, phosphorus, potassium, calcium, sulfur, magnesium, manganese, molybdenum, chlorine, copper, iron, boron, zinc, nickel, and sulfur minerals. Approximately 99 percent of a plant consists of only three elements: carbon, hydrogen, and oxygen.

Think of the plant as a bag of chemicals. Approximately 99 percent of all the chemicals filling that bag is carbon dioxide and water. Carbon dioxide (carbon and oxygen), is 19 percent of a plant. Water (hydrogen and oxygen) is 80 percent of the total plant's composition. Proportionally, 99 percent of everything the plant needs is available and already inside that plant.

All that fertilizer we put on our bonsai is supplying proportionally less than 1 percent of the total elements it needs. We do help out—a small fraction of the total.

Periodic Table of all the essential elements found in bonsai (or any plant)

Credits to Kim Coder, Univ. GA

H																	
												B	C	N	O		
	Mg												Si	P	S	Cl
K	Ca		Mn	Fe	Co	Ni	Cu	Zn								
	Mo															

We only need to be concerned about supplying those other sixteen essential elements a tree might lack (the other 1 percent) (#76).

Commonly used expressions, such as macro, micro, and secondary nutrients, do not have a functional meaning. All nineteen elements are essential or beneficial to all aspects of plant health, but in completely different proportions or concentrations. Carbon, hydrogen, and oxygen are mega elements because they are the highest proportion (over 99 percent) of all the chemicals found in plants. They come from the sun, water, and air—and in all the right amounts and concentrations, readily available and free.

In another life, when I happened to be in a soil science class, the essential elements were remembered by the acronym C(see) H O P K N S CaFe, Mg(Mighty good)—for those eleven elements known to be essential in a plant at that time. That was long before the other elements were discovered to be essential in a plant.

Someone has a more recent acronym, "See MG men mob Cousin Hopkins nice clean café," which includes six more elements: C Mg Mn MoB CuZn HOPKNS Ni Cl CaFe.

Get ready to figure out a new acronym. They'll soon discover even more elements to be essential or beneficial to a plant. *The carbon and oxygen in carbon dioxide are the only elements that can get into the plant without first being dissolved in water* (#77).

Approximately 98 percent of the weight of a tree (and of our own weight) is made up of only six chemicals: carbon, hydrogen, oxygen, nitrogen, sulfur, and phosphorus (phosphate is a molecule) (#78).

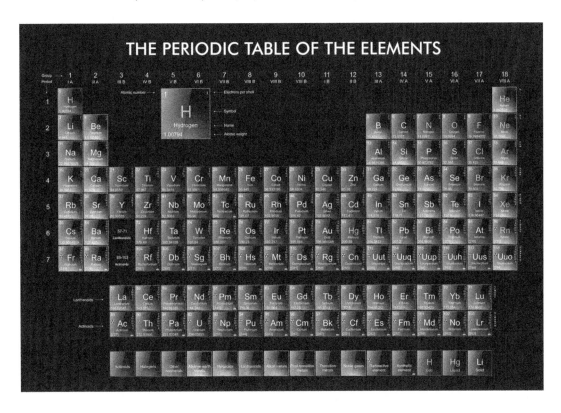

While each element is essential, the plant can tolerate a deficiency to a certain point. *If we can provide half of the total concentration of one particular element it lacks, that tree continues to grow, live, and reproduce* (#79). The tree has a deficiency if it has less than 20 percent concentration of one particular element out of the nineteen it needs.

Nitrogen, phosphorus, and potassium are the big three elements we randomly toss on or spray at our bonsai. When any one of those big three or any one of the other sixteen elements is missing, or applied in excess, it can kill the plant. For example, any one of those big three elements in excess can cause a copper deficiency. Aluminum, arsenic, boron, copper, fluorine, silver, and lead are also capable of causing toxicity in a plant when found in more than a minuscule amount in a substrate.

ORGANIC AND INORGANIC FERTILIZERS

■ **What is the difference between natural organic fertilizer and synthetic inorganic fertilizer?**

The difference between organic and inorganic is simply carbon (#80). Organic fertilizers include the carbon molecule. The

carbon molecule is found in all field soil containing living microorganisms. Carbon compounds in organic matter provide energy to soil life. Since they came from something previously living, carbon compounds may have some residual benefit to soil microorganisms and may last a long time in field soil.

Even if chemistry doesn't appeal to you, look at the element symbol (as on the Periodic Table of Elements) for a synthetic, man-made nitrate molecule. Compare that element symbol to a natural, organic nitrate molecule. They are the same. *Synthetic molecules and organic molecules are the exact same* (#81). Plants don't know the difference and don't care either. From the plant's point of view, organic or natural fertilizer may not be any better than man-made fertilizer. No magic exists in either fertilizer.

"Always use organic fertilizer if you want a healthy bonsai. A tree cultivated on inorganic fertilizer is rarely healthy." It's a common conundrum. Let's look at some of the common scientific facts: *Besides the basic elements they provide, no additional benefit to the plant comes from organic fertilizers than from inorganic fertilizers* (#82). *Bonsai substrate is easily and quickly depleted of essential elements during the first watering after an application of organic fast-release fertilizer* (#83).

You will need to apply much more organic fertilizers than you would need to with inorganic, since a bag of organic usually contains much less of the actual essential chemicals (elements) than the same volume bag of inorganic fertilizer (#84). So in the end, organic usually costs more than inorganic.

Any essential elements in organic fertilizers cannot be applied in precise quantities (#85). You're merely guessing the plant needs it. If you do not know exactly what chemicals are in organic fertilizer, then you don't know how much essential elements gets into a plant.

Mineral components alone (gravel, sand, silt, or clay) cannot possibly change any organic fertilizer into a form beneficial to bonsai (#86).

Organic fertilizers are not available to a plant unless the substrate already contains living microorganisms (#87). *The large organic compounds in organic fertilizer slowly dissolve or metabolize through bacteria and fungi activity before those compounds release any elements to any plant* (#88). That can take quite a while to process.

On the other hand, synthetic (inorganic) fertilizers all come from natural sources (#89). They are:
- Soluble in water.
- Cheap and effective when local sources are used.
- The exact same chemical formula in both imported or local sources of fertilizers.
- Less attractive to rodents than organic fertilizers when stored.
- Inorganic fertilizers can be applied in the precise amounts needed by the plant right when they're needed.

■ What are the risks from using synthetic fertilizers?

The risk of toxicity or lush unwanted growth comes from applying too much fertilizer, no matter if fertilizer is in organic or in synthetic form (#90).

Systematic repotting and normal watering help diminish those risks.

"Chemical fertilizer destroys all the beneficial bacteria in the pot."
The proper use of inorganic fertilizers does not "kill off beneficial bacteria and mycorrhizal fungi." *Some chemicals applied to stock out in field soil can provide energy for beneficial bacteria and bacteria-like organisms. Excess phosphate fertilizer in any form can inhibit mycorrhizae* (#91).

"Natural organic fertilizer is best for the roots of a recently collected plant."
Roots starting out in gravel substrate haven't had nearly enough time to accumulate the microorganisms that allow freshly applied organic fertilizer to be utilized by the plant (#92).

> *Tip*: Most field soils already contain most essential elements and natural organic material. The recent transplant from field soil to a training pot adjusts quite well on its own. In the meantime, hold off the leaf pruning, excess branch pruning, and fertilizing until the plant is able to sort things out.

Your bonsai will be quite OK if some of the original soil clings to the roots. A tree does not usually push out new, finer roots until at least a couple of weeks after potting or transplanting.

The roots can't use any organic fertilizer until it's first converted into inorganic fertilizer and is able to be taken up by the roots (#93). *Oxygen from air and water is used by bacteria to make existing organic matter available to roots in the substrate* (#94). That process converts organic material into inorganic soluble salts. Then it becomes available to the roots.

"Bonsai grow rapidly when fed organic nutrients and must be repotted every spring."
Let's address a few misconceptions:

- The need for repotting is not related to fertilizer applications or to any schedule.
- Bonsai do not require "repotting every spring and fertilizing every two weeks during the growing season."
- To a plant, the (chemical) elements in its environment are no different from either organic or inorganic sources.
- *Neither a bag of commercial organic fertilizer nor a jar of homemade organic cakes is "plant food"* (#95). Chemicals or minerals are not "plant food."
- Plants use elements, not nutrients.
- Fertilizers are supplements, not nutrients.
- The chart of Periodic Table of Elements is not a chart of "nutrients."

■ Can bark or other organic wood products "provide nutrients to a plant"?

Initially, those organic components provide little or no significant source of essential elements. Bark has significant element holding capacity and can release essential elements as needed, if and when available. Essential elements are not considered "nutrients for plants" in the sense that food is essential to our own nourishment.

■ What about using solid fertilizer blocks or "organic cakes" on potted bonsai?

They look quite fancy, and blocks were the modern way to feed bonsai until about fifty years ago. Organic cakes or blocks are labor intensive to make and use. Someone stated, "When you see the organic cakes breaking down on top of the substrate, it means the

plant is hungry and using the food." It really means the cakes are crumbling apart.

They sometimes cause caking on the substrate surface. Some specially made organic fertilizer cakes become a breeding ground for maggots and billbugs. They're not effective in a low humidity or low temperature environment. Organic fertilizer cakes do not work at all for newly planted bonsai on most gravel/grit substrates.

Any potentially useful minerals in fertilizer cakes cannot be converted into ions (simpler forms) to become useful unless bacteria are present (#96). Ions from fertilizer cakes are available to the roots only in the presence of substrate organic matter and with microorganisms to break them down— and when those ions are attached to microscopic soil particles or to the fresh new roots.

"Placing organic fertilizer cakes around the base of the trunk will improve the thickness of the nebari (where roots meet soil line) and make it more prominent."
No, cakes can't achieve that claim. The essential element uptake is through the fine roots, not through the thicker surface roots (root collar).

■ Summarize the advantages and disadvantages of using organic fertilizer for bonsai.

The advantages and disadvantages of both organic and inorganic fertilizers have been debated for over one hundred years. Among its many advantages for use on plants growing out in field soil, organic fertilizer slowly provides a few essential elements over time. In addition, some organic fertilizers benefit field soil by the conditioning properties.

Organic fertilizer would be most effective on developing trees planted out in the field soil (#97) or for vegetable or landscape gardening. More advantages than disadvantages are associated with using inorganic controlled-release fertilizer (CRF) products on container plants. *The container plant benefits from precise applications as needed* (#98). No guessing.

Disadvantages of using organic fertilizer in modern bonsai substrate include:

- *Essential elements are limited in availability and usually in unknown amounts in various organic fertilizer products* (#99).
- Organics are more expensive.
- Some organics may be potentially pathogenic.
- *Organics result in uneven distribution of essential elements, even if those elements are available* (#100). Basic composition of organic fertilizers are not standardized and sometimes not even known.
- The plant may not need a certain chemical. And too much of one chemical may be potentially toxic in high concentrations.
- Fertilizing only with organic fertilizer rapidly increases the acidity of a substrate. Low pH is harmful to most conifers.
- Sometimes the plant needs immediate intervention in the form of inorganic fertilizers.
- *Organic material must be decomposed to be available* (#101). As mentioned, any elements in organics may not be released at all if no microorganisms are in the bonsai substrate to make elements available. Low substrate temperatures also make elements unavailable.

Fertilize Flawlessly

■ What are the symptoms of "nutrient deficiency"?

Those symptoms may be invisible. Essential element deficiencies are a long time in the making. Odd colors visible in a misshapen leaf can result from either too much or not enough fertilizer or from many other reasons. What appears to be a "nutrient deficiency" can develop from some other environmental deficiency.

Here is a tip to see if some plants lack an essential element: elements may either be mobile or immobile in a plant.

Nitrogen, phosphorus, potassium, sulfur, chlorine, boron, zinc, and magnesium are mobile or semi-mobile in a plant (#102). Plants deficient in one of those elements will remove those elements from older, less active foliage and relocate them to younger, more actively growing foliage. Older, chlorotic-appearing, misshapen leaves are the first to show a deficiency of N, P, K, B, Zn or Mg (magnesium).

The other essential elements are immobile in a plant. They don't readily move from an old leaf to a new leaf. Look at the plant's new growth for symptoms of deficiencies in every essential element except N, P, K, zinc, sulfur, chlorine or magnesium.

For an emergency deficiency problem, use water soluble sprays. For long-term care, use CRF pellets. This chapter refers to the controlled-release fertilizer as CRF.

■ How do we know when a tree lacks one of those nineteen essential elements?

The demand for any element depends on the concentration of the other elements; the plant's growth stage and where it lives;

the species; and even the varieties within the species.

Someone once said, "Better to be safe, just in case, and give them a little of all the vitamins, minerals, and nutrients you can." We can't find out when a plant needs fertilizer by simply applying more fertilizer.

> *Tip*: To verify what essential element a tree lacks, we have several testing options. This includes sampling for a soil, substrate, leaf tissue, or water test and finding out exactly what's in it.

■ Do I need both a substrate analysis and a foliar analysis? How do I interpret test data?

Use soil tests either as a diagnostic tool or to identify trends taking place in your substrate over time. Soil testing can tell us what is expected to become available to the plant in the soil. If the results come back intermediate or high, no fertilizer addition will increase plant growth in that soil. Soil tests apply more to plants grown out in field soil than to those grown in containers.

Specialized substrate testing labs can check the chemical and physical properties of a media mix. Most labs can compare the element concentrations in your plant to concentrations in plants of the same species. You can predict how effective your fertilization program is over time. Or you can pinpoint or rule out any fertilizer-related immediate problems in your substrate.

Leaf analyses are from samples taken on both problem areas and healthy areas on the same plant. This test is the most precise way to measure what essential elements or pathogens are in that foliage at that particular time.

Use lab data from a leaf tissue analysis to identify what is in that leaf. We can't infer from a leaf tissue test alone what kind of fertilizer to apply to the substrate or soil.

Sampling your well water or city water may be the first test to get. If your water leaves a white crust on the substrate surface, sodium is a likely cause. Plants hate sodium and water that is too alkaline or too acidic.

■ How do I know how much fertilizer supplements to put on my bonsai?

The concentration of fertilizer supplements required by container plants depends on:

- The plant species, if it's "a heavy or a light feeder."
- Its stage of growth.
- The desired rate of growth.
- Frequency of fertilizer applications.
- How much fertilizer leaches out of the pot after watering.
- Test data from a foliage tissue test, substrate test, or water test to determine any deficiency or toxicity.

Your bonsai can have either too much fertilizer or too little fertilizer (#103). Either can kill them dead. Roots take up whatever elements are offered, but only when those water soluble elements are available and sticking to the tiny new roots.

A tree does not know when too much fertilizer is harmful (#104). We know what's harmful by analyzing data from a substrate and foliar test. Don't guess. Get a test.

Generally, people regularly over-apply fertilizer "just to ensure it gets enough nutrition." Unfortunately, this same practice is seen all too often with overwatering. Bonsai do not require large amounts of fertilizer or water, but they do need a source of essential elements and moisture during their active growth.

You can't put a small, minimum amount of fertilizer in the substrate to "supply nutrition" to your bonsai (#105). The law of minimum applies to crop yields in field soil, not to container-grown plants.

*If one single essential element is missing, the whole plant struggles to survive; it can't adapt to or compensate for that one missing elemen*t (#106).

There is no point in applying any fertilizer to a bonsai if it already has the essential resources required to survive (#107). No one can predict the response of a plant to conditions of deficiency of essential elements.

Find out if a fertilizer application gives the plant the desired response. Find out if fertilizer is vital to produce that desired response. Then apply only the type and amount of essential elements scarce in that plant and necessary to give that desired response.

■ To be on the safe side, should I "overfeed" or "underfeed"?

Be on the safe side and get your favorite substrate tested at least once during your bonsai career. Then find out what amount of essential elements your particular plant needs or lacks.

Each specific plant needs a specific amount of a specific chemical at each specific stage of growth. Cultural requirements vary depending on cultural conditions.

Plants requiring larger amounts of essential elements include Betula, Callicarpa, Ilex, Ligustrum, Lonicera, and Quercus. Those tolerating lower rates of fertilizer include Pinus, Prunus, Azaleas, and Taxodium. Skip the fertilizer application on evergreens when spraying liquid fertilizer.

"Rotate several different types of fertilizer during the year to give the bonsai a broader and more balanced range of nutrients."
This wouldn't be the best idea. If you've used several different types of fertilizer during the year and the bonsai appears healthy, which particular product worked? What essential elements did each type of fertilizer provide for the plant's benefit?

Using random fertilizers randomly would indicate that we didn't test for their deficiency in the substrate. It's as if we're not sure if one fertilizer works well or if something else might work better. Or maybe our perfect growing media or our expert watering technique made our bonsai look so good. It's not necessarily because we "fertilized every week, weakly."

To make it worse, adding more fertilizer only reduces the plant's ability to utilize and take up existing elements already in the substrate. Adding more and different fertilizers only adds to the existing mineral imbalance.

■ Can a tree "take up more plant food than it needs"?

A plant can take up more nitrogen than it needs; it cannot take up most of the other elements that it needs (#108). A plant is not "going to take up all the excess chemicals from over fertilizing and be killed from kindness." Excess elements in solution with water usually leach out through the drain holes.

Salt levels increase inside a pot from excessive concentrations of fast-release fertilizer (#109). Roots can be injured when the water and element uptake is restricted. Toxicity is the result. *The substrate may have excess nitrogen with none available to the plant if not adjusted with either trace elements or proper pH* (#110).

"Superfeeding" high amounts of NPK (elements) to a bonsai can be a total waste. *Apply fertilizer supplements only to compensate for a known essential element deficiency in the plant* (#111).

Symptoms of too much chemicals in a plant include:

- Thin, long, weak branches.
- Twig dieback.
- Chronic leaf tip burn.
- Constant invasions of scale and aphid insects on the new growth.

Excesses cause deficiencies. *More plant disorders result from excess fertilizer than from not enough fertilizer* (#112).

Two essential elements frequently might be antagonistic during plant uptake. For one example, adding super concentrations of iron suppresses plant uptake of manganese. Super concentrations of manganese suppress plant uptake of iron.*

---

* Douglas Bailey and P. Nelson, "Managing Micronutrients in the Greenhouse," *North Carolina Department of Horticultural Science Information Leaflet* 553 (August 1998).

■ Some say, "Always use acid fertilizer." Others recommend, "Always add lime." Should we be concerned about substrate pH?

The pH number tells us how the substrate ranks in terms of acidity or alkalinity. It means hydrogen potential. *Neutral pH is 7.0. The pH can influence the availability of essential elements in field soil* (#113).

Chemical problems in modern substrate are usually not a pH problem but rather a lack or excess of trace elements tying up certain other elements (#114). There is no need to add acid or alkaline (base) fertilizers or any lime to our bonsai substrate. Research indicates the optimum pH of soilless substrates can be 5.6 to 6.2, while field soil can be a whole pH unit higher, 6.2 to 6.8.

Dr. Whitcomb concludes that pH doesn't affect the micronutrient availability in substrates and is not directly responsible for plant problems while in a container (#115).[†]

The recommended pH level varies with species and their tolerances. Plants develop strategies to deal with wide ranges of fertility and pH. So-called acid-loving plants have developed the means to cope with low pH. Salt-tolerant plants tolerate more salts. The common range of 4.5 pH to 6.5 pH in bark-based substrates is completely adequate for almost all bonsai.

There is no need to ever apply lime sulfur, ash, or gypsum to gravelly bonsai substrate (#116). It's probably close to neutral.

High pH does not necessarily "cause chlorosis or stunting." Excessively high or low substrate pH values may possibly indicate water-quality problems.

One commercial perennial plant nursery used a highly acidic organic greenhouse potting mix. He once super-fed some "acid fertilizer" to

---

[†]From his website, www.rootmaker.com.

his container substrate every week for almost a full growing season. The pH dropped from 6.0 down to 3.0 over the year, meaning it became one thousand times more acidic. Those herbaceous plants came to a sudden demise.

That rapid change in pH rarely happens in modern gravelly bonsai substrates with appropriate fertilizer applications made according to previous substrate data.

> *Tip*: One take-home message to remember is that woody plants can tolerate a wide range of pH. Do check the pH of most greenhouse potting mixes. Some commercial organic greenhouse mixes will test extremely acidic. Some well water will test extremely alkaline.

"The more you fertilize, the more the pH of the soil decreases from alkaline to acid."
The pH could go either way. Some fertilizer additions, along with alkaline well water, increase pH in agricultural field soils over a long period of time.

■ Is it important to water the bonsai before applying fertilizer supplements?
Pre-watering is highly recommended, especially before applying liquid fertilizer. The fresh new roots can take up more water when it is offered in a chemically pure state without dissolved fertilizer salts (#117).

Be aware that the next watering after a liquid fertilizer application might leach out whatever elements were added to the substrate. Granular or pelletized CRF products can't leach out as easily as a spray or drench of water soluble fertilizer.

■ At what air temperatures do tree roots quit taking up fertilizer?
Plants can't use essential elements when stressed or when the air temperature is above 100°F (37°C) (#118). Temperatures ranging between 60° and 75°F (16°–24°C) seem to be optimum for CRF uptake by the roots.

FEEDING 101

"Fertilizer feeds bonsai."
False. **Bonsai feed themselves** (#119). Fertilizer may include a particular essential element a plant requires, but all the fertilizer we offer to the plant can't ever give it enough resources for it to survive on. Try not to think of fertilizer as a chemical resource needed for the bonsai to survive. Fertilizer is simply a supplement to help plants make their own resources more efficiently.

We're used to the phrase "Feeding our lawn and feeding our vegetable garden." Lawns and vegetable gardens do need more supplements than trees or shrubs. Animals cannot make their own energy, but they can eat food to get energy. **We do not have to feed our bonsai a certain minimum daily requirement as we feed ourselves** (#120).

Fertilizer can't feed a plant, but too much could injure a plant (#121). Plants

have no kidneys or fat stomachs. Food and nutrients are nutritious but are not fertilizer.

Plants can't eat unless they "eat the sun." Plants are perfectly capable of providing their own energy and manufacturing their own vitamins and supplements. *The energy source for a plant starts when the leaves trap the first rays of the sun; at the other end of the stick, trees get water and other essential elements up through the roots* (#122). They use the sun's energy to provide energy for their own growth with sugars, proteins, and other materials. They can get carbon dioxide through the bottom side of their leaves. "Food from photosynthesis" is more correctly termed "photosynthate."

Let's clarify a few other common misconceptions:

- *Roots can't feed on fertilizer to get food* (#123). We probably should not refer to "feeder roots." Except for carbon, chemical ions (salts dissolved in water) float around in solution with sticky water. Some of that sticky salt solution may happen to stick to the younger roots.
- *Plant "food" is not "absorbed"* (#124). The chemical ions sticking to tiny substrate particles and to tiny root hairs are extracted, not absorbed. Elements enter and are taken up into the plant mainly by osmosis and diffusion, not by absorption.
- *Fertilizer supplements are not an energy source for any plant* (#125). Rather, fertilizer products supply a small percentage of the total proportion of supplements a plant needs to help make its own resources. The end product, photosynthate, is all the elements it requires to live, grow, or reproduce.
- *Fertilizer can provide energy for any bacteria present in the soil but can't provide any energy for root growth* (#126).

- *Fertilizer cannot "cause cell divisions to occur in a plant"* (#127).

"You can't make a mistake with feeds made specifically for bonsai."

That statement is way too debatable. Don't be disappointed when you can't "find secrets, magic, or miracles in a bag, bottle or box." Nitrogen equals nitrogen, but all fertilizers are not equal. Soluble plant food products purported to "feed bonsai simply by spraying their leaves" cannot "flow down from the leaves to the roots." Nor does fertilizer "move from the roots back up to the branches in one lump of food."

■ Does fertilizer "stimulate plant growth by feeding"? Will my "plants starve from lack of fertilizer if not fed regularly"?

The answer to both questions is no. Steroids can "stimulate growth" in animals, but fertilizer will never stimulate a plant to grow. Lack of essential elements can kill plants. *The plant's own growth regulators exclusively produced by that plant switch growth on or off. Lack of fertilizer can't switch off growth* (#128).

Tree roots require essential elements for growth, either produced by the leaves or found in the soil. Established miniature trees developing out in field soil are not necessarily going to die if you skip the fertilizing. Most field soils already contain all of the minerals required by plants. A forest never gets fertilized and does quite well without it.

If any specific essential element (except for carbon, hydrogen, and oxygen—the 99 percent) is limiting in a substrate, the tree goes into a kind of resting period when the rate of cell division slows down. Add that element (a small fraction of the other 1 percent), and the plant continues with normal cell divisions again.

Fertilizer can't "stimulate plant growth" or make any other miracle occur. For one example, fertilizer does not change the quantity or quality of leaves produced. When a plant has all the essential elements in its system within the right proportions, it won't starve and die.

Fast or Slow?

■ How long will fertilizer supplements last on a substrate?

That is debatable. Most fertilizer we apply to our gravelly bonsai substrates will have a short, useful life. Measure it today and the meter shows excess salts. Water it and then measure again tomorrow. Notice the huge difference.

Our job is to find out what essential element is missing in the plant and to supply the supplements that are most deficient at the point when the plant most needs it (#129). *Nitrogen is the one element more likely to be deficient in a plant and its substrate* (#130). Nitrogen dwindles down after about one month in a substrate. Nitrogen gas in the air lasts forever. Though it's the most common chemical in the air, it stays in an unusable form.

One case study discovered an inconvenient truth about one controlled-release fertilizer advertised to last six months. After three months, it no longer measured adequate levels of the nitrogen element. That CRF was tested on woody plants in a nursery container with normal waterings and within normal temperature ranges.

Some bonsai substrate is much coarser in texture than the substrate commonly used in ornamental nursery container production. Fast-release fertilizer added to gravelly substrate quickly dumps its essential elements and leaches out. Apply CRF products twice a year or water soluble fertilizers every three months during the growing season on a gravelly type substrate.

■ What is controlled-release fertilizer? What makes it any better than fast-release fertilizer?

CRF is minerals, either pelletized or water soluble powder but with a coating of plastic or sulfur. That coating binds and holds the minerals for longer periods instead of being dumped all at once. Controlled release depends on the thickness and holding quality of the plastic coating making the beads. Also relevant is the moisture present, the temperature range, and the amount of time it stays on the substrate.

Leaching out of the bottom of a container is the most common way applied essential elements are lost from the root zone of bonsai grown in gravelly type substrate (#131). *Controlled-release fertilizer products provide a continuous supply of elements at optimal levels, but in small enough quantities to minimize the loss of essential elements due to leaching* (#132).

Most modern, professional nursery container growers prefer some type of CRF product. Various formulations are available to last from two to twelve months of gradual release. More expensive CRF products are not always any better. Any fertilizer product will last considerably longer in modern organic/calcined clay substrate than in a gravelly/gritty textured substrate.

One study showed that higher-quality nursery plants resulted from two straight applications of a CRF product compared to split applications with both fast-release fertilizer (13-13-13) and a controlled-release fertilizer.[*]

> *Tip*: A nursery-quality, nine-month CRF product with trace elements can normally be applied once or twice a year. Apply once in the spring and possibly again in the fall. That's it!
>
> This simple but proven and effective practice applies to fertilizing during both the development and the refinement stage of most deciduous bonsai. Skip the spring application of CRF on most evergreens. They won't tolerate as much fertilizer as will deciduous plants.

■ Why are fast-release fertilizers, either granular or water soluble, not normally "the best solution for bonsai"?

Increasing the amount of either granular or liquid fast-release fertilizer has the potential to "burn" both the roots and foliage. The fast-acting granular fertilizers such as 10-10-10 are for agricultural production not for bonsai culture.

Fast-acting water soluble fertilizer products will be short-lived and must be applied considerably more often than a CRF product. They were originally formulated for flowering annuals and perennials or for our vegetable garden. The urea nitrogen found in most of those spray-on products causes leaf burn.

Foliar applications of fast-release fertilizer can't ever supply enough of a plant's essential elements (#133). Even when sprayed on the top of the substrate, all the elements are released all at once to the roots whether or not the tree can accept them. The remaining elements are unused or will quickly leach out the bottom of the pot with the next watering.

Water soluble fast-release fertilizer works better if the plant needs those particular elements immediately. But then the bonsai sits, waiting hungrily for its liquid "plant food" fix again. This process turns into a constant cycle of feast or famine when regularly "fed" water soluble fertilizer.

Controlled-release fertilizer (CRF) supplements are more economical in the long run because we don't need to apply them so often (#134). CRF is usually the best overall solution for supplying that 1 percent proportional share of essential elements not being supplied through photosynthesis, air, and water.

■ What are the differences between the available controlled-release fertilizer supplements?

As with most products, the quality and efficacy of CRF products will vary considerably. Some low-quality CRFs can dump excessive elements prematurely into the substrate (#135). With an unstable thin coating on low-quality CRFs and subjected to increased temperatures and rainfall, elements will be released prematurely. In that case, CRF is no different from any fast-release fertilizer.

---

[*] Scholl and D. Fare, "Fertilizer Source and Application Time Impact Growth of Containerized Oak Liners," *SNA Research Conference* 54 (2009).

■ How do I apply CRF supplements?

Two ways commonly used in container nurseries are surface application and premixed into the substrate. Surface application is best for bonsai. **No benefit exists from premixing any fertilizer into substrate before repotting** (#136). If fertilizer is incorporated into the substrate when repotting, it may become available but leached out before new root growth can ever utilize it.

> *Tip*: Apply fertilizer the same way you apply water—on top of the substrate and for the roots. Controlled-release fertilizer is best sprinkled uniformly on the top of the bonsai substrate with a cup or spoon or by hand. You could spread a thin topdressing of fine compost or fine calcined clay over the plasticized pellets to keep them from washing away. If the pot rim is deep enough and pellets large enough, the CRF pellets or spheres should stay on the surface with each watering or during heavy rainfall.

■ What about fertilizing the plants out in field soil?

Granular fertilizers without the slow-release coatings are inexpensive, easy to apply, and fast acting. Both organic and inorganic fertilizers work well on field-grown plants, if necessary at all.

Only apply fertilizer to plants developing in the field if they require more essential elements than what's already available in the soil—which is rarely the case.

"Use a slow-release type of fertilizer on mature bonsai and fast-release fertilizer for in-the-ground trees."

The majority of plants are prewired to accept a wide range of any essential elements applied. Container plants require much higher concentrations of fertilizer than field plants. Roots either take up a lot of fertilizer that dissolves rapidly in water or else fewer applications of a CRF product that dissolves slowly in water. Essential elements are scarce in our substrates and leach quickly out of the pot.

Established field-grown plants can also use CRF and eventually will survive quite well without any added fertilizer product.

Composts and other organic fertilizers are more effective on nursery trees in the ground than on container trees (#137). If your field soil already contains enough organic matter, you probably won't notice more plant growth when you add most types of fertilizer to field-grown stock.

"Too much artificial fertilizer releases too fast and burns the roots."

Fact: **Excessive amounts of salts in any fertilizer product can dehydrate a plan**t (#138).

Fertilizer products with the name "nitrate" or "urea" in them often have high burn potential. **Organic fertilizers can dehydrate the roots as fast as inorganic granular fertilizers** (#139).

Water dilutes some of the fertilizer salts and spreads those salts around in solution. Water inside the delicate, tender new roots close to undiluted fertilizer is drawn out, and the roots become dehydrated. Excess salts from fast-acting water soluble fertilizers can cause the purer water inside the plant to migrate back out of the roots. That equalizes the salt concentration found in the less pure water of the substrate.

Soluble salts become concentrated and toxic to the plant with insufficient water (#140). Ensure the plant has adequate water both before and after any application of fertilizer.

■ Full strength or half strength? When using fast-release water soluble fertilizer, how much is too much?

Applying fertilizer to a plant is quite different from applying water to a plant. Water soluble fertilizers can be applied at the manufacturer's recommended times and rates. Applying a half dose of 20-20-20 turns out twice as strong as a full dose of a 5-5-5 fertilizer product. Put on a "weaker dose more often" and the plant may not be able to accumulate enough of what it needs.

If you apply too much, it's wasted and possibly toxic. Fertilizer manufacturers would love for you to use as much as you can of their product, even if most of it washes out the drain holes with the next watering.

Water soluble fertilizer applications at less than full strength may not supply enough of some particular essential element lacking in a plant at that time (#141).

LIQUID OR GRANULAR?

■ Which one is better on bonsai substrates, CRF pellets or CRF water soluble applied as a liquid spray?

CRF pellets are hard to beat. Those spheres stay on the substrate for release in precise amounts at the right time.

Since water soluble slow release has the propensity to leach out with each watering, granular CRF would be more economical and efficacious. Most water soluble fertilizers are fast release. CRF usually contains both slow- and fast-release nitrogen.

By definition, natural organic fertilizers are slow release, too. But we can't control or monitor the rate of elements released from any organics we use on modern substrate.

"Plants can absorb nutrients twenty times more effectively through the spray on their leaves than they can from the fertilizer sprayed on their roots."

If that sounds like a false advertisement, it is. For most established plants, applying liquid fertilizer directly on the substrate for the roots is more effective than spraying directly on the foliage. Leaves and branches can photosynthesize and grow quite well by themselves without a single foliar application of fertilizer. Foliar fertilization can be an emergency or temporary solution to a substrate or root problem from micronutrient deficiency.

Some disadvantages of foliar sprays include:

- *Most essential elements sprayed in a water solution just on the foliage will never reach all parts of the plant* (#142). The elements already in a leaf usually stay in that leaf and won't reach the roots. Substrate applications have the potential of reaching all parts of the plant from the roots up.

- *Some thick-leafed species can't take in foliar fertilizers efficiently and*

won't benefit if liquid fertilizer is sprayed only on their leaves (#143).

- Most old, tough, hardy bonsai plants have thicker cuticles than you would find on a younger greenhouse-grown plant. Waxy leaves repel water since no electrical charge exists.

- It's true that some elements can get into the stomata on the bottom of the leaf. *Foliar applications are useless if the spray droplets forming on top of a leaf roll off or crystalize before reaching the stomata under the leaf* (#144).

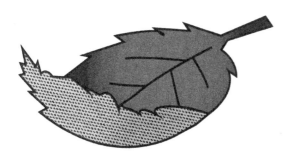

- *Spraying foliar fertilizer is wasted when stomata close off transpiration during excessive heat and when stomata close up during darkness* (#145).

- *If you spray only the tops of the foliage too much and too often, the fertilizer is wasted and the leaves get injured* (#146).

- *Foliar applications will not solve an essential element deficiency in the roots* (#147). Foliar applications can be a good method to verify a deficiency of iron in the foliage, but they won't help satisfy a deficiency of iron in the roots. Iron won't move out of the leaf.

- *High nitrogen in the foliage has been shown to increase the plant's susceptibility to insect pests* (#148).

- *Foliar applications can't ever give the plant enough nitrogen, phosphorus,* *or magnesium because so much is needed of those mega elements* (#149). The uptake of the big-three elements of N P K comes through the roots.

- *Salts from excessive foliar spraying can become concentrated, cumulative, and toxic* (#150). Residue may scorch foliage on a hot, sunny day.

- *Micronutrients (trace elements) are the only essential elements that could ever be useful from foliar application; only a trace amount is required, and only a trace amount of elements can possibly enter the foliage* (#151).

- *The roots in a pot can become weakened if you are only spraying the foliage* (#152).

■ Why can't I "spray only the weaker lower branches of the bonsai with a foliar fertilizer so the total tree growth will be more equalized"?

Maybe the problem of weak, declining lower branches is the result of a lack of sufficient light more than from lack of fertilizer.

■ Should I be concerned about harming the plant by spraying liquid fertilizer on the leaves during a hot, dry day?

That could definitely be a cause for concern. During a long, hot day, leaves are busy with evapotranspiration, using the greater part of the available water they can get up through the new roots (#153). Spraying a salty solution on the leaves reduces the available water both in the leaves and coming up from the roots. Those salts crystalize again before a spray of liquid fertilizer reaches the stomata under the leaves.

■ *Could I "inject liquid fertilizer directly into a trunk or the soil for quicker results and better food distribution"?*

No, the toxicity risk is too great. Trunk injections of fertilizer may possibly help the leaf coloration but cannot help the long-term health of the tree. That's the job for roots to distribute their essential resources up the tree.

You can't "force feed" a plant (#154). Several studies have concurred and concluded that soil surface applications of fertilizer were more effective than either soil or trunk injection. "Burying fertilizer in the soil" also has been proven ineffective.

SPRING OR FALL?

■ *At what stage of growth will bonsai start requiring fertilizer supplements? Should I start the growing season with fast- or slow-release fertilizer?*

Normally, CRF products can be applied after new foliage hardens off in late spring. As the substrate temperature rises, the elements in the controlled-release product become slowly available to assist the new roots for the next growth flush.

Contrary to common practice, bonsai do not "need their biggest amount of fertilizer as soon as the buds start breaking open to strengthen the new growth." This is because:

- *New foliage grows quickly and dies quickly from too early fertilization* (#155). The tree can't stay healthy long with constant, rapid growth.
- In early spring, the branches and thicker roots still hold a sufficient reserve of photosynthates accumulated during the last summer and fall. Those stored photosynthates came from leaf

photosynthesis and then from the leaf before it dropped.

- *The rapid flush of spring growth will first make use of those stored reserves already present in the plant* (#156).
- *After leaf flush, sun, water, and air continue to furnish 99 percent of the total amount by concentration of all essential elements plants require* (#157).
- *Nitrogen and phosphorus leach out the drain holes before benefiting the plant when fertilizer is applied too early in the spring* (#158).
- *Excess fast-release nitrogen causes immediate injury to a plant* (#159).

> *Tip*: Hold off on any fertilizer applications to resting or stressed plants, especially at the height of hot summer or freezing winter.

Controlled-release nitrogen is much safer for the roots than fast-release nitrogen at most stages of growth. Applied in the fall, CRF products are safe and highly recommended to assist in the making and storage of photosynthates for the next growing season.

■ *What time of the year should I start fertilizing my bonsai, and when should I stop fertilizing my bonsai? Is it different for evergreens than for deciduous?*

Roots grow all year. All plants use energy from respiration all year. Sufficient light is necessary all year, especially in evergreens and indoor plants since the rate of photosynthesis must exceed the rate of respiration.

Evergreens grow almost all year in the right temperature range. Generally, they can adapt to lesser fertility when in their natural soils. Some commercial container nurseries apply a good-quality twelve-month CRF product once every late spring on evergreens. *Deciduous trees require more watering and fertilizing than would a similar-sized broadleaf or narrowleaf evergreen tree* (#160). *A deciduous plant needs to pack in an entire year's growth in barely half a year* (#161).

Before packing up for winter, deciduous trees withdraw as many essential resources as possible from their leaves and store photosynthates for the next year's new growth. Trees already have sufficient reserves when the buds open and the leaves start to unfold for their first flush. No fast-release fertilizer applications are necessary in late winter for early spring flush.

Both spring and fall are the appropriate times to fertilize bonsai with a good-quality, long-lasting CRF product that includes both long-term macros and micronutrients in correct proportions (#162).

The plastic coating on some CRF products may be temperature sensitive. A portion of the essential elements may not be available to the plant in the cooler days of early spring or early fall. Apply CRF the first day of spring so the plant gets a constant slow release with every watering or rain, with time and with constantly rising temperatures. Reapplication may be necessary by the first day of fall. Moderate rates of additional CRF applied during the fall don't stimulate new growth.

No scientific evidence confirms that adding fertilizer increases winter hardiness (#163).*

"You don't want to overwork the roots. Stop the fertilizer applications on bonsai in the late fall in order to give the roots a rest."
*Plant cells keep on dividing and elongating with or without our help or the help of fertilize*r (#164).

■ **Is it OK to have some unused CRF pellets left over in the substrate during the entire winter?**

Sure, no harm is done. CRF products will sit there all winter waiting for the temperature to get higher before it is released.

The manufacturer of one CRF product I use twice a year states on the bag that its fertilizer will last eight months under an average temperature of 60°F and lasts only five months at an average 80°F. In contrast, quick-release fertilizer has the propensity for "root burn" if its elements don't dissolve in sufficient water or leach out.

By the Numbers

We've chosen either fast-release or controlled-release patterns. The next choice: what are the chemical formulations?

■ **What would be a good "balanced fertilizer" or "complete fertilizer" for cultivating bonsai?**

In theory, you should be able to apply a "balanced and complete fertilizer" and completely provide "all the food in balanced

---

* F. Henning et al., "Effect of Fall Fertilization on Freeze Resistance of Deciduous versus Evergreen Azaleas," *Journal of Environmental Horticulture* 28, no. 4 (2010): 235–39.

proportions any bonsai is ever going to need."

In practice, you can't. "General all-purpose, complete, balanced fertilizer" usually means a fertilizer with the same numbers. A fertilizer called 10-10-10, for the 10 percent nitrogen element (N), 10 percent phosphorus element (P), and 10 percent potassium element (K), yields a 30 percent total volume of actual fertilizer in that particular package. *Nitrogen, phosphorus, and potassium (NPK) is not a "complete, balanced fertilizer"* (#165).

Aside from hydrogen, oxygen, and carbon, nitrogen is one essential element needed by plants in relatively large proportions relative to the other elements in a plant. It's usually the main element low in a substrate over a period of time. Twice the percentage of nitrogen element may be needed over phosphorus or potassium in a modern, well-draining substrate. *Increasing the nitrogen can decrease the availability of the potassium* (#166).

Both nitrogen and phosphorus leach rapidly from container substrates (#167). If we apply a 10-10-10 fertilizer, then nitrogen and phosphorus are going to be used up or leached out a whole lot faster than the 10 percent potassium.

Are those other essential elements still available in the right amounts and in the right proportions to one another? Without testing, it is difficult to know which elements are missing until a deficiency shows up after the plant has been long declining in health.

If a plant requires a certain essential element, it will use up that specific element more readily than any other elements (#168). The rest of the elements it doesn't use may be sitting there, tied up or wasted.

CRF supplements may also contain iron, sulfur, gypsum, and magnesium or other essential elements needed in much smaller proportions. Scientists have limited knowledge about the appropriate levels of the essential elements needed for optimal plant growth. Too many species and too many variables make for an inexact science when it comes to which fertilizer is best or "complete."

You want to simplify your fertilization program: "Nitrogen is for shoots, phosphorus for roots, potassium for fruits and flowers."
That's not the case. And no essential element can "stimulate" any part of a plant to grow. *The mega three essential elements are not only for the shoots, roots, and fruits* (#169). They're for the entire plant.

Nitrogen does not "stimulate shoot growth" (#170). Nitrogen is a major component of proteins, growth regulators, chloroplasts, vitamins, and enzymes essential to the entire plant.

Phosphorus does not "stimulate root growth" (#171). Phosphorus is essential for photosynthesis, protein formation, and almost all aspects of growth and metabolism in the entire plant.

Potassium does not "stimulate the growth of fruits and flowers" (#172). Potassium is essential for sugar, starch, and carbohydrate formation, for protein synthesis, and for all cell divisions in the entire plant.

Nitrogen, phosphorus, and potassium are all essential elements needed by all the shoots, roots, and fruits (#173). Sixteen other elements are also needed in much smaller quantities and concentrations by all the shoots, roots, and fruits.

Substrate composition can be a recipe. Fertilization is not a "recipe." You can't "lower the nitrogen to slow upper growth" or "increase the phosphorus to speed up the root growth."

■ **Which essential element is most limited in a plant and most likely to be toxic in high amounts?**

Nitrogen requires the most energy expenditure of all elements (#174). Complex nitrogen compounds must undergo changes and release energy before any nitrogen can be utilized by a plant.

Nitrogen is the one element most limiting in a plant. It is needed in relatively high concentrations and must be constantly replenished in the substrate (#175). That element readily leaches out of the pot because it's repelled away from most substrate particles by its negative-charged ions. Then it is leached out with the next watering.

Nitrogen can be applied as both a fast-release form and as a controlled-release form. When we add fertilizer that includes nitrogen, we usually see quick results in plant growth. So we tend to keep adding high nitrogen (the first number on the bag).

Ammonia toxicity is a common result of too much nitrogen. *A high nitrogen level decreases root growth and may even result in phytotoxicity to a plant* (#176).

"Adding high-nitrogen fertilizer increases the rate of plant growth."
We can't add fertilizer to increase a plant's rate of growth (#177). Adding more nitrogen to young deciduous trees reduces the top leader dominance and promotes longer side shoots, but it never makes a tree grow faster, taller, or thicker.

Studies have consistently shown that increasing the levels of nitrogen does not add additional growth in plant height or stem diameter (#178).

Low levels of the nitrogen element favor apical dominance at the top branches but reduced growth in branch diameter (#179). This means that trees can keep on growing up in height without any additional nitrogen.

Phosphorus, not nitrogen, is the main element that governs plant height (#180).

Sporadic, haphazard fertilizer applications lead to abnormal surge growth (#181). In turn, more fertilizer triggers more pathogen activity during the hot summertime.

We can't add fertilizer to a deciduous plant slowing down for its resting phase and expect it to start increasing its growth again. No cause and effect takes place between adding more nitrogen and starting up new leaf growth after dormancy.

Fertilizer applications increase the plant's need for water (#182).

Many pathogens exacerbate plant diseases due to increased nitrogen levels (#183).

■ **Does fresh organic material consume nitrogen during its own decay process?**

Very little. Some nitrogen is required and little energy is consumed during composting before organic materials can be useful in a substrate. Organic matter consists of much more carbon than nitrogen.

"Bonsai must always have something organic to feed on. Organic material supplies enough nitrogen when supplied as a top dressing."
Fact: *No nitrogen in organic material is available to plants until broken down by existing bacteria and changed into a usable form of ammonia or nitrate* (#184).
Organic matter spread on top of inert

substrate cannot supply any essential element to any plant (#185).

■ You know natural rain is the optimum water for plants. Can't "bonsai get most of their nitrogen from rain"?

Only about 5 percent of the plant's total available nitrogen comes from rain or lightning. *Nitrogen needs regular replacing in substrates due to its transitory nature* (#186).

■ You accumulated a lot of leaf litter this fall. Is "finely shredded leaf mulch a good source of nitrogen"? Can I "let the fallen leaves stay in the pot for nitrogen from organic fertilizer"?

Not necessarily. Dead leaves in leaf litter will be low in any essential element. The tree takes the nitrogen from its foliage for itself before shedding its leaves. Don't count on those depleted leaves supplying any more nitrogen.

> *Tip*: It's always a good idea to remove the fallen leaves and weeds from the pot to minimize pathogen activity.

■ You don't want your bonsai to have too much late growth that would only freeze and die. Should I "stop using fertilizer by midsummer"? Does "applying nitrogen in the winter time stimulate unwanted late budding"?

The scientific answer to both questions is no. *By midsummer, most of the tree's energy is shifting to root development and to photosynthate production and storage* (#187). It still needs some available nitrogen all year for growth regulators and

continual cell division. Once new cell division ceases, it's gone.

> *Tip*: Late fall fertilization applications that include nitrogen may also help give the tree an extra boost for spring growth.

Research studies and practical field applications indicate the value of midsummer fertilization for maintaining the flourishing growth of spring-potted plants. *Research results also imply most plants would benefit from late fall fertilization* (#188).

Overwintering bonsai in warm climates may cause the release of elements from a CRF supplement. Not to worry. The available nitrogen does not make the leaves flush out at an earlier time than the buds would normally unfold. Nor does it reduce winter hardiness. *Acclimation to cold temperatures will not be delayed from fall fertilization* (#189).[*]

"Adding more nitrogen thickens the trunk and helps the roots grow."
Fact: The plants' response to nitrogen fertilization is highly complex. Nitrogen does show up in foliage growth. But increasing the nitrogen rate does not have a significant effect on tree height or trunk caliper growth.[†]

A tree doesn't grow as a result of applying more nitrogen than it normally requires (#190).

---

[*] D. Hadziabdic et al., "Spring Growth of Two Woody Ornamentals in Response to Fall Fertilization and Timing," *SNA Research Conference Proceedings* 46 (2001).
[†] J. Robbins, "Effect of Nitrogen on the Growth of Field-Grown Ornamental Trees in Eastern Arkansas after Four Years," *SNA Research Conference Proceedings* 51 (2006).

Root generation decreases with increased nitrogen rates regardless of previous root pruning (#191).

Optimal nitrogen needed for top growth is not the optimal nitrogen needed for root growth. Increased stem growth can reduce the rate of root growth (#192). *Greater amounts of nitrogen go to the top growth, not to the root growth* (#193).[‡]

■ Would "low nitrogen prevent long internodes and lush foliage"?

Low nitrogen, low phosphorus, low potassium, low manganese, low calcium, and low copper, et cetera, stunt growth. All essential elements are essential for the growth of all branches and foliage. Low amounts of gibberellin growth regulators in stems produces shorter internodes.

■ Will "too much nitrogen ruin the established fine stem ramification and existing small leaves" on your refined bonsai?

No, using less nitrogen doesn't "prevent long stem growth." Nor does "more nitrogen promote small leaves into large leaves and cause so much rampant top growth that the roots cannot sustain the overly balanced branches." Excess nitrogen is wasted. We will go into this in more detail in later chapters on balancing branches and roots.

■ Does "nitrogen govern the size of a tree"?

The correct answer sometimes perplexes people. Phosphorus, not nitrogen, governs

plant size. *High phosphate levels result in tall plants; phosphorus, not nitrogen, governs plant size* (#194). *No relationship exists between the amount of nitrogen applied and the rate of plant growth* (#195).[§]

Lower the phosphorus levels, not the nitrogen levels, if you want a more compact plant during its later refinement stage (#196).

■ You observe the nice effects on the foliage when you add nitrogen. What about the other elements? Should I "add extra high phosphorus and high calcium content fertilizer to promote flowers and fruits, shoots, roots, and mycorrhizae"?

No part of that claim can be supported by any scientific literature. Plants do quite well on their own without the addition of extra high phosphate or calcium fertilizers. Phosphorus is in the phosphate form in fertilizer. It's important to monitor and increase the availability of phosphate in acid-tolerant plants.

Additions of phosphate do not "stimulate root growth and shoot growth." Never "add superphosphate to encourage more root and shoot growth."

A substrate low in phosphate can influence a good environment for root growth (#197). *Excess phosphate inhibits mycorrhizal fungi* (#198). Never add phosphate to plants in field soil without first testing the soil.

[‡] J. Owen, "Growth of One- and Two-Year-Old Red Maples under Varying Nitrogen Rates," **SNA Research Conference Proceedings** 53 (2008): 88–92.

[§] P. Nelson et al., "What Really Causes Stretch?" January 2002.

■ **You start noticing the leaves turning red in the summer and you haven't fertilized in a while. Do I "pour on the superphosphate if the leaves are turning a reddish color"?**

Plants need phosphorus when manufacturing the growth regulators, vitamins, lipids, and acids found in most of their cells. *If foliage turns a reddish color prematurely, the cause is less likely from phosphorus deficiency rather than from other environmental stresses* (#199).

Tip: Leaves turn red for many different reasons. Increased intensity of light or cold or drought can change the leaf color to a more reddish hue. A reddish color from anthocyanin acts as a sunscreen. Red leaves hold less water than green leaves. An unhappy deciduous plant with leaves turning from green to red to brown in the summer may benefit from repotting.

This example illustrates why we shouldn't observe only leaf color change to diagnose a plant problem. The phosphorus element may not even be lacking in a substrate containing organic material or mycorrhiza. It might be present but tied up and unavailable. Phosphates are also notorious for leaching quickly out of substrates.

Excess phosphate concentrations can cause leaf chlorosis and may even become toxic to the plant. *Restoring deficient nitrogen in a substrate improves the plant's ability to use phosphorus* (#200).

Tip: In a bonsai forest grouping, the addition of another species of seedling can serve as an early detection monitor of a deficiency of a particular element. A deciduous birch seedling, for instance, can be planted with an evergreen tray landscape and will react differently than the evergreens to any drastic change.

■ **The older leaves on my bonsai are turning yellowish and brownish colors. Should I try some nitrogen or should I try phosphorus?**

Be on the lookout for unseasonal leaf coloring, for wilting, and for any sudden dieback. Try not to diagnose a tree's problems solely from visual symptoms. A leaf turning chlorotic or a yellow color can be a sign of stress from multiple causes, including injured roots or stems.

Nitrogen is mobile inside and outside the plant cells. A deficiency or excess of nitrogen will first show up as chlorosis in the older leaves and spread to the younger leaves. Phosphorus doesn't move around much once inside plant tissue.

Excess or deficiency of the tree's essential elements, individually or in combination, can cause chlorosis or yellowing of the leaves. *The symptoms of toxicity or deficiency don't appear until a long time after the causes occur* (#201).

Adding too much of one essential element eventually makes another element toxic to the plant.

■ **You discover that adding iron to your lawns will green them up in a hurry. If the bonsai foliage looks chlorotic, would it "help to add iron with rusty nails or iron shavings"? Is chlorosis a pH imbalance?**

Chlorosis means the leaf tissue turns yellowish due to lack of chlorophyl. Sometimes it does work to apply iron. Or chlorosis could be a magnesium, manganese, zinc, or nitrogen deficiency. Sometimes chlorosis could be from excess iron or calcium carbonate, or from ruptured cells decreasing the number of green chloroplasts.

Poor leaf coloring and wrinkled leaves could be an indication of many problems. For example, poor root growth; a virus; too much or too little fertilizer; pesticides; nematodes; or a poorly aerated substrate. It might be time to repot. Don't be too concerned with a few yellowing leaves that aren't curling up on the margins.

Some variegated foliage on trees was developed to look chlorotic on purpose. The natural tissue aging appears chlorotic. Some trees are more tolerant of higher pH (above 7.5) and of a constantly compacted wet substrate. A pH imbalance may not even exist in most bonsai substrate.

Chlorosis is more commonly caused by a history of overwatering, especially during the spring, or watering with high pH well water (#202).

> *Tip*: You may need to monitor your watering program with a moisture meter. Or add acidifiers to the alkaline irrigation water from some wells. Monitor the pH on azaleas. Iron, boron, and manganese are notoriously deficient in high alkaline (high lime) soils.

The only good case for foliar fertilization: if you've sprayed the foliage with iron chelate and it greened right up in a few days, you've solved the symptoms. Still, those effects won't carry over to the next year unless you apply the iron supplements to the substrate.

As mentioned earlier, some elements are mobile and some are immobile in a plant. Iron is immobile in a plant and can be tied up and unusable. The lack or excess of iron starts on the outer, younger leaves, and you'll observe it later as those same leaves age. The vein itself remains green.

Solid iron is never available to the plant roots. Rusty nails and iron shavings are useless to plants as the iron is tied up. High pH or addition of lime can tie up iron.

Nitrogen, manganese, and zinc deficiencies start on the inner, older leaves and include the veins. Chlorosis is a lack of chlorophyll secondary to too much or too little N, Mn, or Zn. You can notice a plant developing later chlorosis outward to the younger leaves and including the leaf veins.

■ ***It's time to prepare your bonsai for winter. A "special potash fertilizer" product claims to "fatten up bonsai and improve frost resistance."***

Yes, those products are available but may not live up to claims. It turns out that potassium could be a magical fat booster for potatoes but not a booster for woody plants.

The scientific evidence to date is both conflicting and confusing concerning the association of fertilizer to cold tolerance in a plant. Potassium alone has been shown by different studies to have three different effects on cold injury when applied to non-woody agricultural crops planted out in field soil—positive, negative, and no effect at all. The "K" stands for potash when you see it on a fertilizer bag.

FERTILIZERS ARE SUPPLEMENTS

■ How often should I fertilize?

Some people living in northern countries take vitamin D supplements. Their objective is to supplement the deficiency of naturally occurring vitamin D due to weak sunlight in their microclimate. *Our objective in applying fertilizer is to supplement our bonsai with its essential elements and resources on an as-needed basis* (#203).

Fertilizer products are simply a supplement to help plants create their own resources more efficiently. We add fertilizer to supplement a deficiency in a particular plant. Some tolerate lower concentrations of essential elements. Some plants don't have a deficiency in essential elements and never need a supplement.

"Nutrients are used up so quickly by the plant and must be replaced every couple weeks."

Fact: Some bonsai, especially those grown on or in a rock planting and those that tolerate low light levels, use minimal amounts of essential elements. Fertilizer supplements are not as vital to plants growing out in field soil. Bonsai in some niches are able to thrive for years without a single application of fertilizer supplements.

Growth processes in a specific plant, the rate of crown growth, and the rate of root growth are constantly changing. The chemical, physical, and biological composition of the substrate will change considerably over one growing season.

If you use water soluble fertilizers or fast-release fertilizers, you'll be repeating those applications often. Fertilizer supplements applied in too large amounts accumulate and may become toxic to the plant, or they may be leached out and wasted with the next watering.

■ How much of all those fertilizer supplements that I apply to my bonsai are actually used by the trees?

Many trees don't use more than 20 percent of all the available chemicals in the fertilizers we apply (#204). The rest is tied up and unavailable or leached out. More often than not, nitrogen is tied up and unavailable or leached out. Phosphorus and sulfur are also quite susceptible to leaching out the drain holes.

■ Why do bonsai growing in modern substrate need regular, repeated applications of mineral supplements?

Growth in plants comes from cells dividing somewhere in the plant every day of the year. *Cell division slows down, or stops, if a plant lacks any one of its essential elements* (#205).

Forest tree roots have all nineteen essential elements, all the other natural resources, and all the room they need. Any supplements are superfluous.

Bonsai roots are forced to grow in coarse substrate within a confining space using up some of their own limited resources during the growing season. Container plants could use more supplements to grow if they had access to more resources. Essential elements are used up, washed out, and limited in availability to roots trying to survive in the relatively barren substrate. So we add supplements to their natural resources. Their own resources are used in all plant cell divisions.

■ You apply extra fertilizer to your newly seeded lawn or vegetable garden. Does "adding fertilizer to field plants help fast track them to get started as a bonsai"?

Not according to university experiments. *Adding fertilizer supplements to field soil at planting time does little or nothing to speed transplant establishment of landscape trees from container, balled and burlapped (B&B), or bare root* (#206).*

Field soil test data generally show sufficient phosphate and all micronutrients. Foliage analysis data generally show all essential elements are present and accounted for in landscape trees. There is no need for supplements.

■ How long will micronutrients last when applied to substrate?

Several elements are required in much smaller quantities or concentrations for plant growth or reproduction. Micronutrients (trace elements) can be available as components of a CRF in either liquid or granular form. If additional micronutrient supplements are part of the CRF, it will not be necessary to apply any more micronutrients for up to two growing seasons on most substrates.

Some micronutrients may be still available in composted organic substrate materials or in field soil that was left clinging to the roots of a recently collected transplant. Those supplements can last until the next repotting.

> *Tip*: Most plants won't need all the supplements we give them. Supplements more often cause toxicities in an otherwise healthy plant. Applying micronutrients in an existing situation of toxicity or deficiency will simply increase the problems. Toxicities cannot be controlled without replacing contaminated substrate and repotting the unhealthy plant.

■ You have some pre-bonsai growing out in the garden area. Does field "soil need trace elements added for optimal growth"?

There's no need to add to the trace elements already in garden field soil if they are composed of at least 5 percent organic matter. Container growers stopped using any field soil as part of substrates more than fifty years ago. So our nutrient-poor bonsai substrates can sometimes benefit from extremely tiny concentrations of trace elements applied once every year or two.

Does "adding fertilizer and rooting hormones to recently potted bonsai help them get started"?

No scientific evidence shows that fertilizer, growth stimulants, or special hormones are even necessary for a tree to survive right after potting. Newly potted plants don't need an application of fertilizer until several weeks later. You can cause injury if you "fertilize weekly, weakly."

Adding fast-release fertilizer at potting has been shown to be detrimental to plant growth and results in wasted, leached-out nitrogen and phosphorus (#207).†

> *Tip*: There's no need to mix fertilizers in the substrate because they might be leached out with the initial watering. Wait until you see obvious new top growth unfold, and then harden off before you think of the first fertilizing. Start with a long-term, low-percentage CRF supplement.

* J.R. Harris et al., "Does Fertilization at Planting Speed Establishment of Landscape Trees?" **SNA Research Conference Proceedings** 52 (2007).

† S. Scholl and D. Fare, "Fertilizer Source and Application Time Impact Growth of Containerized Oak Liners," **SNA Research Conference Proceedings** 54 (2009).

Phosphorus won't "stimulate the growth of new roots at potting" and can even inhibit root growth.

Adding "rooting hormones" can inhibit root growth when applied to existing roots (#208).

CAN'T ALWAYS BLAME FERTILIZER

■ Should I "add fertilizer to cure nutritional deficiencies"?

Fertilizer applications can't cure deficiencies caused by insect or disease injury, poor roots, environmental problems, toxicity problems from excess micronutrients, water problems, substrate problems, or many other weakening factors (#209).

"White, crusty accumulation on the top of substrate and under the pot is a sign of too much fertilizer."
Maybe, or it could come from lime deposits from your alkaline water. Chemical salts dissolved in water don't evaporate when the water evaporates.

"Turning the pot around every so often makes the fertilizer work better."
No cause and effect exists in that statement.

■ You find big open scars after aggressive pruning. Would "aggressive fertilization promote rapid wound closures"?

No. Injured plants heal quite differently than wounded animals. With excess fertilizer, injury from improper pruning becomes further enlarged, and any callus formation slows down.

"Aggressive fertilization is the secret to developing finer branch ramifications."
The opposite effect usually occurs. Aggressive fertilization along with aggressive pruning forces a heavy flush of top sprouts with long internodes. Sprouts are the tree's response to start a new crown to accommodate excess fertilizer or pruning injuries.

> *Tip*: Water sprouts suck out energy for themselves at the expense of secondary branching. Then you must eliminate most of those long stems. Time spent pruning back that mass of long sprouts sets back the time needed for developing shorter branch ramifications.

"Flowers are harmed if the tree is fertilized while in bloom."
You can safely fertilize the blooming tree without affecting its blossoms.

"Too much fertilizer causes root rot damage."
Root rot is a fungus problem, not a fertilizer or substrate problem. Injury, not damage, harms plants.

So which biostimulants and other supplements could I add to stimulate my bonsai?

UNDERSTANDING BIOSTIMULANTS
AND OTHER SUCH CHEMICALS

An unbelievable amount of biostimulant products flood the gardening market. They imply unbelievable claims to help a plant in numerous ways—too numerous to be tested. Those products, when independently tested, do not always back up manufacturers' claims. It's not "what can we give our bonsai" to make it healthy. It's holistic plant health, not concentrating on products but on all the factors that keep it thriving.

Various university researchers have collaborated on studying biostimulants and eventually find limited benefit from using biostimulant products for container growing.

You'll find a few patterns in this chapter. Some biostimulant products may be somewhat effective in feeding bacteria in field soil crops but not effective in providing essential elements to plants in modern bonsai substrates. Some biostimulant treatments are even found to cause more harm than benefit.

■ Are biostimulants fertilizer? What's the bottom line for us bonsaiists using biostimulants when we bonsai?

Sometimes classified as metabolic enhancers, biostimulants differ from traditional non-carbon fertilizers in that their active chemical ingredient consists of organic compounds. The category of biostimulants could include fertilizers, vitamins and other chemicals such as auxins, cytokinins or salicylic acid. Or it could include plant or animal extracts ranging from algae extracts to zebra eyeball extracts! (Can you see where this is heading?)

Readily available independent scientific testing results to date are not consistent or supportive of product claims. Most biostimulant products independently tested were verified to have no beneficial effects on plant health. Testimonials don't count. Testimonials are advertisements.

Tip: Biostimulants are not going to make any difference to plants in any substrate deficient in essential elements or in microorganisms. If the conditions in a substrate are not right for biologicals to work, they won't work. What works in field soil crops won't work at all in a bonsai substrate devoid of organic matter and microorganisms.

Plant health is more determined by plant species and their environmental conditions than by any biostimulant application (#210).

Why does a plant continue to have the same problems no matter how much or what type of biostimulant is applied to it? Why do we not find any consistent effect of different biostimulant products on a specific species of plants? Because no consistent active ingredient is found in biostimulant products. Even when the active ingredient is the same, there's no consistent beneficial effect on all plants. ***Most of the time biostimulant applications are wasted anyway as they usually leach out with the next watering in our coarse-textured substrates*** (#211).

No miracles or magic are behind biostimulants. Instead, consider saving your money to buy a good watering hose and a good-quality, controlled-release fertilizer product. *Bottom line*: Bonsai live quite well without any biostimulant product. To date, no scientific rationale exists for using metabolic enhancers on bonsai.

Research studies cannot verify any consistent and significant biological activity or ability to stimulate life from adding any biostimulant to substrate (#212).

Few substrates on the market are truly "sterilized." Bonsai substrates consisting of fresh gravel might be completely devoid of living microorganisms. Therefore, no organic fertilizer ever becomes available to a plant.

Add as little as 5 percent compost or hammermilled bark to the total volume of a gravelly type substrate; the mix will be loaded with microorganisms (#213).

Field soil is a completely different story from modern substrate because natural soil already contains so much organic matter and so many soil organisms. Bacteria found in field soil love to consume biostimulants. Any microorganisms already present in the natural soil are the first to use any fertilizer or carbon-based "biostimulants" we apply. Any essential elements left over, after the microorganisms first consume what they need, may be available to the roots of stock growing out in garden field soil.

Animal byproducts such as animal manures may contain a small percentage of slowly released nitrogen. The actual usable nitrogen depends on how finely those products are ground up and whether the nitrogen is tied up or able to be broken down. ***Microorganisms present in the organic matter of soil break down the nitrogen compounds into usable ions*** (#214).

The potential contribution of "organic biostimulants to stimulating biological activity" is minuscule when compared to the reliable contribution of a CRF supplement to remedy a deficit in any essential element. Simply add water and minerals whenever the plant is limited in water or any essential element.

While not totally true, it has been generalized that plants live on inorganic matter and animals live on organic matter.

■ Will "adding hormones stimulate growth"?

Not at all. A plant produces all the growth regulators it needs for all its own growth (#215). Growth regulators produced by the plant itself include the auxins, cytokinins and gibberellins.

We do not need to add hormones to plants. We can't stimulate any plant growth with any hormone or other biostimulant product (#216). We can stimulate animal growth with growth hormones, for example, by adding steroids.

■ Where are "growth hormones" produced? Can we do something to encourage plant growth?

"Growth hormones" is an animal term. Growth regulator is the term applied to plants. Growth regulators act different from animal hormones.

The plant makes its own growth regulators in the growing branch tips and at the ends of the roots. We don't need to add any more growth regulators or vitamins than a plant already makes itself. *We cannot add anything or do anything to stimulate our bonsai to grow* (#217).

Some herbicides, fertilizers, biostimulants and other chemicals have the propensity to cause undesirable, deformed growth in plants.

■ Vitamin B-1 is often advertised for use on bonsai. Where is the scientific evidence supporting any benefit?

It's quite nonexistent! Now, next question, please.

The then-famous "advertised study" from the late 1930s attempted to get detached pea roots to "regrow" after being placed in a sterile petri dish in laboratory-controlled conditions. In sterile culture media, vitamin B-1 (thiamine) was added to the pea roots to see if any regeneration growth response could occur in the roots. Growth was measured.

The problem with that experiment was the fact that thiamine is already manufactured in plant roots and the plant never needs more vitamins. Still, it won the 1940 World's Fair gold medal. The very next year, further independent testing failed to replicate any root growth on any plants, pea or otherwise.[*]

Since that time, other detached and intact roots of other plants have been independently studied for B-1 response but always failed to duplicate any type of growth response. Neither laboratory nor field conditions have ever replicated the same "regrowing" results from the 1930s. Now we know for certain that when B-1 is applied to normal plants, there is no plant response to that vitamin— perhaps because woody plants already produce optimum doses of what they need.

People don't cut off bonsai roots to see if the roots alone will respond, regenerate and turn into a bonsai! One study did show that plants watered with plain water grew better than plants watered with B-1.

It seems we should see some scientific evidence supporting B-1 since it's been around, overblown and heavily promoted for so long. For some reason, those B-1 ads keep coming on.

Plants respond but can't "regrow or regenerate" with anything we put on them (#218). Sugar from photosynthesis connects with the plant's own vitamins to release energy. This process is called respiration. *We cannot replicate photosynthesis to trap energy, replicate respiration to release energy or replicate metabolism to use energy* (#219).

Vitamins do not need to be added to a plant at any time because they are made by and already in the plant (#220). Adding B-1 has absolutely no effect at all on bonsai or on any other plant.

_____

[*] A.E. Hitchcock, "Further Tests with Vit B on Established Plants and on Cuttings," *Boyce Thompson Institute* 12, no. (1941): 143–56.

■ Where is the scientific evidence of any benefit of using "super-absorbent water crystals"?

Also nonexistent. Most products marketed with the word "super" in them probably will be shy of super.

Many times and in many ways, hydrophilic polymer, sometimes called superabsorbents and hydrogels, have been proposed as additives "to increase the water-holding capacity of bonsai soils." The two original objectives of that product were to improve substrate aeration and drainage and to keep the bare roots from drying out when transplanting or shipping.

Scientists discovered that the benefit of adding water gels was insignificant. The highest increase of water-holding capacity was shown to be only 5 percent more.

Since the 1980s, scientists have concluded that superabsorbents have little or no use in sustaining plant growth or in transplanting (#221). In fact, the gels start to absorb water away from the root system as it dries out, giving the plant even more drought stress. They break down during the growing season. Save your time and money.

■ Will surfactants "help increase the available water" to a substrate?

Surfactants, such as soap, are chemical additives used as wetting agents. They break down the surface tension of water and are sometimes used to increase the wettability of materials such as dry peat moss or pine bark.

Any dry materials we use in our substrate are hydrophobic (hard to wet at first). Almost all dry substrate materials, once wet, can easily be kept from drying out completely without the additional use of surfactants.

Unfortunately, scientists say the effects of surfactants on a plant's foliage or when added to the substrate are poorly understood. Many surfactants are toxic to a plant in excess. All become inactive over a short time.

Organic materials decompose, and most inorganic materials break down and eventually turn into powder. The surface tension builds up on those finer-textured particles and causes them to hold too much water. At that point, we definitely don't want any surfactants added to our substrate.

This is another product that may do more harm than good.

■ Will "rooting hormones and vitamin B-1 treat root rot"?

No. Those products are not fungicides, so they can't treat root rot, which is a fungus.

■ Will "rooting hormones promote root vigor and help pruned roots regenerate"?

"Rooting hormones" can be useful in the propagation of fresh cuttings with no existing roots, depending on plant species, the time of year and the initial application rate. Rooting hormones might even hinder new root initiation when applied to existing pruned roots.

Roots will never regenerate, replenish, renew or reestablish. Root vigor is genetic.

■ Can table sugar promote root growth and reduce transplant losses?

Sugar—or more accurately, sucrose—is the end product of photosynthesis. Studies have suggested that applications of a weak drench of table sugar slightly enhances root growth after transplanting out in garden field soil. Practically speaking, the results were insignificant and inconsistent.

It is claimed that table sugar kills weeds. Too high of a sugar concentration can kill plants; it encourages soil pathogens. Better think again.

■ *"Transplant shock will set a plant back," we've always heard. What about "soaking the bare bonsai roots in a biostimulant to help them recover from stress or from transplanting shock"?*

Scientists have discovered no evidence of any benefit from the application of a biostimulant to aid against transplanting shock. Also, biostimulants will never "reduce heat or water stress in a plant."

■ **What common organic fertilizers have a good percentage of nitrogen?**

Bat guano, corn gluten meal and feather meal have a good percentage of nitrogen. A high percentage of nitrogen doesn't reflect the actual amount of available, usable nitrogen.

Any form of nitrogen fertilizer is completely reliant on nearby living microbes to break it down and convert it to usable ions (#222). After releasing it, those microbes get first choice to consume it. Any usable nitrogen left over is available to the plant.

TOP TEN ORGANICS

	PERCENT NITROGEN
Blood meal	12%
Fish meal	10%
Soybean meal	7%
Cottonseed meal	6%
Fish emulsion	5%
Rapeseed meal	4%
Alfalfa meal	3%
Bone meal	3%
Liquid seaweed	1%
Wood ashes	0%

One of the supposed benefits of organics is a safe, slow release of nitrogen. The point is, all this nitrogen is potentially not available to the plant.

Urea can be 45-0-0 (percentage of NPK), inexpensive and readily available to the plant. Why risk the likely toxicity? Any urea sprayed on plants might cause scorched areas on the foliage. Check the first ingredient listed for urea and think twice before using that product.

Urea applications are usually wasted to the outside air or out the drain. Its reaction with water releases ammonia gas. *On a slightly windy day, the nitrogen blows away before it reaches the substrate* (#223).

■ **You have access to some free fresh organic farm manure. Can the "nutrients from animal manures benefit bonsai"?**

Animals cannot manufacture any essential element for any plant's benefit (#224). In reality, the value from manure for plants consists purely from what food the animal consumes. Using manures in container nurseries went out of style over fifty years ago.

Organic fertilizers, especially fresh manure, can "burn" plants. Manure needs more than half a year to compost by itself. Stinky-type manure may be too salty, drying out the roots and scorching the leaf edges. Fresh manure can also contain a lot of pathogens.

Even non-smelly-type "composted" manure is sometimes overrated in terms of how much available nitrogen is in the bag. "Sterile compost" may contain toxic elements and lack other essential elements.

Now popular, anaerobic digesters can "compost" materials, including manures, in a week to ten days. Data is mixed on how much the end product will benefit container plants.

Bags of composted manure we typically find in the big chain stores might show only a NPK percentage of 1-1-1 That amounts to 1 percent nitrogen, 1 percent phosphorus, and 1 percent potassium, with 97 percent inert, chemically inactive materials in the whole package.

■ You could buy so many different products advertised "for healthy bonsai." What are the facts behind the products?

Scanty. Some products, such as some ureas, may decrease a plant's defense system—one other point to remember the next time you put a product on your bonsai. The dosage you use should decrease with the age of the bonsai. Less pruning, less fertilizer and less amendment is usually healthier on older trees.

"Liquid seaweed is a good tonic to use on bonsai by adding hormones and minerals."

Not unless the bonsai is legitimately deficient in "hormones" and minerals. Again, plants manufacture their own growth regulators. Seaweed extracts have proven to have no effect as a growth stimulator. Applied to field soil, seaweed extracts are quickly degraded by soil microbes.

Applied on the foliage, seaweed extracts add nothing to foliage growth. Scientists have also concluded that seaweed extracts have no reliable effect on a plant's resistance to disease or environmental stress. The percent of NPK is only 1-0-4.

"Yucca plant extract helps reverse dry, compacted soils; serves as a frost control when applied to bonsai foliage; and repels bad bugs."

Sorry, but it can't help bonsai. Yucca extract was promoted as a surfactant/wetting agent but was found to be almost ineffective even when applied to fresh substrate.

"Compost tea suppresses disease on bonsai."

There is no scientific evidence exists to support that hype. Some aerated compost tea has been tested positive for E. coli. Compost tea is expensive to make, too. Also, don't count on coffee grounds to "control pH on bonsai soil."

"Epsom salts (magnesium sulfate) cure a bonsai with sick-looking, yellow-colored leaves by adding magnesium."

Is your bonsai deficient in magnesium? Magnesium sulfate may help reduce excess toxic phosphorus in agricultural field soil, but only if that soil has been over fertilized with super phosphate. Oftentimes, adding magnesium sulfate or another product, gypsum, is beneficial to agricultural field soil because of the sulfur. Sulfur can and will "green up" certain plants in certain situations.

"Humic acid significantly accelerates root pad development."

This is true only in bonsai product literature. Humic acid does help make available some existing chemicals tied up in some field soils with high pH. Non-stressed roots growing in a modern substrate are not going to respond to any addition of humic acid.

■ Does moss growing on the soil "help the bonsai roots by giving off humic acids"?

Also tag this as a proven false statement.

"Blood meal adds significant nitrogen and iron needed for green leaves."

This is not much help except in attracting a few pests to its smell. The big plus for blood meal is its quick release of nitrogen out in field soil. Keep in mind, live microbes grab it first.

"Alfalfa meal stimulates root growth."
Sorry, it won't happen. Does the bonsai need root growth stimulation? Its NPK percentage is 3-1-2.

"Bone meal adds significant potassium, greatly reduces transplant shock and promotes healthy, extensive root systems for your bonsai."
With NPK percentage of 3-20-0, bone meal has zero potassium. Besides, neither its calcium nor high phosphorus levels reduce transplant shock or stimulate growth. Bone meal is not a growth regulator. Too much phosphorus can be toxic to a plant and to any beneficial root mycorrhizae.

"Soybean meal helps the trunk thicken up rapidly."
Do bonsai need soybeans? The NPK percentage is 7-2-1. Any available essential elements are first used by soil microbes, then foliage and then by roots before the stems even begin to thicken up.

"Cottonseed meal makes the soil more acidic."
Is the soil too alkaline? Most modern substrates are already in the right pH range for growing bonsai. The NPK percentage is 6-1-1.

■ Fish emulsion is highly recommended in bonsai literature. What's in the scientific literature?

It turns out that a radish seedling was grown once out in sandy field soil in a controlled environment in the United Arab Emirates. Fish emulsion was shown to promote the existing rhizobacteria present in that agricultural field soil.

Any rhizobacteria in field soil gets first choice of whatever it can pull out of the fertilizer when it's first applied. Little, if any, leftover elements from fish emulsion are available for the actual plant roots to use.

Does fresh sterile substrate test positive for rhizobacteria? No. Can anyone stand the smell of fish emulsion? And did you know that too much fish emulsion is also potentially toxic to a potted plant? Fish emulsion has an NPK percentage of 5-2-2. Fish meal has an NPK percentage of 10-4-0.

■ Rapeseed meal cake is also recommended.

Some farmer long ago probably once used rapeseed meal cake for pig food and then decided to try using it on his field crops. The NPK percentage is only 4-0-0, and its nitrogen can last up to a couple months in field soil That's an expensive source of little available nitrogen.

■ Do organic meal cakes "give pep to bonsai"?

Cakes give too little pep for the trouble.

■ Will horticultural charcoal benefit bonsai?

That's still out for debate for now. Horticultural charcoal, sometimes called biochar, can be mixed into garden crops planted out in field soil. As any added fertilizer starts to fill the pores of the biochar and allow microbial diversity to develop, chemicals are held longer when in field soil. The organic carbon present in fertile field soil is easily oxidized and thereby short-lived. Biochar is long lasting and ties up the chemicals so the plant may not ever be able to use them.

Still experimental, the use of biochar can't be recommended yet by horticultural scientists for plant use in containers. Wood ash's NPK percentage is 0-2-5 and short-lived. Charcoal briquettes can be toxic to plant growth.

"Always use liquid rooting hormone, a water soluble fungicide  *and vitamin B-1 when changing the soil and repotting."*

Snake oil, urban legends, bonsai myths and misconceptions = false.

Now we can get to the dirt on roots in the next chapter and branch out from there.

Chinese elm.

GROWING SUPERB ROOTS

Trees consist of three growing parts that respond to one another: the fibrous root hairs, the growing bud and stem tips and the tissues connecting them. Each component has its own sensors and signals. To keep things simple and to relate to common bonsai terminology, *Modern Bonsai Practice* refers mainly to roots, foliage and branches.

Growing roots get their resources from water, essential elements and stored photosynthate. Growing stem tips and buds get their resources from light, carbon dioxide and essential elements. Connective tissues transfer essential elements between the stems and roots.

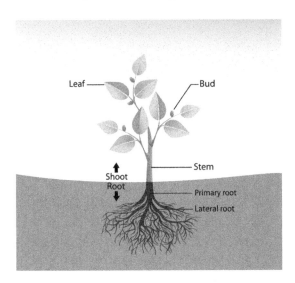

THE PERFECT TREE

You've seen artistic renderings of a "perfect tree" drawn within a perfect circle. Impressive roots below evenly fill the bottom half of the circle, and the trunk and branches evenly fill the top half. Are the "roots below a mirror image of the branches above"? Definitely not. ***Roots and branches are not balanced or mirror image of each other*** (#225).

In real life, the amount and the depth of the roots are never the same as the amount and height of the branches. The amount of roots is considerably less.

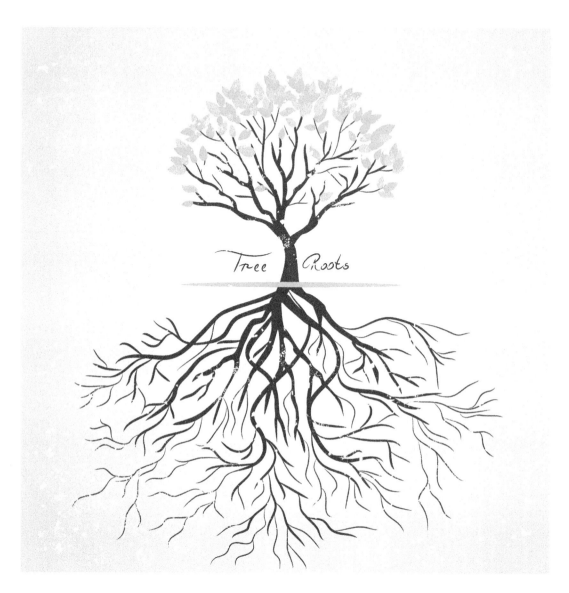

Tree Roots

Roots continually develop and change according to opportunity and necessity; branches develop according to opportunity and necessity (#226). Those roots are going to grow in one direction while the branches may grow in another direction. Both roots and branches do adjust to each other with a continual feedback process in order for the whole tree to survive.

If a tree has many small finer roots, the crown above does not necessarily "have many small ramified branches." If a tree trunk refuses to grow straight, a "curled-up taproot" is not the cause. If the tree branches have curves, tree roots are not necessarily "curved the same as its branches."

When thick branches are mostly on one side of the tree, that does not necessarily mean "thick roots will be on the same side underneath." The presence of "two very strong roots" doesn't always mean the tree has "two very strong branches." Count them next time. The presence of healthy-looking thick roots does not necessarily "nourish and make strong, thick top branches."

Out in nature, root development is shallow and wide in all species (#227). The tree's roots can't get enough oxygen and proper moisture deep down in the subsoil. *Pruning the roots and placing the bonsai in a smaller pot does not "automatically weaken the top branches if they're not pruned also"* (#228).

Pruning the top branches without pruning the roots does not "cause root damage." The pruned root system won't "become overworked" if you do not cut off some of the top growth to compensate for the root loss." If you prune the long, straight and thick roots, the new branches aren't "going to grow better controlled."

If you prune off the big taproot or most of the big bottom roots during repotting, the branches won't "start to die." You won't find any taproot on mature bonsai. *Roots do not bud back toward the trunk the same way branches bud back toward the trunk after pruning the apical meristem* (#229). *Roots have no buds* (#230).

When "the top growth continues to decrease in vigor," that does not "mean you must prune the roots to invigorate the branches." Shortening the roots more on one side does not mean the "branches on that same side will grow less vigorously."

SINK YOUR ROOTS

◼ Do roots grow twenty-four hours a day?

They sure do. Roots are slowly pushing into any available substrate pores. If not in waterlogged or frozen environments, some root cells are dividing all throughout the year.

During daytime, roots are busily transporting up water and essential elements from the substrate to the developing crown. Carbohydrates are translocated down in the phloem to other parts of the tree. During nighttime, roots are still busily growing after receiving photosynthates from crown growth.

◼ Is the tip of the root alive? How can it possibly "shove and jam forward in the soil"?

No is the answer to the first question. Cells at the tip of a lateral root elongate, die and then differentiate into a firm, mature plant structure called a root cap. It's coated with a slimy substance. Root caps act as a shield protecting those tiny hairs as expanding lateral roots are being pushed into any available pore spaces.

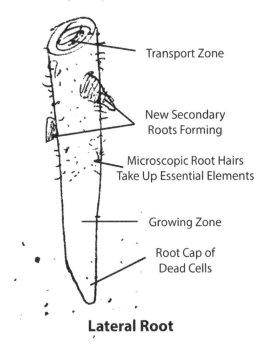

Transport Zone

New Secondary Roots Forming

Microscopic Root Hairs Take Up Essential Elements

Growing Zone

Root Cap of Dead Cells

Lateral Root

Back from that root cap is the area where root cells divide, elongate and then differentiate into the mass of root hairs. The live, delicate new root hairs are lateral extensions only one cell thick. They are constantly replaced.

Live cells dividing and elongating in the root's growing zone is the mechanism for pushing the dead root caps into pore spaces wherever they can fit. Elongation occurs only near the apex of the lateral root. That growing, sensitive, delicate section of the root elongates its way into pore spaces and around any substrate particles.

When a flexible root hair reaches a solid particle, it flattens out, bends around and fastens to that particle. Then it stops growing in length. Tips of the roots can't "shove and jam forward."

■ What affects the generation of new root hairs? Are the root hairs different sizes in trees? Do "all trees have root hairs"?

Near the end of a constantly dividing root tip is its apical meristem. A growth regulator called cytokinin switches on the process of growing the new, finer, lateral roots and masses of root hair extensions. *A root hair is simply a tiny microscopic extension on the end of a single cell* (#231).

The delicate root hair is one flat, elongated cell about 1.5 millimeters long. Those fine root hairs in the smallest bonsai are the same exact size as root hairs in the largest tree, if it has them. Some trees don't have fine roots. You'll be lucky to find any root hairs on old, mature trees in the forest. Other root extensions help take up water and elements in mature trees with no root hairs.

When a tree is put in a container, it adapts by developing a mass of fresh new root hairs. Those root hairs grow fast and die fast. *As the newer roots die, they add organic carbon to the substrate* (#232). This carbon makes it easier for any subsequent new roots to take up organic fertilizer.

Most root hairs function for only a couple days during the growing season before dying (#233). They are constantly replaced at the root apical meristem, which is right behind the root cap.

New root generation, their cell division and growth rate vary by several factors:
- Species and age of the tree.
- Temperature of the substrate.
- Availability of water.
- Availability of essential elements.
- Concentrations of natural growth regulators in the roots
- The presence of oxygen in the substrate. *With less than 12 percent oxygen, root cells can't divide; with less than 3 percent oxygen, the roots die* (#234).

■ Which part contributes more to the function of a tree, the roots or the stems?

Both roots and branches have the same overall importance. Each has a different function and response, but one is dependent on the other. *Roots and branches compete with each other for vascular pathways, connections and resources* (#235). *The top supplies photosynthates to the bottom; the bottom supplies water and a few essential elements to the top* (#236).

Growth of roots depends on sugars manufactured in the foliage, not on anything we put on or in the substrate (#237). Unfortunately, we may not find as much information in the scientific literature about roots as we do concerning stems (trunks and branches). Why? The plant has to be killed to study its roots. Besides, it is dirty work.

Like branches, roots are woody with bark or non-woody without bark and are able to survive more than a year. Unlike branches, non-woody roots live less than one year.

Roots usually die before the branches die since roots depend on their energy coming from the foliage. Plant genetics also tells roots when to die and branches when to die.

■ **What is the relationship between the formation of new roots and the formation of new stems?**

New roots can grow with or without any stem or foliage growing at the same time (#238). *New roots form prior to new stems forming* (#239). The entire plant reserves its energy and slows down top growth while waiting for fresh ultra-fine root hair tips to start growing. *New vascular pathways to future stems are built from new root growth* (#240).

The turnover rate of newly forming roots in the root system is much higher than the rate of newly forming stems (#241). Auxins in the stems signal root growth. New root growth produces cytokinin. *A combination of both auxins and cytokinins promote stem growth and leaf expansion* (#242).

Newly formed roots are the only way to quick start the entire growth process in our bonsai. During spring, most of the stored photosynthates in the roots are first used by the roots and then by the upper crown. Photosynthate goes first to new foliage, then to new stems, and then to stem thickness.

Stem growth is put on hold at the expense of the new roots forming after potting or pruning (#243). When the root/shoot cycle from the auxins and cytokinins begins to move around, then the stems can start growing again. New top growth along with new root growth together help get the water and essential elements to the top of the plant. All those plant growth regulators are constantly switching on or switching off those root-to-stem growth cycles.

Only fresh new roots on the entire root system can take up and distribute water and essential elements (#244).

The signal to start new roots comes from existing stems. With stem and root pruning at the same time, both stems and roots lose.

Roots aren't able to adjust to sudden, extreme temperature changes as well as stems are able to adjust (#245). Both stems and roots have apical meristems and apical dominance. *Both stem tips and root tips hinder lateral growth closer to the trunk* (#246).

Older, thicker, waterproof roots, similar to batteries, are energy storage facilities for photosynthates that are manufactured in the foliage above (#247). *During summer, the new foliage is busily photosynthesizing sugars to be utilized for the crown growth and for restoring photosynthates in the roots* (#248). *Even during the resting period, the roots continue to store photosynthates and continue to grow if the substrate is above 40° Fahrenheit* (#249).

Plants grow up before they grow out. A tree normally has more total roots and stems than it needs in order to survive. *Both the stems and the roots grow independently, and both will die independently* (#250). Both grow if and when the rest of the tree can sustain the new growth. Stems can die without roots dying. Roots can die without stems dying.

Robust root growth is independent of robust stem growth (#251). Independently, both roots and stems can keep on growing all the time or in flushes. *Unpruned roots have enough stored photosynthates during winter to supply bud break and stem elongation for the crown next spring* (#252).

Root pruning without stem pruning initiates new growth in stems, roots, and flowers (#253). This concept can be a useful practice.

Stem pruning taxes the available root resources. Weakened roots soon become vulnerable to pathogens and infection.

While most roots are very good at compartmentalizing infection, stressed roots soon can't take up essential elements to the overly pruned stems. Essential enzymes for photosynthesis become unavailable.

Stem pruning can promote new shoot initiation, but shoot initiation does not cause root initiation (#254). Stems and roots never regenerate; they generate. *Water pressure can build up in the roots from low rates of leaf transpiration up in the stems* (#255).

◼ Which live longer, the roots or the stems?

The newer, finer-textured roots are deciduous, and they have an extremely high turnover rate. Some delicate new roots live for only a day or two.

> *Tip*: Some older roots eventually die and turn into organic matter for beneficial bacteria and fungi to live on. We do our roots a disservice if we try to constantly remove all the dead organic material from the substrate each time we repot and also if we omit all the organic matter from our substrates.

Larger, thicker support roots do live longer than their aboveground counterparts. In bonsai cultivation, we limit older, thicker underground roots while allowing the growth of newer, finer roots. The newer, developing, short-lived roots have invigorating cell divisions occurring inside the pot and keep the entire plant going strong.

"Each particular branch is fed by only one particular root."
The problem in that statement is with the words "fed by only." Branches aren't fed. Most species get the vast majority of their essential elements from their leaves, not from their roots.

Someone could make an interesting experiment to prove this. Does one particular stomate under one particular leaf get water through one long, continuous tube coming up from one particular root?

There are many stomata per leaf. Long vessels in some stems may be a couple feet long, but they still have an end cap. Pores connect the capped vessels to one another starting from the roots upward.

The linear vein on junipers is one example of a more direct phloem pathway from foliage to root. "Live veins" are a series of dead tubes stacked one on top of one another carrying photosynthates down the tree. On most deciduous bonsai, the indirect connective vascular system continually adjusts and changes pathways. We can expect those vascular pathways to adjust after each time we wire, twist, bend, fracture, leave the training wire on too long, or remove half of the crown and most of the roots at any one time.

◼ You observe the roots of a landscape tree cut and injured on one side from excavating for a new sidewalk. Is "root damage on one side of the tree going to affect only that same side of the branches"?

It depends on the species and the stage of growth. More specifically, the answer is most likely yes for an old oak tree but not always for a maple tree.

From personal observation only, I've noticed opposite branching stem systems such as on Ligustrum, Pinus, Picea, and Acer seems to have similar branching root system architecture. Alternate branching stem systems of Malus, Prunus, Juniperus, and Quercus also seems to have similar branching root systems. Azaleas, among others, have whorled branching on both roots and stems. Wound responses, pruning responses, and transplanting responses differ on those three different branching patterns.

Mature Acer, Pinus, Ligustrum, and other trees with opposite roots and stem branching can have random branch injury throughout the tree even if a small part of the roots on one side is injured (#256). *Mature Quercus, Malus, Prunus, Juniperus, and other species with alternate roots and stem branching show branch dieback only on that same side of injured roots* (#257).

"Roots absorb and feed on fertilizer. Moisture and nutrients need to be in a gaseous form before the roots can absorb them."

Roots can't feed, and they don't "absorb fertilizer" as a sponge absorbs water. Try to picture a sealed syringe extracting water up a tube instead of a sponge soaking up water. Except for the younger microscopic root hairs, the older, thick roots are waterproof and can't ever absorb water.

A single bonsai might have thousands of delicate root hairs. Younger, fresh root hairs are tiny extensions of a single new growing cell on the skin of a secondary root.

Masses of tiny, microscopic hairs have developed (through an adaptive process when a plant is containerized) to take up water and elements mainly through osmosis (never "in a gaseous form"). The process of osmosis is not "a matter of balancing the water inside and outside the plant." Osmosis basically means water pressure differences will trigger the plant to take up water. Water always moves to an area containing less water. Simply put,

lots of water in substrate is sucked up by less water in the roots all the way up to even less water content in a leaf.

The higher concentration of purer water in the pot comes through the cell walls of a root hair into the plant, where lower concentrations of pure water (in sap) equalize the pressure differences. Higher negative pressures outside the plant (in water vapor) continue to draw up the water in low pressure that sticks to the xylem tube walls.

The solid minerals in fertilizer become dissolved mineral salts in water. Microscopic root hairs are so tiny that not all larger molecules of dissolved mineral salts can stick to, or pass through, the root hairs and enter the living plant cells. One key to understanding water movement in plants is that it sticks to itself and to other things.

Fact: *Few, but not all, of the essential elements in the sticky water solution stick to nearby microscopic root hairs or to microscopic substrate particles* (#258). The root hair already contains sticky sap (sugars and acids in water solutions), making conditions ideal to pull in sticky mineral salts through osmosis.

Essential elements in a water solution move into the root cells by osmosis and diffusion (#259). *Elements are sucked up in solution through the active transport process (diffusion) and by the energy of proteins pumping up those sticky salts* (#260).

"Roots grow toward water or food."

If fertilizer was placed only on one particular part of the pot then, yes, roots will grow toward that spot. Most fertilizer products can be applied anywhere on top of the substrate. Mineral salts eventually mix with water. Those essential elements in liquid solution flow toward different parts of the substrate.

■ What makes tree roots grow downward?

Gravity—or more specifically, geotropism—governs downward-seeking roots, even on the biggest trees. Roots on mature trees find more available pore spaces for growing around the top layer of soil than in deeper, hardpan subsoil. They concentrate in the top several inches where oxygen is more available. Downward-growing woody roots are mainly for support.

The forces of gravity on the roots are insignificant in a shallow bonsai pot. The opportunistic roots take advantage of any available pore space the root caps can push into.

■ Which roots are the "feeder roots"?

No one has yet discovered the answer to that perennial question. People are still looking at roots under a microscope for "feeder roots." *Eventually, they conclude the obvious: no roots are feeding* (#261).

■ Why do the roots of potted bonsai look longer and denser than the roots of plants grown out in field soil? Are the "roots of field-grown trees of such poor quality that they may never be able to be fixed for good-quality bonsai"?

Have you noticed quite a few of the best award-winning bonsai are from old collected trees? Some practitioner has "fixed" those roots. *Containerized plants end up with a larger proportion of younger, laterally growing roots than the same species growing out in the ground* (#262). As a result of root pruning, more pore spaces for the roots, and better moisture conditions in a container, bonsai have potential for superb roots.

■ What time of the year do roots grow the fastest and when do they grow the most?

During early summer, at between a 65° and 90°F air temperature, roots grow the fastest in terms of speed of growth. The total amount of root growth is another subject. Most woody plants have two flushes or periods of root growth during one growing season. A growing season is a one full-year cycle.

One short spurt of root growth occurs in the spring, and another huge spurt of root growth occurs during the fall (#263). Roots start their first flush in early spring before bud break at 40° to 50°F air temperature. The rate of growth slows down when the branches extend in spring. After the branches finish shooting out, the roots are still growing until the fall spurt. Then, at around 45°F, or 7°C, roots usually slow down their rate of cell divisions.

Only about one-fourth of the total season root growth has been measured to occur in maples by the end of August. By the end of November, the other three-fourths root growth is mostly finished.[*]

> *Tip*: The optimal time for transplanting, grafting, or repotting maples, and maybe other deciduous trees, might not always be in the middle of spring before growth hardens off. That's when the roots have already slowed down their rate of growth from last fall's huge flush of root growth.

---

[*] J. Sibley, J. Ruter, and D. Eakes, "Monthly Growth Patterns for Red Maple Cultivars," *SNA Research Conference Proceedings* 43 (1998).

The first of summer may be a good time to start propagating air layers. Right before winter might be a good time to remove and pot up the air-layered plants. Tender handling and vigilant aftercare of newly planted air-layered roots is vital to their new root growth after repotting.

Longer photoperiods under artificial light has proven to assist new root establishment in newly propagated air layers or cuttings. *Transplant or repot in the fall to take advantage of the most root growth before spring bud break* (#264).

■ Do roots breathe?

Absolutely. Breathing is called respiration in roots, foliage, and stems. *Smaller, finer roots have a much higher respiration rate than what occurs in thicker, coarser roots* (#265). High nitrogen concentrations due to excess fertilization can also result in higher respiration rates in all parts of the plant.

More root respiration results in a slightly more acidic soil or substrate. That's good, as most tap and well water is slightly alkaline. Roots grow in pore spaces in order to breathe. The reason plants can grow hydroponically in water is the provision made for air continually bubbling through the water so the roots can breathe all the time.

■ When the flowers are growing on the plant, does that mean the roots and flowers cannot grow simultaneously?

Correct. *The plant is either growing flowers or roots, never both at the same time* (#266).

How Roots Respond

■ How do roots respond to scarce resources in a harsh, contained setting?

Roots slow down their rate of cell divisions under stress:

- Too hard or too soft substrate.
- Too large or too small pore spaces.
- Too much or too little water or fertilizer.
- At the far ends of extreme temperature ranges.

Under stress:

- Photosynthate production from photosynthesis is reduced.
- Synthesis of growth regulators decreases.
- Uptake of essential elements is reduced.
- Root metabolism slows.
- Stem growth slows.
- Stem diameter growth slows.
- The quantity and size of leaves is reduced.
- Total increase in height of the plant slows.
- Roots, just like stems, consume oxygen and release carbon dioxide during respiration.

In conditions of limited oxygen, roots cannot utilize any energy generated and sent down from the foliage (#267). Excess carbon dioxide builds up quickly inside the substrate of a pot. That excess carbon dioxide needs to get out into the air for the work of photosynthesis.

Air outside consists of:

- 20 percent oxygen
- 0.3 percent carbon dioxide

Air inside the walls and constrictions of a pot consists of:

- 0–20 percent oxygen
- 0–20 percent carbon dioxide

Confined roots in pots are subjected to much more debilitating conditions than unrestricted roots allowed to grow out in garden field

soil without any side walls. Pay extremely close attention to the health of confined roots. *In a restrictive environment, stressed roots can somehow send up an inhibitory signal for branches to toughen up and slow down the rate of stem and foliage cell growth* (#268).

Roots grow at optimum temperature ranges. Temperature inside a pot or even on the substrate surface is not the same temperature as outside the pot. At the lower end of that temperature range, roots use less water.

Fewer environmental insults occur to the hidden roots than to the exposed branches. For example, there is no wind inside a pot, and temperatures fluctuate less in a substrate. *Roots inside pots can't tolerate high or low temperature extremes as well as the plant's aboveground parts* (#269). Both the shallow root system of bonsai and the pot itself are not good insulators.

■ Explain the adventitious root system we sometimes find on nursery stock.

The adventitious root system is a response to stress. Normally, trees have only one root system. The original, natural root collar forms on a tree at ground level in nature. However, an additional adventitious root system is commonly seen growing higher up on the trunk of nursery stock that is planted too deeply.

Depending on how shallow or deep the original rootstock ends up transplanted in the ground or potted in the container, sometimes "false roots" continue to form on the trunk. You'll find them right above or below the original natural root collar. Sometimes the adventitious roots become more robust and start to dominate and supplant the original natural root collar. The part where the trunk meets the roots is called the root collar. Adventitious

roots usually form on the trunk, which is physiologically not part of the root collar.

Adventitious false roots can be detrimental to the tree. A buried root collar has no method of adjusting to constant wettened conditions. The oxygen level is considerably less. No gas exchange means no carbohydrates can ever get to the real roots. The plant is trying to save itself from decline, so it sends out roots above the root collar in order to breathe. *Newer adventitious roots form because the original lower hidden root system is stressed for oxygen and in decline* (#270).

> *Tip*: Gently rake back the top layer of soil or substrate and discover the thickest spreading roots. It is like uncovering hidden treasure. When you find those best roots, prune off the smaller, upper adventitious roots close to the main trunk. Don't remove adventitious roots larger than one-fourth inch right away. Wait until the next growing season after repotting to address those largest adventitious roots. Those larger secondary roots might be providing a considerable amount of moisture and essential elements to your new tree. Temporarily expose the best root collar.

A nursery-grown seedling may have been potted a little too deep in its first container. Deeper planting could have been an effort to reduce watering or to keep the top-heavy seedling from tipping over. Each time it's progressively upsized to a larger pot, the roots get shoved down and crunched deeper into the new substrate.

Tip: The graft union on low-grafted nursery stock can be slightly wounded and buried in an effort to hide the unsightly bulge of the union. New, small, lateral roots begin forming randomly above the original top roots.

What's wrong with most grafts; for example, top scion with red foliage on green understock?

Green-leafed rootstock adapts easier and faster to its niche than the top red scion. Genetic vigor on the green outgrows the red. Graft union do not always "eventually blend into a smooth trunk."

On trees with a slanted trunk, what makes the surface roots thicker at the trunk's base on the opposite side the tree is leaning? Did the "sun pull the roots up"?

The sun wasn't at fault. Trees lean from physical forces such as wind or erosion. You notice more surface roots on the side opposite from the way the tree is leaning because they were pulled up by physical forces. Or the tree was pushed over to expose the roots. You don't see as many surface roots on the leaning side of a tree because compressive forces hold the roots down.

Tip: When potting a leaning bonsai, remember the thicker, stronger surface roots look more natural on the opposite side from the way the tree is leaning.

"No roots will grow if the bonsai is in deep shade."

Shade affects branches and foliage, not directly the hidden roots already growing in the dark.

What is the optimal temperature for root growth?

Optimal temperature range for root growth is between 50° and 85°F, measured in the root zone (#271). In full sun, on a dark surface, the pot's substrate temperature can quickly and easily get up to 150°F. Since pots are not insulated, bonsai roots tend to become hotter in the summer and colder in the winter than tree roots growing in the ground.

You can use an inexpensive meat thermometer to check substrate temperature inside and outside the pot. An infrared thermometer is non-contact and also can quickly measure substrate surface temperatures. The usual recommendation is to minimize the exposure of tree roots to constant temperatures higher than 100°F. That is also the temperature at which the process of photosynthesis will start to break down.

At 95°F, root growth slows by as much as 90 percent. Higher than 170°F, which is 42°C, the roots can't take up water and essential elements and can die.

Tip: Keep evapotranspiration in mind when your prized bonsai in a shallow, dark pot is sitting on or in front of a scorching reflective surface in full, hot sun. Some bonsai may not tolerate those harsh conditions. Trees may have foliage that tolerates full sun, but shallow roots can't tolerate extreme heat and can't supply enough water during long periods of higher evapotranspiration rates.

"Frozen water will freeze damage the roots and force them to explode."
This won't happen. Sap in the cells of thick, fleshy roots keeps them from freezing. ***Water in the substrate can freeze without affecting or freezing the roots*** (#272). Woody bark of mature roots may split but not explode when exposed to extremely low and rapidly falling temperatures. Frozen substrate can expand and possibly crack its container.

■ After the foliage is gone, do the roots on a deciduous tree continue to grow?

The roots do keep on extending in the right environment after leaf shed. ***When new root hairs are not produced, bonsai is not taking up water or essential elements*** (#273). ***Decreasing photoperiods from the first day of summer trigger the beginning of the resting process in the crown and slow down the rate of the foliage growth spurt*** (#274).

Excess photosynthates from the dying foliage have been relocated and stored in the stems and roots as available energy during the slower root growth. However, roots find a difficult time growing if the temperature in the substrate is too high or too low.

Increasing temperatures in the late winter trigger the roots to begin their first big growth spurt after the resting process. Once you notice the substrate drying out more often between waterings, then you know the roots have broken their semirest period and are taking up water.

Substrate temperature in a bonsai pot may be quite different from the ambient temperature above. Aboveground growth in pines seems to be more dependent on air temperature than on soil temperature. However, some pines, spruce, and azaleas cannot grow new roots when in constantly frozen temperatures. The roots of some tender tropical species cannot tolerate below 50°F for extended periods.

■ Can roots take up essential elements from the substrate during winter?

Absolutely, if they need it, have it, and the temperature is right. If the substrate around the roots is frozen, the plant can't pull up any water or soluble mineral salts.

Plants can and do dry out in the freeze of winter. That is one reason we don't water our bonsai when the substrate is frozen. If even necessary, we water a drying-out substrate prior to an extended freeze. ***If a plant dies in the winter, more likely the cause is from dehydration or disease than from lack of available water or fertilizer*** (#275).

Roots don't cold harden as do the aboveground parts and can possibly become injured by extremely fast-falling temperatures (#276). They're the first to die back, and then we notice stem dieback. The cambium layer of the branches dies if the stored photosynthates are used up and not replaced with new foliage or new roots. We won't realize it until next spring when the stem buds don't open up.

■ If only the central trunk of a multi-trunk plant dies, does that mean the inner root system is not getting enough water?

Could be. Water can flow easily down the inside of the container wall and out the drain holes before wetting the middle part of the root system. That situation frequently occurs in established container plants, although the root injury is not readily noticed.

"Allow the substrate to dry out completely on the top surface between waterings."
Under watering is not always a good idea. Tiny new roots can rapidly dehydrate and die if even the upper half of the substrate profile is dry. Secondary roots can shrink and lose contact with the substrate. Sudden death during a summer's hot, dry period can be the result of a root collar buried too deeply. The root collar (lower trunk) may be wet while the top surface of the substrate seems dry.

Highly soluble salts, low moisture, and high temperatures also kill tender roots in the top part of a substrate. Increasing evaporative conditions and excessive leaf transpiration can quickly dry the entire root system and wilt the leaves.

Available water is either leaching out, taken up by the roots, evaporating, transpiring, or freely sitting at the bottom part of the pot (#277). Meanwhile, the top surface could appear to be bone dry.

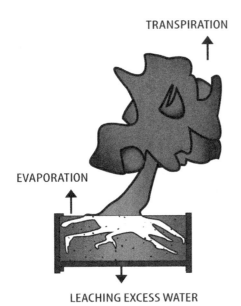

TRANSPIRATION

EVAPORATION

LEACHING EXCESS WATER

Where does the water go?

■ How do I know when the substrate has too much water?

Sometimes you observe the new foliage nodding or starting to wilt, and the substrate still appears moist. Or you notice the root system holds little additional water. If you can, check the bottom roots to see if they are dark, smelly, and mushy. If so, they've been soggy to the point of rotting.

> *Tip*: A brief drying-out period between waterings lets the carbon dioxide out and the oxygen in the substrate pores.

If the tender new roots are trying to grow in heavily compacted or poorly aerated substrate, they'll suffocate from lack of oxygen or too much carbon dioxide, not from excess water (#278).

■ How do roots respond to drought stress?

Different species respond differently in terms of how much and how fast they recover from insufficient water through the root system. Root growth slows down any time a plant has drought stress. Finer roots are short-lived anyway. Conducting water up to the rest of the plant is hindered. Parts of the foliage decline and die. *Plants recover from drought stress solely with a flush of new root growth* (#279).

"Surface roots will die back if the bark on the lower tree trunk is injured."
This is debatable. Trunk defense mechanisms are different from root defense mechanisms. Their vascular patterns and response to injury are different. Pathogens can, however, enter the wounded zone at the base of the trunk.

ROOT PRUNING

■ What are our objectives for root pruning?

- To develop a mass of fibrous roots.
- To fit the bonsai in a smaller pot.
- To refresh compacted or old, broken-down substrate.
- To correct a severely pot-bound root system.
- To remove any visually unpleasing surface rootage or improve the visually pleasing root crown.
- To remove diseased, dead, or broken roots.
- To let the new roots develop their growth regulator, cytokinin.

Dead or pruned roots leave a root stub, similar to branch stubs (#280). Stubs become tempting invitations to pathogens. Make clean cuts. Root saws work well on cutting larger roots or when shaving to reduce the size of the root ball.

Sometimes a heavily foliated crown on a newly transplanted large landscape shade tree is reduced by pruning for safety reasons. Often it is also staked to reduce the risk of wind blowing it over in the ground.

■ What are we working toward in a well-developed bonsai root system?

The majority of horticultural techniques in *Modern Bonsai Practice* are geared more toward early development than to refining more mature, show-ready bonsai. Whatever the stage, our purpose is developing a dense mat of actively growing, younger, paler-colored, ultra-minute, delicate, fine-haired roots on a compact fibrous root system.

Why do we like to see those masses of fresh, tiny, fibrous roots colonizing the pot? The youngest, light-colored, hair-like, delicate roots are responsible for the water and essential element uptake. And those root hairs are basically invisible to the naked eye.

Thicker, mature, more woody storage roots rapidly take up valuable real estate growing below in a small pot—all at the expense of masses of newer roots whose job is to take up water and elements to the rest of the tree. Those few, short, thick, exposed surface roots (root collar) we like to show off on our refined bonsai also have a practical purpose. *Root collars also serve as a storage facility for the winter photosynthate reserves* (#281).

When we have any thick, dark, slippery-feeling roots, the problem could be root rot stemming from lack of available oxygen in the substrate (#282). At one time, those thicker roots were waterproof until they were weakened by excess moisture and attacked by pathogens.

> *Tip*: Before we buy a car, we usually check under the hood. If you can, pull the plant out of the pot and look at the roots.

■ What are some so-called design flaws commonly seen with the surface rootage?

- No trunk taper or root collar visible.
- Root collar is not uniform or does not look stable. The root collar should have a settled-in look. Choose a same species seedling with a bent root and root graft where needed.
- Surface roots not in the same horizontal plane or radiating from the trunk at the right places.
- Big voids seen between the roots around the base of the trunk.
- Excessively different-sized top roots.

- Redundant and crossed surface roots.
- Thick surface roots with the ends chopped off. Big, partially cut-off roots can be split in half with a wood chisel or tapered down with knob cutters. Try repositioning the whole tree at the next repotting to bury those thick, blunt ends.

■ How can I tell the difference between active roots and aging roots? Should I "try to remove all dead roots"?

Actively growing, flexible roots are paler in color, with delicate-looking, finer-textured, fresh young root tips. Older, stiffer, thicker, woody roots look darker or decaying with no fibrous roots actively extending. Roots that die make good organic matter. Leave them for the good bacteria to break down and add good qualities to any substrate.

■ Do roots ever become "physically defective" inside the pot?

Decayed roots are defective. Roots grown in a nursery container may well have been crunched into their pot and the substrate packed tightly to stabilize the plant. They are not defective. **Roots can deflect and curve around next to the inside walls of the container or go up and down** (#283). That is not necessarily a defect or even a future problem. Usually the first thing most people do when repotting is to prune those longer roots. Surface girdling roots may restrict the vascular pathway due to wire damage at the base of the trunk.

"Girdling roots" won't "choke the tree." You don't ever need to "slice the root ball vertically several times when you remove the plant from a nursery container to prevent girdling."

Existing curved roots neither "straighten out by themselves" nor "always continue to keep on circling even after they're pruned" (#284). New roots extend outward toward any pore spaces until they reach an inside wall or other obstacle. They continually extend and deflect, extend and deflect.

> *Tip*: Root ball shaving is the modern method to address redundant perimeter and bottom roots. Simply remove the outer substrate and periphery roots with shears or a root saw.

"Crossed roots will choke a tree."

Some rules are concerned with how crossing roots appear, but the tree will not "suffocate or suffer" from the direction any roots happen to be heading. Allow them to graft together as they grow. You find more crossed roots in nature than "wagon wheel spoke" roots.

■ Which roots should I prune first before repotting?

For the aesthetics, you can start by removing these roots:
- Large, dead, diseased, or dying.
- Kinked, deflected up or down, knotted.
- Long, circling roots.

> *Tip*: Shave off the perimeter roots necessary to fit the root system into the desired container. Point the upper surface roots radially away from the trunk if possible.

"If you don't prune them off, air roots on ficus will weaken the trunk and branches." Aerial roots are adventitious roots caused by growth regulator pockets below in the hidden roots. Their job seems to be helping to prop up the tree. Air roots can be an attractive feature and a healthy part of ficus, schefflera, and other plants.

> *Tip*: If you have several air roots forming, let them grow. Stick a wide straw in the substrate up to an aerial root in a direct pathway from the aerial root down to the substrate. Substrate moisture and geotropism help draw those air roots down.

■ **After root pruning, when can I expect the roots to start developing and sending more water and essential elements up the plant?**

New roots can be formed on the ends of newly pruned roots in as early as one to two weeks (#285). Only the newer root hairs are able to uptake any essential elements. Existing foliage continues the process of photosynthesis and sends down photosynthate through the phloem to the roots. Photosynthesis is also a prerequisite for developing a concentration of root growth regulators. *New root growth is switched on by auxins flowing down through the phloem from the growing tips of branches* (#286).

■ **On my field grown miniature trees, I want to develop a denser root system closer to the trunk. Should I "shovel prune a circle around the tree each year while it's still in the ground to stimulate roots branching back toward the trunk"?**

That's not the way roots work. Don't expect the roots to back bud the same way as the branches back bud. Roots have no buds. If you spade a circle around the outside diameter of the ball, you'll find out later that the new roots are growing away from the trunk. *New root growth starts at the ends of the cut roots and grows away from the midline of the trunk* (#287).

Scientists don't yet know all the factors of how new roots form on an undisturbed root system. On a disturbed root system, they know roots do compartmentalize, or wall off, after pruning or injury much more easily and faster than after pruning or injury on branches.

> *Tip*: Resist doing any branch pruning or fertilizing until at least several weeks after the roots have been pruned and any new foliage growth has hardened off. Make clean cuts, and remove any injured areas on the roots. Root saws usually make cleaner cuts than pruners. Calluses quickly form, and new roots will initiate from the callus formation. Remember, roots grow outward away from the trunk.

Root Spading
Around Perimeter

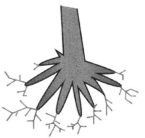

Next Year

Tip: Once your tree is planted out in field soil, don't mess with the roots every year. It may take two or three full growing seasons for the roots of a large collected transplant to grow robustly. Then you can spade prune for a smaller ball to ease in future transplanting to a pot.

More root growth this year means a whole lot more overall growth next year (#288).

■ Will root pruning reverse the aging process?

Continual but slow cell division keeps plants eternally young. **Root pruning keeps young roots active** (#289).

"Root pruning stresses and thereby dwarfs the tree."
Fact: **Root pruning can remove part of the stored photosynthates destined for later top growth** (#290).
Explanation: The restricted conditions of roots in a small pot can also restrict top growth. Confined, pot-bound, lignified roots eventually lose their ability to store photosynthates. Restricted roots can contribute to restricted branches.

Systematic, proper root pruning and repotting helps encourage the new growth of root hairs and helps keep a compact, fibrous root system healthy. Correct root pruning causes little stress to the bonsai. The same holds true for correct branch pruning and for any cultivating practice we apply to bonsai. We can bonsai first-class trees without ever subjecting them to any high stress.

■ Do bonsai need any of their big support roots?

Aside from those thick surface roots, healthy refined bonsai do not need any of their thicker, woody bottom roots (#291). Those few big roots on the root collar are available as a storage facility for accumulating photosynthate from foliage right before leaf drop. Potted plants do not need large bottom roots.

Larger roots confined in such a small space tend to grow woody (lignified), thus their cell-dividing and photosynthate-storing abilities decrease. Water and the soluble salts of essential elements stick to tiny root hairs, not to the waterproof big roots.

You can remove as many older, thicker bottom roots as you need in order to gradually fit the fibrous root ball into a proper-sized pot. Thick, out-of scale roots can be chomped down with a knob pruner and buried. **With an active root system composed of newer, fibrous, pale-colored, finer root tips, the bonsai is sustained quite robustly in the confinements and niche of its pot** (#292).

"The taproot supplies sap to important parts of the tree and will grow back if pruned."
Fact: **The taproot pruned from a young tree never grows back and has served its purpose for earlier survival and support** (#293).
Explanation: Every part of the new seedling utilizes the sugars found in the young taproot before it matures and becomes woody. When the tree gets a little older, the thickened, waterproof taproot functions more as a semi-anchoring support than as a storage facility for photosynthates. Waterproof woody roots can't "pull sap up from the soil."

■ **What time of the year is best for root pruning and "regeneration"?**

You can prune roots at any time of the year. Some say, "Roots don't grow in the fall or winter so if you root prune then, they'll get root rot." That statement is obviously false. Some say, "Roots need to be kept warm and under heat to regenerate after root pruning." That would also be a misleading statement.

> *Tip*: Keep plants cool in partial shade only for a short while if they happen to be pruned during the heat of the summer. Otherwise, summer transplanting with root pruning is not a big deal. Roots need foliage for energy.

No root regenerates, restores, replaces, renews, repairs, or rebuilds; roots are generating systems (#294).

"Prune the roots in the summertime and the supply of water and nutrients ceases, causing the tree to wither and die."
Fact: **Bonsai easily adjust to the heavy root pruning if sufficient foliage is left on for photosynthesis and transpiration** (#295).
Explanation: Any available foliage left on for photosynthesis and evapotranspiration is ready to pull up water and essential elements when the new roots get going again. Normally, it takes only a couple weeks or so.

"You'll suffocate pot-bound roots."
Pot-bound roots can't "suffer and suffocate," but their processes of cell division can slow down in response to a restricted environment.

■ **Can I prune all the big roots at once when first collecting and transplanting from field soil to container? Should I prune a few big bottom roots this year and some next year?**

Make certain the tree is in good condition before transplanting. Leave some existing native field soil clinging to a few roots. That helps increase the overall water-holding capacity of the new substrate and decreases the time needed for new roots to establish.

Then let it be a tree for a while. Resist the urge to park it too soon in a small bonsai pot just so you can call it a bonsai. Your reward of quick growth and long-term health will be several times more.

> *Tip*: Remove a few large, redundant roots when containerizing a transplant for the first time. Give it a year or so to sort itself out before addressing a few more large roots at the next repotting.

"Keep a newly root-pruned bonsai at least one month in full shade."
This is when it needs a more appropriate level of sunlight for the manufacture of photosynthates. Top growth replenishes photosynthates lost from the larger, pruned storage roots.

THE ROOT COLLAR

■ **How do I get a larger-diameter flare at the base of the trunk and force the tree to form a bigger root collar?**

Different words are used to describe those nice, old-looking, swollen surface roots merging with the base of the trunk. The correct word to use is root collar, not "root flare."

The upper main horizontal mother root collar is also referred to as basal trunk flare, the base, trunk crown, root crown, trunk collar, nebari, root spread, buttressing, radial spoke roots, or exposed surface rootage, among other terms. As mentioned, "root flares" are nonexistent. Discover a root flare and you might even get nominated for a Nobel Prize!

Trees might eventually develop a trunk flare or root collar but will never develop a root flare (#296). The root collar is part of the trunk down where the roots join. When you look at nebari, you're more likely looking at the trunk than the roots. And the root collar is not "the circle of roots at the bottom of the pot."

As we know, the trunk is built quite differently than the roots, and both react differently. Roots can usually tolerate periods of constant soil moisture. Most trunks have no mechanism to survive constant wet conditions. ***Wet trunks cannot move photosynthate to the roots because gas exchange cannot occur in incessant moisture*** (#297).

Bald cypress trunks in swampy conditions produce knobby projections out of the water

Would you call this a root collar or "root flare"? Where does the trunk stop and the roots begin?

called knee structures. That visibly thickened trunk structure is usually the result of natural flexing and movement of the trunk at the soil line starting from a young age. Knees are said to serve as an oxygen collector or a support to the tree. Their function has never yet been proven for certain.

You won't see root collars on nursery stock if the young trunk has been planted too deeply. Large surface roots are not "an indication of the good health of a bonsai." They are merely an indication that the bonsai looks good now and has the potential to be developed into a specimen. A nice root collar at the base of the thick trunk holds so many design possibilities.

■ Several techniques have been used to thicken the root collar on the trunk and enhance the appearance of surface roots.

Sometimes all you need is to take the developing bonsai out of its pot and plant it in the ground for a couple growing seasons to speed up trunk and root size and enhance the root collar. Put the refined bonsai in a narrower but deeper pot temporarily. Lower trunk root collars thicken at the expense of upper trunk growth. If lower suckers start to develop, let a few strong ones grow for a season. Bring any potentially useful buried roots up toward the surface.

Several small bare-root seedling trees can be clumped and tied together at the base to develop into a larger, multi-trunk base. The trunks soon graft together.

While the tree is young, prune redundant roots and spread out any promising surface roots radially from the trunk. Wrap a wire around the base of the trunk for a temporary tourniquet as is done in air layering. Large surface roots can be split with a small chisel or root splitter. Some people have split the main trunk longitudinally to correct reverse taper. Pin large, arching roots down to the surface of the substrate.

Root grafting is another easy technique used to add surface roots. Scar or cut a few small notches in the base of the trunk where you want new adventitious surface roots to initiate. Cover up that area of the trunk and check back in a few months. One famous bonsai master was caught trying to lightly pound the base of the trunk with a small hammer.

Starting from young branched seedling or bare-root liners, first prune the bottom roots and spread the top roots radially from the trunk. Let roots freely colonize in the ground or in a large container for several seasons with the lower branches intact.

"Leave roots uncovered to make them grow faster."
Fact: **A root collar temporarily covered over in porous, slightly moist substrate tends to increase in diameter much faster than when left uncovered** (#298).
Explanation: Surface roots exposed to the air tend to harden up (lignify) and grow slower.

> *Tip*: Bury the developing root collar slightly to thicken it up. Uncover the roots later on when the refined bonsai is show ready.

GETTING BACK TO ROOTS

■ What are the advantages and disadvantages of planting bare-root liners to start a bonsai?

A liner can be a couple inches tall or even a plant that is well over your head in height. They can be rooted cuttings or seedlings or even recently rooted grafts. Advantages for starting out with bare-root plants include:

- An opportunity to check for incorrect or structural root defects or hidden pathogens.
- An opportunity to root prune and promote denser new root growth.
- An opportunity to arrange the top surface roots to improve the cosmesis of the root collar.
- The top growth of a dormant bare-root plant will wait for new root initiation before sending out fresh foliage.

> *Tip*: A slurry can be created with soaked greenhouse potting mix to dip the bare roots in prior to potting. That slurry helps the bare-root system keep uniformly moistened. It prevents large air pockets and ensures the substrate settles around the roots.

One disadvantage to planting bare root could be that the root system quickly dries out if not handled properly before potting.

■ Scientifically, what is fertilizer burn or salt burn or "root burn"?

It's dehydration from reverse osmosis. Fertilizers are chemical salts that can become concentrated in a water solution. Plant cells already contain salt solutions in the form of sap. Osmosis into the roots is when pure water from a purer, lesser concentration of substrate salts start moving into a solution of less pure, higher salt concentration in the root cell's membrane.

In some cases, the fertilizer solution in substrate has a higher salt content and is less pure than the salt content (sap) already present in the roots. Again, water always moves to areas that have less water content.

The upward movement of soluble salts in roots can reverse. *It is possible for that weaker solution inside roots to be drawn backward out of the roots into a stronger solution of substrate salts* (#299). Then the roots dehydrate. Sometimes you can see the tips of the leaves turning brown and crinkling from the so-called root burn. It is actually dehydration.

"Seal the cut ends of the roots with a fungicidal wound compound after disinfecting any nematode infected parts." Forget all three: the sealant, the fungicide and the disinfectant. Sealing pruned roots might seal in harmful bacteria or decaying fungi. Disinfectants can cause even more die back on cut roots. Nematacides work on nematodes if they're present. Fungicides work on fungi. A fungicide can kill any good mycorrhiza and not touch any nematodes whether good or bad. Many more good nematodes than bad nematodes exist in natural field soil.

"Roots can't grow without mycorrhizal fungi. Inoculate all bonsai roots with mycorrhizae." Mycorrhizae refer to the fungi living in close symbiotic association with some root systems in field soil. Only 10 percent of all plant families in nature commonly have mycorrhizae. Those include some species in the birch, oak, pine, juniper, and rose families. Mycorrhizal fungi usually colonize on those roots in field soil by their own effort.

Root cells of ericaceous plants in field soil, such as azaleas, eventually get infected with an endomycorrhizal fungus. That fungus colonizes inside the root cells when in field soil. No one can see endomycorrhizae. Try not to bare root azaleas or replace their existing field soil all at once when first transplanting.

All mycorrhizal fungi in natural field soil serve as root extensions. They're beneficial to the roots' growth on those trees growing in the ground because they increase the surface area. *Mycorrhizae are organs* (#300). You cannot inoculate with organs.

Mycorrhizae are not essential for plant growth (#301). No direct scientific evidence supports that adding mycorrhizae works for all trees.

Coarse-textured substrates, frequent repotting, root pruning, and regular fertilization discourage mycorrhizal growth in a bonsai pot (#302). Mycorrhizae are instantly killed with a small pinch of nitrogen fertilizer in the form of ammonium nitrate.

■ **Is mycorrhizae fungus or tree?**
Both.

■ **When you buy a "bag of mycorrhizae" and open it up to add to your tree's roots, are there any mycorrhizae in that bag?**

No. *Few studies back up claims on the product's efficacy or its shelf life. Mycorrhizae are a combination of living root and living fungi* (#303). If you buy a bag of mycorrhizae, any roots in the bag are dead. On the shelf, they don't have constant moisture and suitable organic matter to live on. How do you know how much is even viable by the time you incorporate it into the substrate? *Researchers conclude that commercial products with mycorrhizae do not and cannot provide endomycorrhizal fungi* (#304).

■ **Taking bonsai out of the wired pot is a big hassle every year. Do I have to "prune the roots on bonsai every year"? And must I "always wire all bonsai firmly to its pot"?**

Tree roots don't like to be continually disturbed. However, juvenile top growth on junipers and aggressive top growth on deciduous trees can be promoted after root pruning. *Bonsai continue to flourish in the same container if the roots haven't yet colonized the substrate* (#305). Pruning healthy roots won't make them healthier.

> *Tip*: It may not be necessary to wire a developing bonsai to the container if the plant has a dense root ball and is not top heavy. You can easily pull the bonsai out of the pot and check to see what's going on inside. Roots don't "get damaged" if the root ball is not wired to the pot.

Surface roots wired down to the pot can push the root ball up into the wire as the root system develops and expands. Cut the wire before the surface roots get injured by growing into the wire.

"Apply starter fertilizer before spring and after root pruning to give the roots a jumpstart."
Contrary to some advice, fertilization cannot help root initiation. *Excess fertilizer salts inhibit the root growth of a newly pruned root system* (#306). *In an effort to conserve water, the the photosynthesis process is less on the foliage of a newly root pruned plant* (#307). Excess fertilizer salts can accumulate in the fresh substrate and increase the plant's need for water. *Adding fertilizer after root pruning has been shown to decrease new root growth in some instances* (#308).*

■ **What is the difference between root rot and crown rot?**

There is no difference. It is sometimes also called collar rot if the tree gets Phytopthora rot around the soil line. The same pathogen can infect below the soil line and everything at or above the soil line.

"Yellowing leaves or needles are the first sign of root rot."
Root rot can show up in late summer on the leaves. You'll observe more of a brownish, purplish, or reddish color on wilted foliage. Sometimes you'll notice soft, mushy, darkened brownish areas on the lower trunk and surface roots. Root rot is the culprit if it looks stressed for water but doesn't recover when watered.

Root rot is often confused with a constantly soggy substrate and with winter injury. The difference is that root rot smells bad.

"Either too much water or an injury to the root causes root rot."
Fact: *Fungi or fungi-like microorganisms swimming around in flooded soil pores lead to root rot* (#309).
Explanation: Bonsai planted in overwatered, over-fertilized, and poorly aerated substrates can get infected from a root decay pathogen. Pathogens do seem to know when the root tissue is immature or injured.

Survival rates on older trees for root rot are much better than on infected younger trees. If one of your valuable plants is killed

---

* Warren, "Fertilizing and Pruning Dogwood," *Journal of Arboriculture* (March 1993).

with kindness from too much water, don't let it happen twice.

Fact: **Root rot fungus can also affect leaves, leaf petioles, and fruit** (#310).

> *Tip*: Let any infected areas dry out. Prune infected roots and try to peel off any infected bark tissue. Ensure that the pot drains. Drain holes do clog up over time.

"Roots rot in just one day if watered too much."

Fact: **You may not observe any dieback or decline symptoms in an infected plant for weeks or even months after the plant tissue has been invaded** (#311).

Explanation: Watering too much doesn't explain why roots rot. Rotting depends on pathogens swimming around in long-term waterlogged conditions.

Fact: **Root rot kills by starving and suffocating a root** (#312).

Explanation: The roots are good at isolating the root rot pathogens out in natural field soil. Storage space and energy reserves in a pot are reduced for roots in poorly aerated substrate. Over time, the tree starves from lack of energy and suffocates from thirst while the roots may be surrounded by more than adequate fertilizer and water.

Drought-stressed roots may also result in root rot. Injured roots will not take up water. If you dunk injured roots in a tub of water, they eventually get rot, not hydration.

"If you place moss on the other side where roots are needed, then roots grow and thicken up."

Sorry, this is yet another myth begging to be debunked!

Ponderosa pine.

KEEPING BRANCHES HAPPY

Stems are the supporting woody parts of a plant coming out of the ground from the root collar. Branches, shoots, twigs and trunks are all stems. Trunks are the main stems.

Branches and limbs are stems more than one year old and smaller than the parent trunk they're attached to. Shoots are stems less than one year old with foliage.

Twigs are also stems less than one year old but without foliage. Shoots morph into branches at a branch collar. Branches morph into the parent trunk at a branch collar belonging to the trunk. The main trunk morphs into the roots at a root collar.

BRANCH PARTS

■ **What is the difference between the phloem, the xylem, and the cambium? And why would we need to know any tree anatomy and physiology?**

A basic knowledge of plant anatomy is as essential to us bonsai aficionados just as a thorough understanding of human anatomy would be vital to someone starting out in a health field career. First, we'll try to clear up a few misconceptions.

The cambial zone is not the only living part of roots and stems (#313). This cambium layer is not only single layer of cells. ***The cambium is not green*** (#314). The green color we see when we scratch the bark of a stem or root is the outer layer below the epidermis of the stem or root called the cortex. ***Cambium does not "produce wood"*** (#315).

Sapwood, where the sap flows, is not living tissue but dead or dying transport vessels .

Bonsai are usually woody plants, meaning a plant with a cambial zone. Grasses and annuals don't have a cambium. Phloem and xylem tubes are the plant's vascular transport system, sometimes called the tree's pathways.

Where does the tree's corky outer surface come from? The cambial zone controls

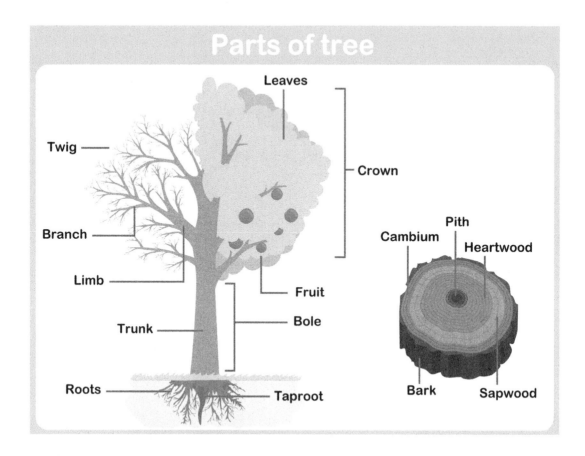

Parts of tree

Leaves

Twig

Crown

Branch

Limb

Trunk

Fruit

Bole

Roots

Taproot

Pith

Cambium

Heartwood

Bark

Sapwood

growth of new phloem, which expands outward from the cambium. Where does the woody sapwood come from? It comes from new, thicker xylem expanding inward from the cambial zone.

Plant cells can't specialize until they elongate into continuous tubes and quit dividing. Lots of toughening natural cement called lignin forms in the walls of the cells. Lignin gives staying power to recently wired and bent branches.

When lignified (becoming hardened), living phloem turns into outer dead corky bark. Xylem turns into inner woody sapwood. The amount of outer bark or inner wood produced does not have to be equal in width on both sides of the cambium or even in one area of the branch.

Phloem is a vessel that allows photosynthates to flow downward (mostly). Phloem vessels go

anywhere the tree needs energy. If a branch is trained to cascade downward, the first movement of photosynthate is upward in the phloem toward the trunk before squeezing downward to the roots.

That thin pre-bark layer outside the cambium layer is a pathway distributing the sugars (photosynthate) produced in the leaves from photosynthesis. Sap does not move down "from gravity." Photosynthates are squeezed downward.

Sap flow is active in the phloem tissues of younger stems. The outer bark of younger stems can usually be stripped down nearly to the wood without harm to the rest of the plant.

The xylem pathway toward the inside is full of sap and water. Annually, that thin, inner, ringed layer of xylem dies and is replaced again by a new ringed layer.

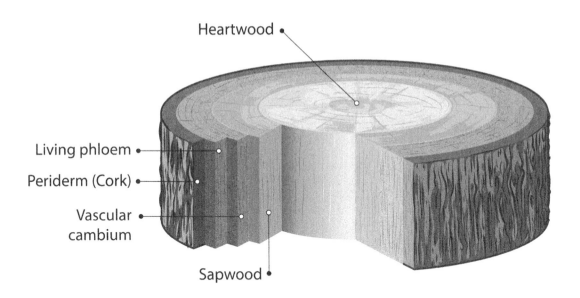

Xylem is a tube vessel that allows resources to flow up (mostly). As the leaf evapotranspirates water into the air, that gas exchange contributes to water going up a tree. Water in the foliage is replaced like a syringe drawing up liquid. Starting at the top of the tubes, the whole water column flows up from the roots in a vacuum.

The water molecules, stuck together by cohesion, are attracted to the inside of the solid xylem pathway and drawn up the sapwood under vacuum (#316).

Water and essential elements in water solution continue to be sucked up and dispersed throughout the plant. Capillary action is a factor in water movement within substrate but not a factor in moving water up a stem.

The continuous stem flange of thick-walled cells plug the base where the cambium of one branch meets the cambium of another branch (#317). This protection zone resists the spreading of pathogens.

When cambium is ruptured by a pruning cut, wound tissue begins to form. Wound tissue has a survival benefit because it adds strength to some part of a branch, and it isolates the living part of the tree from a scar.

Wound tissue formation after wiring can help set a branch where we want it to stay.

Older branches take much longer to set in a new position because they have more pith (heartwood), and their resistance to bending is much greater to overcome (#318). With age, some pathway vessels (phloem and xylem) start to clog up and reroute.

Girdling or flush cut pruning injures through the cambium layer into the living xylem layer (#319). That injured area cannot produce cork on the outside or sapwood on the inner side of the cambium. *Once injured, it is always injured* (#320).

"Cells fuse together in grafting when both cambium layers match exactly."
Bonsai is somewhat like sculpture: take away what doesn't belong and add a branch or root where it will add to the aesthetics. Often the looks of a tree can be improved by grafting a branch or root just exactly where we want it.

The stem grafting procedure involves exposing the vascular system of both the understock and the upper scion. The tree fundamentally responds to a new graft the same way it would respond to the propagation of a new cutting, to a scar from proper pruning, or to an injury during air layering. It almost immediately deposits a layer of pectin glue to wall off the cut from pathogens and to slow down the loss of water. Undifferentiated, protective callus cell formation then originates from the most recent dying phloem and xylem cells. Mostly from the new phloem. Callus tissue expands to fill in the gap between both foreign stems and to further restrict the movement of decay into the two stems. Only the new callus tissue bridging the gap will interlock cells. The water and photosynthate can passively move through the callus without the cambium, phloem, and xylem matching or even remotely connecting.

New xylem originates only from the top scion part bringing up water to help offset any moisture loss from transpiration. Often you will notice callus formation originating only from the top scion. It is reasonable for both foreign cambial layers to be in the vicinity of each other, but it is not "absolutely vital for both existing cambial layers to touch and match so they will fuse together."

They'll never fuse. In some species, the phloem and xylem vascular tissue differentiates directly from the callus even before the new cambium cells form. New cambium cells can eventually bridge to the original cambial cylinder. Existing vascular cambium only alters the undifferentiated, unspecialized cells in the new cambial tissue, making them differentiate and eventually specialize as the new cambium bridge. Callus cell formation has a high requirement for oxygen, so do not apply any sealant to new callusing wounds on recent grafts, pruning scars, cuttings, or air layers.

Another tidbit about the cambial zone: You can strip an entire ring of bark from a two-year-old seedling, effectively girdling it. Invert and graft that thin cylinder of bark back on the seedling upside down. New callus tissue bridges the gap. Reverse polarity will still graft, but the decreased downward movement of auxin permanently dwarfs the tree parts above that ring graft. Water from the roots is still passively extracted up and through the callus tissue.

■ What connects the growing roots to the growing leaves?

The cambial zone is the center of all tree growth (#321). We need to keep that thin cambial zone active on the parent stem, untouched and uninjured. Cell division in the cambial zone adjusts in response to the tree's changing conditions. Cambium activity is also affected by a resting stage or by an injury. The cambial zone closes up like an accordion during its resting stage and opens back up again for the entire growing season.

"The trunk stops and the roots begin at the soil line."

First of all, the trunk is not the roots. Biologically, the trunk (and all stems) have pith down the center. Roots don't have pith. Stems have internodes and buds. You won't find internodes or buds on a root. At the point below the trunk, the roots begin, not necessarily at the soil line. Roots can be buried deep or exposed high above the soil line.

Second, when measuring the trunk diameter for size, don't include the roots. For accuracy and consistency, bonsai trunk diameter is normally measured one inch above the root collar flange. If a graft is obvious, measure one inch above the graft union.

Often, you come across an unusually large base with an unusually thick flare extending more than an inch above the root collar point. Measure at that point where the unusual trunk flare ends. Height of the bonsai is measured from the top of the root collar to the top of the crown.

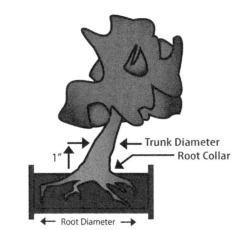

Trunk Measurement is taken 1″ above the Root Collar

Measurements "taken from where surface roots meet the soil" are just that: surface root measurements.

SWITCHING SYSTEMS

■ What is the role of auxins, cytokinins, gibberellins, and abscisic acid?

These growth regulators are all switching systems. Chemical growth regulators (unlike human hormones and steroids) coordinate growth and synthesize plant growth substances in respond to stimuli. It takes only a tiny quantity of one or two growth regulators to induce considerable changes in a plant. Plants respond quickly to the slightest environmental stimuli.

Each plant growth regulator has several switch-on or switch-off effects. This depends on its location and its concentration compared to the other growth regulators. When the growth regulator is diminished, the signal pathways have a process to turn that signal off.

Knowledge of how plant growth substances interact is helpful in bonsai cultivation. We understand better how our bonsai respond to internal and external signals, to environmental stress, or when we prune, wire, or transplant.

The health and growth of an entire branch depends on its terminal bud and the switching systems controlling it (#322). Latent lateral buds wait in the axial (elbow) of every shoot and leaf. They're on standby waiting to compete and push out as soon as the dominant active apical bud is repressed or gone.

Auxins at the tips switch off and repress the growth of latent buds below (#323). Pruning or nipping off the top bud switches on standby buds below to become more active. Auxin levels increase—they do not decrease—in axillary buds of decapitated plants.

The auxin regulator accumulates not exclusively at the tips but also on the shaded side of the tree. When auxin moves away from light, the stem grows toward the light.

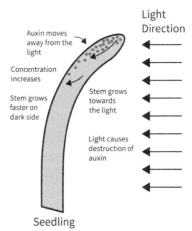

Auxins flow downward from cell to cell in a direct line to the roots with the help of proton-pumping proteins. Their distribution has nothing to do with gravity. If we bend a branch more horizontally, the auxin flow is temporarily reduced as it relocates to the bottom or more shaded side. ***Vertically oriented branches have more efficient growth regulator flow than downward-bent branches*** (#324).

Why doesn't a new branch grow back exactly straight up and down when you've pruned its original upright leader down to a lower bud? One reason is that the concentration of the auxin growth regulator was apparently low in the lower branch at that time. The new weakened leader started to grow more horizontally for a short time. Soon, auxin accumulates at the new top. The new leader eventually grows out of that crooked angle.

> *Tip*: To help that new leader look straighter, stake it. Leave a short, temporary stub of the previous leader to stake and wire the new leader vertical until it lignifies.

Horizontally oriented surface roots grow more rapidly on their upper side than on their lower side due to geotropism and auxin concentrations. Lateral root formation is switched on with high auxin concentrations.

Auxins are part of the cell elongation process. Both auxins and cytokinins switch on cell division and cell differentiation. ***Auxins and cytokinins do not "act antagonistically" to regulate axillary bud growth at the junction of the petiole and leaf*** (#325).

Levels of auxins increase in the axillary buds after nearby pruning. After a branch is pruned, calluses form, and finally wound wood develops at the parent collar. Callusing starts only when the cambium zone at the parent collar (stem flange) is intact and when both the cytokinins and auxins switch on.

Cytokinins are nitrogen compounds produced around the root tips. As they travel upward in

early spring, they release the resting stage of the branches. Their presence retards aging of plant organs. Gibberellins regulate plant height by switching on leaf and stem growth.

Abscisic acid is produced in response to drought stress in mature foliage and switches off growth. If the roots have a water shortage, it gives an early warning signal to the foliage. The abscisic acid accumulating in subordinate buds is thought to switch them off, while auxin in the dominant terminal buds switches them back on.

We cannot make our bonsai grow better by simply adding a "hormone product" (#326). The concentration of growth regulators alone does not determine or control plant growth and development. Switches don't act alone. One part of the plant signals another part of the plant to adjust and correct deficiencies if all other resources are available.

Deficiency of nitrogen, for example, can initiate root growth. With excess nitrogen supplements, the plant is signaled to start depleting stored photosynthates and initiate shoot growth. ***The formation of new shoots is usually a response to low energy reserves in a plant*** (#327). A deficiency in stored photosynthates in one area can initiate a flush of shoot growth. New shoot growth initiated in response to a deficiency in photosynthates is fairly defenseless against pathogens. Temperature and seasonal changes also affect the regulators in a tree.

Switches in both roots and stems signal and allocate resources. They determine if undifferentiated cells become a leaf, stem, or root. Switches also decide if a particular root or stem thrives or dies.

"We can take some of the tree's available energy from part of a branch and balance or distribute it around the rest of the tree."
Fact: ***We cannot take electrons (energy) from one plant cell, balance the electrons***

between cells, or distribute its electrons to another cell (#328).

Explanation: The energy-generating surface provides photosynthate for the plant's own establishment, survival, growth, and reproduction. All the energy in a plant is made in living cells and stored in living cells. Plant cells don't even share their own electrons with one another. They do distribute essential elements from one part of a plant to another part.

Fact: ***We can allow growth in one part of the tree or try to repress growth in another part of the tree but only when the tree switches on or off its own growth regulators*** (#329).

Explanation: Our objective in training bonsai is to allow the tree to switch on its resources in the branches we want to keep for development. It is hoped those branches will improve with age.

"We can encourage an existing dormant bud to grow on a tree."

Fact: ***Latent buds and future adventitious buds are not dormant in the sense of being inactive*** (#330). They're fully developed with dividing cells and fully capable of forming a future stem.

Explanation: Even while repressed, those active, lower resting buds are slowly dividing cells. They remain in the bark, standing by, waiting for the signal to differentiate into a stem, leaf, or flower.

Buds normally occur at internodes. All stems start as a bud, and all buds have tiny, preformed leaves called bud scales. At the base of every bud scale exists yet another future bud. An adventitious bud may form anywhere else on a stem except on a meristem (area of actively dividing cells). Adventitious budding, or budding farther back along the branch toward the trunk, is generated in the cambium in response to stress coming from higher up

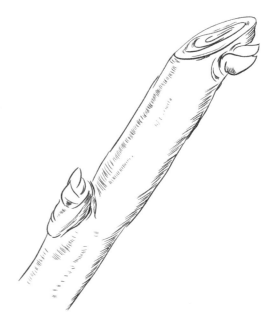

the tree or farther out on the branch. Stress can come from excess pruning or fertilizer applications. One of the best times to prune for future adventitious bud development is during the first flush of foliage growth.

The top bud, called the apical bud, is the lead boss. It produces the highest concentration of the auxin growth regulator. Switches in the top bud repress the subordinate buds below it from overgrowing the top. Environmental conditions remind us constantly who is the real boss.

Tip: We manipulate time and again the natural process of apical dominance at the tips of branches. Developing lateral buds can be encouraged to grow by pruning the active bud at the stem tip. Selecting the lateral bud facing the direction you want forces stems to grow in an interesting zigzag pattern. Notching away a small wedge of the bark above that lateral bud before new foliage appears can also encourage that standby bud to pop out.

BRANCH RESPONSES

■ Do plants respond to touch?

They do. Scientists call it thigmotropism. Other terms include mechanical perturbations, seismomorphogenesis, or mastic movements. Don't we love the imaginative terminology scientists give us?

Any natural grove of stunted-looking, gnarled trees with short internodes, thick stems, and tight, compact canopies has been dwarfed by nature's touch. Those short, stocky trees responded to the heavy touch of wind, water, snow, and other plants and animals. A tree standing alone in an open, unprotected field is thicker and sturdier than a slender forest tree in the middle of a more protected group.

Naturally dwarfed trees show a decrease in internode length, needle length, leaf size, number of flowers, and total height. They show thicker branches. The stems become short and flexible instead of short and rigid, so they're less likely to snap off.

Compact trees have shorter and smaller vascular pathways, less overall cells, and a greater cell wall thickness than larger trees. Shorter stems with shorter vascular pathways result in quicker response time to environmental stimuli. Many of the larger commercial greenhouse growers now successfully use mechanical brushing to reduce internode length, promote stiffer stems, and promote more roots relative to stem mass.[*]

More disturbances equal more plant responses. The more we touch, handle, prune, and wire our developing bonsai, the more touch response changes are evident. We're toughening up our bonsai every time we water by brushing against the foliage with the end of the water sprinkler (rose) head.

---

[*] J. Latimer, "Mechanical Conditioning to Control Height," *Horticulture Technology* (December 1998).

Soon after we start wiring and bending a branch, the disturbed plant's tissue starts to lignify more on the concave side, preventing further bending or fracture. A wired and repositioned branch soon starts to hold its shape. Then we remove the wire. Mechanical stress such as wiring and bending slows branch elongation, but the branch still thickens in diameter. The stem holds new curves as those lateral cells expand.

"A wound in the cambium area stimulates a branch to thicken and activate new growth."
Fact: **Only the tree's own growth regulators can activate and continue its growth** (#331).
Explanation: Wounding wood, by itself, does not automatically cause new cell division. Bending and partially snapping a branch can cause an incomplete fracture of the cambium layer. The process of cell division can thicken up around that wounded area.

> *Tip:* Sometimes growers can influence the process of cell division. They girdle a branch temporarily with wire. They cut, poke or drill little holes in the area they want to thicken up. Plant responses can initiate the process of increasing cell divisions in that area.

■ What is reaction wood, adaptive wood, tension wood, and compression wood?

Those words describe a growth response in the stem or root. Trees form asymmetrically as a result of asymmetrical stress. **Denser wood fibers may form on one side of the branch or trunk in an attempt to prevent further bending or cracking** (#332). Branches and leaning trunks eventually form reaction wood in response to their environmental conditions.

The reaction (tension) side of a leaning trunk is the upper side where the roots are pulling out of the ground. The root crown, where it meets the soil line, has more cellulose on that upper side. The tension side of the roots thickens as the top crown pulls the roots up.

The compression side is the lower side of the trunk lean pinched into an acute angle. It's also strong wood. Knee roots are compression wood trying to support the weight of a leaning tree.

Compression wood is also produced on the underside of branches. This occurrence is especially noticeable on conifers since the bottom side has extra lignin. When you look at a cross section of a large branch, you'll see closer rings on the upper side and wider-spaced rings on the thicker underside.

■ How does a surface wound turn into a cavity?

A surface wound is when the bark is injured. Large stubs or snags left on for more than a growing season can easily become rotten and hold moisture. *The rot can spread farther into the trunk through the punctured live cambium layer; a cavity wound develops from rotting wood and is not reversible* (#333).

"A cavity or hollowed-out area in the tree trunk means the tree is starting to die."
Fact: *Any natural cavity or void in a tree means the tree is doing a great job in defending itself against dying* (#334).
Fact: *Wound boundaries cannot form when the unhealthy tree lacks stored energy resources* (#335).
Explanation: Trees wall off an injured place to minimize the exposure of healthy wood to the decay process. A barrier is formed to protect the cambium layer and help resist the spread of infection. New wound wood is produced, which essentially moves the phloem area away from infection.

> *Tip*: Cavities add great character to the aesthetics of a bonsai. Emphasize those existing natural-looking hollows to your advantage as a focal feature in the design process.

"Heartwood is dead in the middle of an old tree."
Fact: *Heartwood is protection wood composed of dead tree cells and full of live microorganisms* (#336).
Fact: *Trees are living organisms. They survive by their chemical response systems* (#337).
Explanation: A hollowed-out tree has a better chance of survival if the decay stays in the middle of the tree. Wood was alive when first formed in the cambial zone. As mentioned at the beginning of this chapter, some cells later die and specialize into support and transport systems. The cells that live longest store the photosynthates manufactured during photosynthesis.

As heartwood dies, it attracts microorganisms. Progressive breakdown within the cavity by old wood fungi and other types of live microorganisms help release stored essential elements. Decay is the process of breaking down cellulose, basically sugars. As a big plus in that sugar breakdown process, the tied-up nitrogen from air changes into an essential element from which the whole tree profits.

You've sealed a cavity scar years ago with seal paste. Now you notice a small hole going into the center of the trunk. Removing the crusty old cut paste, you discover a big, gaping rotted hole. Somewhere you read, "Dig out the decay

Tip: Instead of filling the cavity, show it off as an interesting design element. In a living tree, the high moisture content of the wood protects against the spreading of decay. Charring inside a cavity with a propane torch also seems to protect against fungus decay spreading further. You can leave cavities alone in the tough wood of boxwoods and junipers, for instance, and no harm is done. Don't feel as if you should drill a drain hole through the trunk cavity into the substrate.

to expose green, healthy wood. Fill the cavity since standing water causes rot and a flat surface heals better."

Fact: **Fungi causes decay** (#338).

Explanation: Microorganisms cause rot. Decay didn't encourage the fungi to come and feast. Those decay organisms can't live in conditions of either too much or not enough water. Water cannot cause wood to rot. Too much or not enough water, by itself, will not cause rot to form or make it spread to other parts of the tree. Fungi uses excess water to move out of one wet area into new surrounding wood.

Fact: **Tree cavities don't "heal and repair themselves"** (#339).

Explanation: Decay actually stops when a tree cavity fills with water. Those decay organisms can only grow with sufficient oxygen. Constantly wet wood is preferable to decayed wood. Filling up the hole with anything is contraindicated.

Digging out or draining a cavity breaks down and removes the tree's own natural protective boundaries (#340). Carving out cavities past those boundaries causes—it does not prevent—decay.

■ **What is the optimum temperature for branch growth?**

About 70° to 85°F. Photosynthesis can slow down or stop when temperatures are higher than 100°F.

"The onset of shorter days usually prevents the onset of the new growth."

The second day of summer is the onset of shorter days. Deciduous plants then start to get the signal to prepare for their resting stage and start storing photosynthate. Growth may slow down, but the only time cell division stops is when the plant is dead.

THE FORM OF TREES

The form of a tree can be defined by the inherent size, shape, quantity of branches, and position of branches. We would expect plants of the same species to vary greatly in form as each different plant adjusts to its own particular niche. The genetic background for most trees came from a forest environment where they easily adjusted to their niche.

Plants in a restricted, forced environment do not adjust as easily

One tremendous advantage our physically smaller bonsai do have over their physically larger older brothers is that they have shorter regulator pathways. Compact plants respond and adjust quickly to internal and external changes. Here's another reason to leave on as many roots and branches as possible during initial transplanting of a collected tree: if no carbohydrates are available to a weak lower branch we've selected to develop, a more active, stronger branch above it will carry the main switches while the lower, preferred branch weakens and dies.

Pruning both roots and crown at the same time must somehow appeal to our sense of balance and symmetry. The tree adjusts (it does not balance out) both roots and branches much better by itself than we ever can. Sometimes growth starts with new roots; sometimes growth starts with the branches. It depends on where the resources and growth regulators are accumulated. This is yet another reason to have more patience with our bonsai.

The tendency of natural processes is to level out toward change, decay, and balance. When a plant reaches balance, no movement exists. **With equal balance and no regulator signals for adjusting itself any further, the plant dies** (#341).

"A triangular silhouette with an apex ensures a more functional branching habit with equal parts of sunlight. That shape will keep any bonsai healthy for many years."
If you think about it, trees with a regulation triangular shape will receive "equal parts of sunlight" at exactly high noon on the one day of summer solstice. Maybe we could refer to the top of the branching system more correctly as the crown form, the canopy, or simply the crown.

Green meatballs and other curious shapes as seen from the "best front view."

Triangular shapes, single trunk, lazy S, and zigzag patterns alternate branching, and those dense layers of foliage pads seem to be more artistic judgment than based on horticultural principles. Too often, "S-shaped trunks" and "triangular-shaped fronts" appear monotonous. And they sometimes look more flattened when viewed from the side. That triangular silhouette with an apex is for looks, not for function. A two-dimensional triangular silhouette with an apex reminds some people of the Christmas tree shape, not of a bonsai.

Consider how you would sculpt a free-form miniature tree. Picture how it will look as it grows. Look for the most interesting form, feature, or design possibility. Maybe emphasize the ugliest feature and change it to the dominant focal point. Look at the possibilities in all three dimensions—from the front, the side, and from the top.

Most of your bonsai won't conform to a predetermined mold. Emulate natural things without silencing self-expression or idealism. Allow each individual tree to suggest all the possibilities of its own future form, shape, or

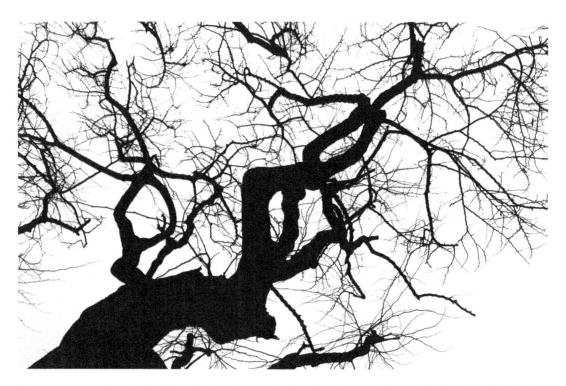

Some trees appear quite majestic with freeform branches roaming throughout the crown. Can you identify any branch pads with flat bottoms?

outline. Our bonsai usually let us know when they agree with their natural identities.

Older branches do not automatically grow horizontally or downward in nature.

Young trees usually stretch up before they stretch out. Acute angle branches form at every crotch. As they get older, some trees develop a more rounded but irregularly shaped crown. The angle of the side branch continues to be an acute angle with the adjacent parent trunk even if the outer part of the branch develops more horizontally or downward. On the whole, natural tree forms, shapes, or outlines are not usually symmetrically balanced on one main trunk line. Nature typically tends toward asymmetry, unpredictable movement, change and disorder, tension and instability, and, finally, decay.

Genetically, trees grow in two basic crown forms: rounded and conical. "Genetically predetermined" means that a genetically rounded tree likes to stay rounded.

> *Tip*: Keep genetics and hormonal dominance in mind every single time you prune, repot, or shape bonsai.

Here in the eastern United States, most of our native trees come with rounded crown forms. Some are more conical with a strong top, such as maples and sweet gums. However, feel free to alter the growth habit of any tree. Elms may typically form into vase-shaped branches with several trunks in nature. A bonsai elm can tolerate pruning its side branches while training it to have more interesting curvy branches on a curvy single trunk. You're adding the illusion of age. The same goes for pruning the top of a central leader–dominant species such as bald cypress to make an older-looking, rounded-spreading crown form. Hormonal dominance can be interrupted and overcome by pruning.

How are the different forms of trees classified?

Most trees can be classified as either rounded, branch dominant, or conical, central leader dominant.

Branch dominant species include Ficus, Quercus, Ulmus, and Zelkova. Genetically, that group typically has a more rounded spreading form with strong apical dominance. Many co-dominant (same diameter) branches fork from the main trunk. Co-dominant leaders grow up and spread out randomly at a similar rate from the main leader. The central trunk has weak apical control with side, secondary trunk-like branches originating from the same area. Those branches fork, ascend, and grow faster than the central trunk. That central axis continues to grow slowly or may even die and be replaced by the many other spreading branches. Co-dominant scaffold branches usually are less than half the size of the main trunk on bonsai.

Rounded spreading crown habit typically has strong apical dominance. Several terminal buds have strong dominance over lateral buds. Multiple scaffold shoots elongate at the same growth rate. Lateral buds initiate this year but elongate next year. It also has weak apical control. Lateral buds initiated last year and released this spring outgrow the terminal shoot. Co-dominant branches compete and elongate with the same strength as the central leader.

Central leader dominant species include Acer, Cedrus, Liquidambar, Pinus and Taxodium. Genetically, that group typically has a more conical form due to strong apical control of one central trunk.

Conical crown habit typically has weak apical dominance. Terminal buds have weak dominance over lateral buds. Lateral buds initiate and elongate the same year. It also has strong apical control. Central terminal leaders with a distinct main axis overpower side branch elongation. Terminal internode growth with longer internodes overpowers lateral bud growth with shorter lateral shoots. Terminal buds and terminal leaders have stronger apical control. The tree develops into the conical form with that triangular silhouette.

"All trees must have an alternating branch arrangement to ensure that air and light will reach all the branches."

Not to worry, the tree branches get enough air. Branches can be manipulated through wiring and bending to receive enough light. Pots can be occasionally turned or relocated to a sunnier area.

Branches don't "assume their position." Patterns in nature are not accidental. Nature will evenly space branches. All the branches along the parent trunk are not always symmetrically balanced. Whorled, alternate, or opposite branching patterns make no difference to the well-being of a tree. Whorled or opposite branching is not a "defect."

What are a few differences to consider when working with alternate branching and opposite branching trees?

The bud opening sequence differs between alternate and opposite branching. For alternate branching species, the opening sequence starts with the last bud on the tip with the strongest and longest internode. That bud will be first to unfold. Then the buds unfold in turn, starting from the tip and going back toward the main branch or trunk. Alternate branching trees have their shortest internodes closest to the main trunk or branch.

Phyllotaxy or leaf arrangement

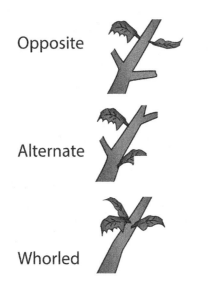

Opposite

Alternate

Whorled

Both opposite buds open at the same time with the same strength on opposite branching species, such as maple, serrisa, boxwood, and ligustrum. Prune those opposite branching species to the desired length. Pinch or rub off one bud and let the other opposite bud aim toward the desired direction.

Overall, you'll find more leaves and internodes on an opposite branching tree than on an alternate branching tree.

■ What are some differences to remember when working with junipers?

Junipers are said to be the most popular plant used in bonsai. Phloem vascular pathways in junipers, cypress, and a few other narrowleaf evergreens develop linear "live veins" over time. The phloem tubes transport photosynthates from foliage down to the rest of the plant. "Live veins" do not "carry water and nutrients up from the roots." That's the job for xylem, located deeper inside the trunk. A "live vein" is in fact a stack of dead tubes serving as a freeway to transport photosynthates down to the roots.

Foliar fertilization doesn't seem as effective on junipers as substrate fertilization. Injured juniper tissue has difficulty callusing sideways to wall off and close over a wound. Wedge cuts or saw kerf cuts should not be used to bend larger branches or the trunk on a juniper because of possible injury to a nearby vein.

The isolated, exposed, wounded cambium in the "lifeline" of a juniper seems to grow at a faster rate than the rest of the trunk. As the vein ages, it bulges and changes from flattened to a more rounded shape. Juniper veins (the phloem) can be separated from the rest of the trunk all the way down to the root.

Bark eventually falls off on its own on old junipers composed of mostly deadwood. People appreciate seeing some aged-battered bark on aged junipers. However, debarking is sometimes appropriate on larger, more mature junipers that consist of mostly deadwood and little live foliage.

Presoaking and then peeling off the flaking mature bark on junipers can minimize fungus-causing rot underneath on their deadwood (or invite pathogen attacks). The debarked trunk can be smoothed with a plumber's brass wire brush to find the outline of the vein and the contrasting outline of deadwood.

Older junipers start to show more spiraling than linear dominance of their veins. Some veins spiral clockwise and others spiral counterclockwise. I've seen one vein spiraling one way on the main trunk and the opposite direction on a branch of the same tree.

That twisting in nature is caused by genetics, twisting cambium, drought and disease, the sun, circling vines, or strong winds whipping the trunk around. All conifers consist of a vascular system where water can move both linearly and laterally throughout its cells. You don't often see twisted trunks on deciduous trees since water usually only moves up or down in its tissues.

Shimpaku (Sargents's juniper).

New pathways develop to connect roots and foliage. They twist as they ascend up the trunk, growing around dead branches or other obstacles. Those lifelines usually concentrate on one side or the other of the tree.

Juvenile or shaded foliage can be prickly to the touch. Sometimes wrongly referred to as "needle junipers," the correct term is awl-like foliage. Needles are found on pine, spruce, and fir. Juniper foliage is overlapping needles, or needle like.

This newer foliage is sometimes called awl-like, such as displayed on Blue Alps and Foemina juniper. Awl-like foliage tends to eventually turn into scale-like foliage with age, while in the sun, and when the roots of those trees become pot-bound.

The Chinese junipers such as Shimpaku (Sargents's juniper, shown on page 111) and the J. *procumbens* Nana juniper are examples of softer adult type of scales.

San Jose juniper is one example that displays both juvenile and adult foliage at the same time. Heavy pruning or fertilizer applications or other stresses on junipers can introduce a new batch of awl-like foliage. In time, prickly foliage eventually settles down to a more normal, softer, scale-like foliage. Soft, adult foliage, with small scales compressed down onto the stem (scale-like), is easier on the fingers and more huggable.

> Tip: Junipers don't respond well to a couple of pruning techniques. Both the clip-and-grow technique and the let-it-grow-and-chase-it-back technique can sap the resources from juniper's essential new foliage. Try preserving as many new growing tips as you can when shaping juniper. Individual branches die because they lose their energy and regulator signals to grow.

BRANCHING OUT

How can I get a new branch to grow where one is needed at a significant place?

Graft on a new bud or branch at almost any appropriate place on the tree. Prune back gradually to concentrate auxins in a preferred, closer, promising bud. Maybe you want to save that tip of a branch but allow a lower bud to pop out a little farther down the branch. Cut a small notch or a few vertical slits directly on top of a developing bud that is pointing in the right direction This bud notching technique interrupts auxin at the tip and allows auxin to stop repressing the lower bud. Keep some of the new growth close to that place to develop density around that area. Develop those branches later by wiring and shaping to your selected silhouette and form.

■ How can I strengthen chronically weak branches?

The weak get weaker and the strong get stronger, just like the economy. A weak branch is sitting alone, depleted of stored photosynthates and steadily declining in health. Prune it back to a robust branch.

Fact: **The healthier neighboring branches with plenty of their own resources will not share any of their resources with any other branch** (#342).

Explanation: Branches aren't altruistic. They don't "decide to drop in order to save the rest of the tree." We can't do much to strengthen a particular weak branch. The tree keeps its strongest and healthiest branches. Eventually, the tree walls off that weak branch to limit loss of resources, kills it, and lets the next heavy wind take it down.

Fact: **Branch thickness will increase faster if the terminal bud on that branch is left intact** (#343).

Explanation: Active cell division is forming new tissue near the meristem tips. New photosynthate production and this year's new storage centers are continuing right behind the growing tip.

> *Tip*: Allow potentially useful smaller branches to grow if they have enough light and are otherwise healthy. Don't prune their tips. Instead, prune the tips off the branches above them.

■ How can I "stimulate more bottom branch growth" with the top part growing so robustly and the bottom limbs seeming so weak?

Unfortunately, we can't ever stimulate a branch to grow. We can prune back some of the flourishing top growth to discourage the less flourishing competition below. Growth exclusively comes from the plant's own regulators. Usually those switches are located at the growing tips of both the branches and roots.

Wire and bend the weaker limb away from the shade of the top branches. The first priority is getting sunlight to the bottom foliage so it can produce photosynthate for itself.

Let it grow wild. Don't fuss with it until that weaker branch begins to elongate and thickens up. Then prune it back to a more proximal node or closer to the trunk. Continue this process until the branch is the right thickness and length. Lastly, work on lower secondary branching and distal ramifications.

Remove the repressed low branches. Trees in a forest habitat rarely have large, healthy lower branches intact.

■ What time of year do tree trunks grow the most in diameter?

Branches start budding out in spring. The trunk's most significant caliper growth period starts in late spring and continues all summer through early fall. Tree trunks don't grow much in diameter during winter.

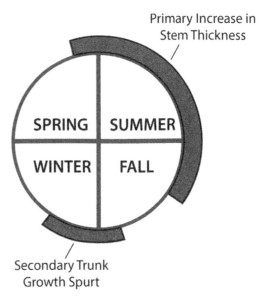

Trunk Growth

One study showed an average pattern of early trunk growth from mid-March to the first part of August and a smaller percentage of later growth from the first part of August to the first part of November. *Some trees have their greatest increase in trunk diameter and thickness right before fall* (#344).*

Another study provided information on trunk growth of maples. The growth in height was completed by the end of August. Interestingly, while more than 75 percent of height and trunk diameter growth was

---

* J. Robbins, "Trunk Caliper Growth of Nine Species Measured over Two Growing Seasons in Central Arkansas," *SNA Research Conference Proceedings* 53 (2008).

complete for most maples before the middle of August, only 25 percent of the final root growth had occurred by the end of August.[*]

> *Tip*: Mid-summer may be an excellent time to prune back maple branches for ramification during the refinement stage. Keep checking any summer wiring job every couple of weeks or so on deciduous trees. Don't "put all your bonsai in a greenhouse to force more trunk growth to develop over the winter." Hardy deciduous plants need their allotted resting period.

■ How do I develop the thickest trunk size in the shortest length of time?

Stems and roots develop in length quicker than trunks and root collars develop in thickness. Thickening in diameter starts from the cambium layer. Several new cell layers form on the inner ringed side and fewer layers form on the outer bark side of the cambium layer. As new cells die, they specialize into transport vessels, become woody, and continue to add bulk.

Fact: **Small bonsai kept in small pots have no opportunity to become big bonsai with thick trunks** (#345).

Fact: **Larger root systems develop thicker trunks and root collars** (#346). **In his 1993 book,** 100 Tree Myths, **Dr. Alex Shigo, tree biologist, found that most of the wood for the whole year in forest trees is formed six to eight weeks after the spring flush** (#347).

---

[*] J. Sibley et al., "Monthly Growth Patterns for Red Maple Cultivars," *SNA Research Conference Proceedings* 43 (1998).

> *Tip*: Developing large trunks requires growing and training for many years in large containers or for a few years out in some good field soil. This proven practice also applies to collected, nursery-grown, propagated, stressed-out, poorly formed, and thin-trunked material. Remember, if you start out with a bad-looking trunk, it's always bad looking.

> *Tip*: If you want to own big bonsai with an impressive thick trunk and a stunning root collar, first invest some big money. Buy a well-cultivated, quality bonsai with an existing good-looking trunk and root collar. Some people like to collect ready-made specimens.
>
> On the other hand, a quick and easy way to develop thick trunks and root collars is to start with a seedling—from small investments come big rewards. Start shaping a seedling into a good-looking trunk now and it can only get thicker and better looking in a few short years. Once you fast-track and get the framework established for your plant, you can start regulating and refining it in a pot.

■ The homegrown method: how to get a two-inch-caliper deciduous tree trunk in six years starting from a seedling.

Two years in a nursery container: Allow a cutting or seedling to develop by itself for two years in a nursery container. If you remove the top apical meristem too soon, the plant doesn't produce sufficient photosynthate at that stage. ***The roots will determine how many top buds can be sustained on a seedling*** (#348). An overly pruned stem may not be able to serve the energy requirements for the roots.

Two years in the ground: After the roots have fully colonized the container, take the plant out of the pot. Wire the trunk loosely into a couple slight curves, as seen in three dimensions, from the front and sides and from the top. Leave the roots unpruned but flatten and straighten out any top roots radially. Plant the small root ball at a slight angle in the ground or in a wide, shallow nursery pot. The nursery pot can be filled with nursery-grade potting mix. Let the tree settle in and develop by itself for another two years before you shape it. Except for the diseased, dying, or dead branches, no serious pruning is necessary. You'll still have to prune and wire the trunk.

Gradually cut the trunk down in stages. Start with trunk quality and trunk line for good bonsai design. Branch placement and ramification comes later. The aim is to develop roots, root collar, trunk size, and taper. Upsize the pot each time the roots colonize it. Ensure the container has several large drainage holes on the bottom and sides. Don't slow them down. In spring and fall, apply controlled-release fertilizer to the substrate or soil surface. Except for the lower limbs, the crown can be hedge-sheared back somewhat if aggressive top growth needs to be chased back down. For instance, a two-year-old tree might be two to four feet tall. Hedge trim the height down to six inches. Next year, you might hedge trim to twelve inches, then down to eighteen inches. Winter is a good time to clean up and smooth down the remaining snags. By then, the main line of the trunk will be obvious. Lower limbs are left to develop wood for trunk taper, but sprouts, suckers, and redundant shoots are eliminated. At this stage, expect extensive strong growth from a young tree.

Two more years in the ground: ***After supplying energy for stem growth and root growth, excess photosynthates finally allocate resources to increase the thickness of the trunk growth*** (#349). When the the lower trunk has developed thickness and taper, you can start shaping the lower main branches. Wait until mid-spring, after the first foliage flush hardens off and the roots have dispersed their stored photosynthates. Pruning at that time shouldn't promote longer internodes. Collar cut the thickest redundant branches back close to the trunk. Top shearing works at this stage to control height and delay crown density from overpowering lower developing branches. Don't forget to propagate the cuttings. Clean up the main branches during the winter when you can see the structural bones better. Twiggy ramification development comes after the trunk taper, root collar, and primary branches are acceptable and the plant is finally ready for a bonsai pot. Within the confinements of a bonsai pot, the rate of cambial cell division decreases. That's good. You want the plant to enjoy regulated growth during the unhurried refinement process.

Grab your knob cutters now and learn how to properly prune without injuring the branches.

Korean boxwood.

PRUNING AND MANIPULATING STEMS

WHAT IS PRUNING?

Pruning removes plant parts. By subtraction, pruning also adds mass due to lateral bud break and resulting new branching. Eventually, pruning adds to the aesthetics or hurts the aesthetics. The end result is either the best thing or the worst thing we do when shaping our bonsai.

It would be difficult to find a tree in nature following our "pruning rules." If our objective is to train and develop the shape of the bonsai, we first try to understand the way of nature—the innate natural shape a particular species wants to take by itself. Consider the normal growth habit when pruning or manipulating bonsai. You'll work less to keep it healthy. Your reward comes when your bonsai eventually reminds you of an old tree in all its glory.

RESPONSES TO BRANCH PRUNING

■ First, how does a plant respond physiologically to pruning?

The more we prune active branches, the less the plant grows (#350). For a short while.

Pruning temporarily removes some of the photosynthetic ability of the plant. Fewer leaves mean less resources available in the weakened plant to initiate new growth. Some plants do not adapt well to regular pruning.

Nitrogen and phosphorus uptake stops immediately after a heavy pruning job. No resources are being generated to break down those two elements into a usable form by the plant.

Pruning one single active stem or bud can affect more than the overall form of the tree. It can also affect the tree all the way to the roots. Loss of essential elements, growth regulators, and stored photosynthates stunts both stems and roots.

Pruning creates new space for new growth (#351). Prior to the cut, cells were tightly packed in the woody tissues. They had the capacity to develop into a new shoot but no space to grow. Finally signaled for release by the regulator switches, new shoots develop into their new space. The pruning cut provided plenty of new space for the new shoots to spread out and do their job.

Pruning during extended periods of higher temperatures releases valuable stored photosynthates and can weaken the plant (#352). After those resources are used up, the plant needs new foliage to supply new photosynthates. *Broken vascular pathways become temporarily weaker due to low defenses* (#353).

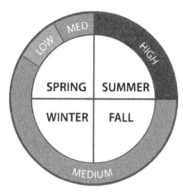

Trees Defense and Energy Reserve Systems

Pruning can disrupt the connection between the growth regulator switches in the growing branch tips and the growth regulator switches in the roots. Major, healthy, temporarily disrupted pathways can enable new connections that can become stronger.

A flush of new shoots increases new vascular pathways but retards new root initiation (#354). *Chemistry is a plant's defense* (#355). The tree's chemical defenses and energy reserves fluctuate during the year. Summer is a good time for major pruning, bending, and grafting. Fall growth repairs the damage.

■ **How do bonsai respond to different pruning cuts such as flush, concave, stub, or collar?**

"Cut flush to the trunk so the wound heals flush."
Until fifty years ago, a flush cut was considered correct pruning. Timing the pruning was important, and large flush cuts hardly ever "healed over" the way they were intended. That method is mostly taboo now.
Explanation: Now, we know flush cuts, concave cuts, and large stub cuts allow air and moisture to bring decay. Fungal decay enters the branch through the exposed live cambium and through the phloem. More wound surface equals more area for infection to enter. Rot follows those pathways, and a cavity forms. Digging out decay to "expose healthy wood" removes the protection boundaries.

Disease quickly penetrates deeper into the branch before the tree has time to isolate the wound and cover it over. The tree is then more susceptible to other problems ranging from cankers, rots, cracks, fissures, sprouts, trunk injury, pathogen injury, and frost or heat injury. Plus, it becomes a good home for unwanted wildlife.

Fact: *Flush cuts and concave cuts destroy some of the cambial zone and the parent stem flange* (#356). Protective chemicals the tree needed for callusing over the wound are mostly eliminated.

■ **Do shrubs and trees differ in their responses to time of pruning?**

There's not much difference between any of their responses. Large deciduous shrubs and small deciduous trees don't differ physiologically. *The dosage of pruning is more vital to the shrub or tree than the timing of pruning* (#357).

Shrubs do seem able to withstand repeated shearing and heavy pruning more than trees.

Most shrubs have more active lower stems and produce multi-trunks. Most trees have more active upper branches and considerably fewer trunks. Shrubs can be pruned down almost any time to ground level or to the thickest branch in order to start developing a thicker trunk. Roses and other shrubs with a hollow pith center have difficulty compartmentalizing their cuts. Those and other plants with cane-type growth may not be the best candidates for bonsai.

Shrubs readily produce sprouts and suckers when we attempt to prune them to a single trunk. Prune those suckers diligently. They'll eventually give up. Younger deciduous trees can usually tolerate being pruned down to a main trunk or to multi-trunks.

■ How do the different classes of evergreens differ in their response to pruning?

Evergreens are sometimes classified into narrowleaf and broadleaf. Not all narrowleaf evergreens have seeds in cones. Not all gymnosperms (non-flowering) are conifers (cone-bearing). Conifers have two subgroups, whorled branching, and random branching.

Whorled-branching, needle-producing conifers such as pine, spruce, hemlock, cypress, or fir produce only spring and summer growth. Yearly pruning is not recommended. Don't prune that group to a stub. Instead, remove developing new shoots or branches to the point of another outward-facing branch or bud. Knock off or pinch off all buds except the one you want to branch out facing the selected direction. Most narrowleaf evergreen tree branches grow and fork in horizontal planes.

All of the random-branching narrowleaf evergreens are further subdivided into yews and then into others such as junipers, true cedars, and Chamaecyparis. This conifer subgroup produces berry-like fruit instead of cone fruit. Yews back bud the most readily from a stub cut. Most broadleaf evergreens can't tolerate regular heavy pruning.

"We prune to invigorate a plant and make it healthier."

Fact: Pruning may improve the appearance and health of individual branches but cannot "invigorate the whole tree." Pruning only retards long-term growth.

Explanation: We see the remaining branches pushing out lush, bushy new growth as a result of pruning. That does not mean pruning is "healthy for a tree." The root system is now delivering more water and essential elements to fewer branches after pruning. Short-term growth is the result.

BEFORE MAKING THE CUT

The four parts of the pruning process include:
- How to cut.
- Which branch to cut.
- When to cut. (Timing is not important when you understand collar cuts).
- How much to cut.

■ What does pruning achieve?

Different pruning objectives can include:
- Adding to the aesthetics.
- Weeding out branches that look awkward, look as if they are not part of the tree, are in the wrong location, or are inconsistent with the line of the trunk or redundant.
- Removing branches not in scale— either too thick, too thin, too long, or without taper.
- Removing whorled, rubbing or crossed branches to achieve a less obtrusive appearance.

- Removing too long or too straight internodes.
- Removing or reducing the length of the lesser-quality co-dominant stem. Co-dominant means duplicate trunk leaders of equal diameter growing from the same point without taper.
- Removing all but two narrow-angled, adjacent, or most appropriate side branches at a triple fork.
- Removing energy-draining top sprouts and bottom suckers.
- Removing energy-draining thin branches from the crotch of a fork.
- Removing an aggressively growing but unimportant coarse branch.
- Manipulating or training the overall form.
- Maintaining the preferred form and structure.
- Controlling or directing future growth in both buds and stems.
- Repressing resources or rate of growth.
- Improving light penetration.
- Improving the breeze pathway through dense foliage.
- Thickening or thinning the crown.
- Encouraging compact growth in one particular area on the tree.
- Discouraging congested growth.
- Taking cuttings for propagation.
- Eliminating wood-bearing disease or wood-boring insects.
- Eliminating diseased, dead, or dying branches.
- Maintaining the natural vigor of one part of the plant.
- Increasing the lifespan of the tree.
- Reducing or stunting overall size.
- Allowing a plant to reallocate resources.
- Promoting future smaller leaf size and closer internodes.
- Making the wiring process easier.
- Influencing flowering or fruiting.
- Removing spent flowers, seed heads, or fruit.

- Building believable deadwood that appears old but not contrived.

Be adaptive if you accidentally ruin an important branch. Can a glaring flaw be a promising good feature? In nature, ugly can look both old and beautiful.

"Pruning is some mysterious method bonsai people do in order to dwarf a tree."
Explanation: Proper pruning is a proven method we use to improve the appearance of a tree and bring out its best features. All branches left after pruning should be capable of improving the aesthetics and health of the compact tree over time.

■ Is your bonsai in development or is it ready for refinement?

The two main stages are the early development phase and then the later refinement phase when the tree nears maturity. Maturity is when the bonsai is at maximum horticultural and artistic quality. Refinement is the process of maintaining the mature bonsai in its overall best vigor at its overall maximal quality.

In the early development or training stage, we first build the trunk and the trunk line. Next come the main branches, and then the trunk taper and root collar are developed. You'll always have time on your side in the early development stage. Secondary and tertiary branches are trained later in the refinement stage. Maintaining the overall health is the primary goal at all stages.

For your deciduous bonsai, make a decision if you want to eventually display the plant in a winter silhouette with twiggy branch structure or in full foliage.

Our pruning objectives differ depending on the growing stage and the growing season. What are we trying to achieve?

If our main objective is encouraging the most robust growth for development, we prune deciduous bonsai branches in winter (#358).

During winter, the tree has an abundance of stored photosynthates. Crown pruning won't use up the stored reserves. The tree is still working with existing growth regulators. Winter pruning can make it ready for the first burst in spring with a high sap flow and a flush of aggressive branch growth. We would hesitate to heavily prune refined bonsai during dormancy. Newer growth regulators that would switch off a second flush of undesirable aggressive growth aren't yet manufactured.

If our main objective is to get the smallest leaves and the closest internodes on new stems during refinement, we do not prune both branches and roots at the same time in the winter or early spring; shorter internodes are related to root pruning that reduces the amount of gibberellin in the stems. (#359). Longer internodes, larger leaves, and aggressive new shoot growth occur from winter branch pruning.

For more flowers and fruit on those trees that produce summer flowers on the current year's growth, we prune in winter. This applies during development and refinement. *Root pruning alone, without branch pruning, on a dormant, refined tree usually results in shorter internodes and smaller leaves* (#360).

If our objective is finer secondary branching (ramification or twiggyness) for refinement, we prune in late spring or early summer, right after the leaves harden off; this limits the most overall growth (#361).

Summer branch pruning results in shorter internodes. This is a good time to rewire branches if needed. Mid-summer is also a good time to remove the apical meristem for any back budding;

We can't increase branch or root back budding; we can prune to remove repression on branch back buds (#362). Roots have no buds.

Summer branch pruning also promotes new foliage growth. The resulting increase in photosynthate production sends energy back toward the developing buds and the roots. Be aware of possible bleaching of those leaves in full sun. *Wound wood response is quicker during mid-summer to repress the potential for decay* (#363).

Both mid-winter and mid-summer branch pruning have less negative impact on the roots (#364). *Late fall pruning can hinder new bud generation* (#365). It can also reduce the supply of photosynthates normally pulled out of deciduous foliage before leaf drop.

If our objective is to stop further crown growth for refinement, we allow the terminal bud to set and don't prune branches in late summer when the roots are still growing strong (#366). The loss of the apical meristem removes repression on the lateral buds. Each bud competes for the limited amount of resources on each individual branch. Pick the best one for development and prune the least desirable buds.

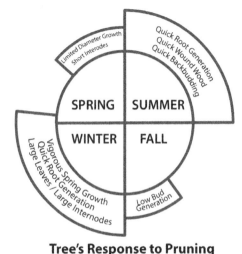

Tree's Response to Pruning

At potting time, we can eliminate dead, dying, diseased, or broken branches. Root growth is put on hold at the expense of allocating resources for establishing new stem growth. After stem growth, let the roots colonize the pot. A plant is formed by its own growth regulators. We allow or repress its growth regulators in anticipation of the plant changing itself.

■ What is the earliest stage of development I can start pruning a young plant?

Developmental pruning could wait until the new spring flush has hardened off for at least three weeks for the photosynthates to become fully operative.

Wait on a young seedling until its roots are well established and occupy their container. During the period of four to six years from a seedling seems to be the time for most aggressive tree growth and is the easiest time to train the structural bones. Plan the final height range you anticipate for the tree at this stage. When you must choose between two major branches, pick the one with the most potential to look better in the future and prune the other.

Start developing trunk taper and old-looking surface roots. Branch development on deciduous trees can wait until after the trunk taper starts. Restrict the top growth, then selectively remove undesirable branches with long internodes and keep the most promising branches with short internodes. Some people let it grow and then chase it back.

When developing evergreen trees, you work with any existing branches. Simplicity and patience are key. Bonsai is not a race, as someone once observed.

■ Along the same line, is it safe for the health of the tree to prune at any time of the year?

Most plants can safely be pruned at any time of the year. In fact, you do the tree a favor if you remove the diseased, dying, or dead branches whenever you discover those stress inducers. Prune past the point of injury. You can snap off slender, dead, or broken twigs anytime with your fingers.

Insects and diseases know when a tree is injured or stressed. Pathogen infection risk is lower when you prune during winter and early spring. Trees in nature know how to respond to a stem breaking off at any time.

■ Is there any risk to the plant when I both wire and prune my deciduous bonsai during the cold of winter?

During a resting stage, many more factors need to be considered. If the tree is otherwise healthy, go ahead and wire and prune your bonsai when they're dormant. Pathogen problems are fewer.

PATHOGEN ACTIVITY

If cold injury occurs and some of the cambial zone is destroyed, bacterial disease may further weaken the plant when temperatures rise. With bare stems, you can see much easier what you're working with. The wood may be more brittle in the cold and snap easier when wired and bent. Some of the stored photosynthates are lost when pruning after leaf drop.

Allow some in-between recuperation time if you apply more than two major insults to a tree at the same time. If you wire and prune, wait until a spring growth spurt before repotting. Some bonsai decide to give up after a major pruning and wiring and potting operation.

That Was a Kind Cut

■ The three kinds of pruning cuts are removal cuts, reduction cuts, and heading cuts.

Proper removal cuts eliminate a smaller branch back to the collar. Correctly termed the stem flange, collars belong to the larger parent stem. Proper removal cuts are only to the stem flange and not into living tissues. Reduction cuts eliminate a larger branch back to a smaller-diameter side branch to lower the height or width of the tree. Heading cuts eliminate the branch's growing tip to release the repression on the side buds

■ What is the stem flange (collar), and why do we try to preserve it?
The living stem flange of a parent stem provides a natural barrier against pathogens (#367). Protective chemicals in the stem flange close over faster and leave no visible scar. For the most part, older trees

have a stem flange collar where the big branches join the trunk or bigger branches. Collars are either nonexistent or not obvious at all on younger trees, smaller side branches, and even on several genuses (genera). Don't be concerned about lack of collars or any minor pruning cuts on those bonsai.

Picture the cambium layer as a thin, completely cylindrical pipe around the parent stem. Jagged pruning cuts or any wounding prevents that cambium from forming a complete cylinder around that stem. New cork must now form from the cambium to slowly join and complete a protective cylinder again on that particular parent stem.

Another analogy is the wall of a plastic plumbing pipe that could correspond to the living cylinder of the outer trunk on a young tree. When you start to connect another side pipe to the first parent pipe, a coupling is needed between the two pipes (stems). The coupling is similar to the stem flange of a tree, except for the fact that a stem flange is a critical part of the parent trunk. Attach a new pipe to the coupling (collar). The wall of the new side pipe (cylindrical living part of a branch) is separated from the wall of the parent pipe (the cylindrical living part of the tree trunk).

A stem flange starts to develop only when a side stem is more than half the diameter of an adjacent parent trunk or thicker stem. The upper bark ridge, the lower thick collar area below, and the cambium cylinder belong to its parent branch, not to the pruned smaller branch. Annual growth rings are separate in the branch and the connecting parent trunk. Side branch xylem does not connect to the parent branch xylem.

Growth rings on the side branch and growth rings on the parent trunk meet and fold in between each other as both grow separately. Wood at the base of a branch turns down to wrap around the wood of the trunk where the

Flush Cuts and Collar Cuts

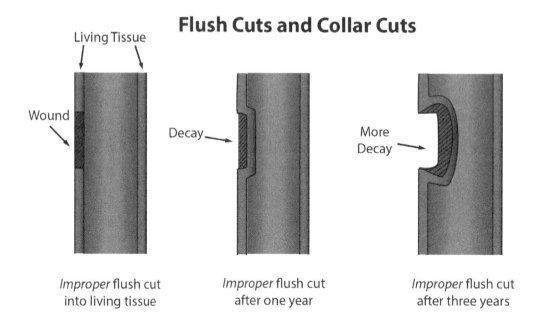

Improper flush cut
into living tissue

Improper flush cut
after one year

Improper flush cut
after three years

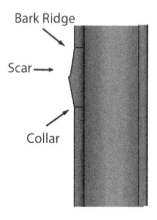

Proper collar cut
preserves all parent
living tissue

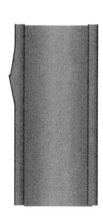

Proper collar cut
after one year

Proper after three years
new growth covers
scar with living
tissue intact

two stems join. The larger stem owns the stem flange. Like pieces of a Tinker toy, stems are individual structures separated with a node or a larger parent stem.

The stem flange becomes more swollen looking with age on the bottom as the bendable branch must resist gravity, wind, and mechanical pressure. Collars do not "hold the branch on the trunk." That thickened area is an accumulation of protective regulators ready to be switched on for defense when needed.

A bark ridge is the top part where the two stems join on larger branches. Both the dark line of the bark ridge above the crotch and the swollen flanged area of the branch collar on the bottom help identify where the proper angle and proper cut are made. Both stand out clearly on a dead stub because that distinctly outlines where the tree would normally seal and drop off a dead branch.

If visible, save the entire parent stem flange on every big cut you make. Cutting into the live zone of a branch collar means no defense zone remains at that junction. *The parent collar has its own growth regulators in the cambium to deal with its cut or broken branch* (#368).

Proper collar cuts are not considered wounds because the defense zone remains undisturbed. And some minor wounds will not cause any problems later on. Wounds are the discontinuity or disruption when bark or cambium is removed, as in flush cuts, concave cuts, stub cuts, branches breaking, cold damage, cracks in the stem, and other open injuries on the trunk or branches.

When you see wood starting to fill in ovally on the two sides, you know the branch collar flange was nicked or injured on both the top and bottom of the branch collar. That wounded area above (the bark ridge) and the area below (the collar) had no active resistance to decay. When you see smoother, lighter-colored wood forming inside a donut-shaped area after a proper collar cut, you're looking at wound wood. Wound wood eventually fills in that donut all the way to the middle. Soon, new growth in thickness and formation of new bark hides any evidence of that proper cut. No part of the tree was ever wounded.

Switches in the parent collar flange tell the callus to start forming soon after an injury. New wound wood with new vascular cambium then starts isolating the scar and going around that area. *Wound wood does not "heal and repair" pruning scars, but it can quickly cover scars and go around them* (#369).

"The healing process" is not "stronger on the sides and top of a wound." Branch collar pruning on larger branches will callus much faster than flush cuts, concave cuts, or stub pruning because it causes no further injury to the trunk. *Wound wood doesn't differentiate between proper and improper pruning* (#370).

Another problem with flush cuts is the unnecessary extra dead areas above and below the cut. The larger wound dies back farther on the top and bottom, making the telltale oval-shaped, callused wood and inevitable decayed, ugly hole.

■ What are the different pruning techniques?

Unfortunately, pruning techniques are easier to show than to explain. Heading cuts are used when pruning back branches to a robust bud pointing in the desired direction. Thinning cuts remove the entire bud or branch at its point of attachment. They are not made to "open up the interior of the crown for letting in the air and light and the birds." We do want a good breeze to reduce pesky insects and bring in carbon dioxide. Sufficient light penetration also benefits photosynthesis. Adding fertilizer after pruning can't "replace the function of the pruned branches when there's less energy."

Pinching off foliage with fingertips is said to help control growth on the edges of new foliage. Brown leaves and weak buds are the result. Heading back with scissors to a forked node causes less stress to the plant than pinching a leaf in half. Hedge shearing with clippers or scissors in early development is even easier, faster, and more effective than pinching or heading back branch by branch. After summer shearing, you can correctional prune the drying stubs back to an appropriate internode the next winter.

Breaking off smaller, unwanted branches of younger trees with your hand by snapping and splitting down with the grain works for the deadwood look. Small scars cover quickly. Any small stubs could be later scissored back to an internode. Cut a stub closer to the trunk if you want secondary branching to start closer than the first internode.

A two-stage pruning process can be used to eliminate an unwanted thick branch with less risk of trunk damage and without unwanted disfiguring callused growth. Wound wood is quicker to form on the upper side than the bottom side of a cut. Normally, callused wood forms slower on the bottom side of a cut branch because a thicker branch has more lignin on the lower side to support the heavy branch on the trunk. Therefore, cutting off the entire thick branch all at once causes the development of uneven callused wood formation.

> *Tip*: For a smoother trunk appearance, you can saw a V-notch on a thick branch. Saw along the collar flange line from the underside of the joint halfway up the branch connection. Then wedge a small stick or rock into the notched area from the bottom to temporarily support the heavy branch. Normal callused wood forms on the lower cut portion over a growing season. Next year, saw off the remainder of the branch from the top, again carefully following the line of the bark ridge. In a few growing seasons, the scar should be engulfed in the new growth.

"Top branches will die back if you let root suckers grow."

Those unwanted masses of young vertical sprouts grow straight up from the trunk or main branches. Masses of suckers grow up from the root collar or roots below ground. Both are a natural response to create a new crown after injury. Most can be rubbed off, snapped off, or cut off. Get those sprouts off as soon as possible, since short pathways to the roots make those new stems grow more aggressively than the older stems. Initially, they contain little lignin for hardening off. Sprout and sucker growth are similar to electric appliances left turned on and stealing electricity even when they're not operating. Although they can suck away valuable resources, root suckers won't "kill any top branches."

■ To pinch or not to pinch. Which is horticulturally correct?

The simplest type of pruning—pinching (nipping) off the leaf ends with the fingertips—removes a growing tip in an effort to refine or maintain the overall form. *The main problem with pinching is that the broken leaf veins prohibit any of its photosynthate from passing down to the rest of the tree* (#371). That's why you see those brown (dead) tips soon after pinching. Leaf veins include both xylem and phloem.

Pinched or cut leaves will die. Plant regulator switches must adjust to isolate any pinching injury and drop that leaf when it completely dies. Another problem with pinching, or nipping, is that weakened buds lead to a weakened second growth flush. To be horticulturally correct, don't pinch developing trees.

PRUNE LIKE A PRO

■ On deciduous trees, should I leave a small part of the leaf petiole or small part of the branch stub?

You don't have to, but it's highly recommended if your objective is to preserve a promising bud close by. Don't prune too close to the internode or a promising bud even if it means keeping a small part of the leaf petiole (stalk) or leaving a small branch stub. If you cut too close to a fork, one fork will not share its energy with any other adjacent fork.

During the development stage, you may want to preserve an unnecessary branch or bud closer to the more desirable main branch. In case of dieback, you'll be left with a future option. Remember, each bud holds a promise of an almost unlimited number of future leaves. Saving the leaf petioles when pruning can preserve a future bud waiting in the elbow of the base of a petiole. Petioles, the leaf stalks, fall off eventually.

As mentioned previously, you could leave an initial stub or snag on the branch until it dies back and the new desirable sprout has extended itself. Let the dying stub dry out and shrink a bit for a season. Then prune closer to the outside edge of the more obvious parent collar during the resting season. Remove any frayed ends. Even smaller flush cuts leave less obvious knobby growth if made during the resting phase.

The two-step stub technique works for most deciduous pruning. A short snag promotes faster and thinner formation of wound wood back at the parent stem flange. The second step is removing the dead stub.

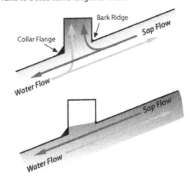

1. First Cut
Prune to a stub same length as width

Sap flow to stub diminishes as collar walls it off

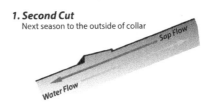

1. Second Cut
Next season to the outside of collar

Stub Pruning Technique promotes quicker formation of wound wood and compartmentalization than from flush cut pruning.

This technique doesn't apply to whorled-branching conifers such as pine, spruce, or fir.

◼ How do I prune to get future shorter internodes?

Some people chase the longer internodes back toward the trunk in an attempt to get shorter internodes the next time. The shorter internodes usually originate from buds on the first section of the branch closer to the main trunk. Shorter internodes are not "the result of a shorter growing season." *The first flush of spring growth produces a predetermined internode length* (#372).

Established, refined bonsai form shorter internodes:

- if they're not repotted every year.
- if they're in the highest light intensity they can handle.
- if branch pruning and fertilizer applications are postponed until after springtime hardening off of new shoots.
- if roots but no stems are pruned during the plant's resting period.

You've probably noticed that if both stems and roots are pruned during a resting stage, trees usually send out the new spring growth with longer internodes and larger leaves. That is the result of being overstimulated with growth regulators. Cells are longer in long internodes.

Winter and early spring are not exactly the best time to repot refined bonsai unless you are not pruning any branches at the same time. After new foliage has already hardened off (lignified) in late spring or summer is the time to prune the existing branch growth for a winter or spring potting operation. Then the new shoots, with a minimal amount of stored photosynthates, continue to develop shorter internodes and smaller leaves.

A high quality and quantity of light signals a stress response for shorter cells in shorter internodes. Move the plant into enough sun—not to full shade—to trap the sun's energy after late season pruning.

◼ How do I keep the short internodes short on those nice, tiny ramified stems?

Not to worry. *Short internodes will stay short* (#373). They can get thicker, but existing internodes don't increase in length. They'll grow out from the tips if you let their buds grow. Nip 'em in the buds. Shear to maintain the desired silhouette. Keep pushing back new growth to shorter internodes closer to the trunk.

◼ How do I handle multiple pruning wounds in the same area?

Consider staging any major pruning over a couple of growing seasons. The lowest part of a wound is the slowest part to generate wound wood. If possible, wait until an earlier lower wound has callused over before pruning a major branch directly above.

We may need to prune several branches in the same area. Irregularly shaped scars, as seen in nature, often appear more convincing than perfectly rounded edges. Combine and define the entire border of neighboring scars by inscribing. Inscribing is a wound treatment to enhance the closing process of large wounds. Use a half moon chisel instead of a sharp knife to shape the perimeter of the irregular multiple pruning wounds. Fall or winter is a good time to inscribe *shari* (Japanese term for a deadwood feature on the bark) after the tree has finished the growing cycle for that year.

Whorled branch patterns commonly seen on pines and azaleas may cause the trunk or branch to look swollen at an internode where several branches originate. If that swollen look detracts from the trunk taper, then you can carve off some of that excess adaptive wood.

■ What about those ugly callus growths and knuckles and knobs that sometimes develop after improper pruning?

Gnarly, swollen growth comes from callus production made after cell elongation. Usually, knobby growth is evidence of improper flush or gouging-into-the-live-wood pruning cuts. You'll know you made a mistake and cut into the cambium layer when you end up with a swollen knobby growth.

If they add to the story and communicate an air of antiquity, then show them off. If they draw attention to where someone improperly pruned, cut them off. Lose the knobby, man-made look by opening up the lower part of the wound by carving a more natural-looking elongated hollow following down and into the trunk.

Burls are woody growths protruding from some older tree trunks. They are good for the tree and good for cosmesis. Uncontrolled knobby growth on the trunk is harmless and can be an appealing feature.

> *Tip:* Don't be too concerned about proper pruning cuts on seedlings. Most any cut closes over properly on young trees. No collars are even formed until the larger parent stem needs to protect itself. When an adjacent smaller stem starts to branch off and grow more than half the diameter of the main stem, that larger parent stem grows a stem flange to protect itself. Some larger branches may not show signs of an obvious flange. You can hold a large knob cutter at a slight angle away from the trunk at the bottom of the branch junction to ensure the branch collar stays with the parent trunk.

In nature, smaller adjacent side branches may get snapped off somehow from the larger parent branch. Not a problem. The parent branch walls it off at the junction, sets up hormonal defenses, and sheds what's left of the smaller side branch. Thickening bark and callusing growth will drop off small, dead twigs.

Some species tend to develop and keep ugly scar formation even after proper pruning. Postpone the pruning operation until that plant is well into its resting period. The same normal growth that thickens a stem will eventually smooth over a proper pruning scar (not wound) if the remaining parent tissue is untouched. In a few years, any evidence of a collar cut is engulfed into the new thickening bark.

■ How do I recognize well-pruned bonsai?

Good pruning on a refined bonsai eventually does not look as if it has ever happened. Improper pruning is obvious and ugly. Learn to recognize the difference in proper and improper pruning. Avoid lion-tailing, where you see foliage only at the edge of the crown and on the ends of branches. Avoid fish-boning branch scaffolding.

It's OK if the plant looks a bit shabby after a good pruning during development. Don't aim for the final silhouette, shape, size, and crown composition. Trees need years to develop. Resign yourself to the fact that major scars may require a few years to wall off and cover over.

Proper pruning scars will end up rounded and smooth, not oval shaped with callus bulges on each side. If you're faced with a bad-looking cut, make a deadwood feature out of it. Many prize-winning bonsai have been designed around a pruning mistake. Emphasize interesting scars and dead branches.

Mimic the typically normal habits of a beautiful old tree. Maybe emphasize lower co-dominant forked trunks instead of "always eliminating the slingshot look." Many mature double-trunked trees in nature developed a second trunk after some trauma. The main trunk may have broken off when young and a bud was waiting to take off as a leader or co-leader. As time went on, part of a weaker trunk dies. Allow the tree to proudly display deadwood as its unique badge of life's profound experiences. Reveal the unique personality of your own tree to your own standards. Do what you want to do to your own plant. Ugly transforms into beautiful. Who can argue with that?

■ How can we make believable deadwood?

Believable deadwood should convey a reminder of a history of scars and survival after natural disasters and hazards. Try not to let it look like a tree attacked by a human. Deadwood is not evenly distributed on all sides; it's concentrated on the most exposed side. Make it appear as if the branch or trunk broke down, not up. Most wood on the trunk is lost from the bottom of a branch, not the top part.

On deciduous trees, most of the deadwood will be found on the lower trunk (bole). Begin carving coarse and finish fine, but not too finely smoothed and always textured. Major wood carving on the trunk is much easier after the wood has a chance to dry out. Minor stem debarking works better before the wood dries out.

Stem flanges, the swelling where the branch joins the parent stem, usually stay intact on the upper side. Knotholes, if any, are on the top part of the former branch, not on the bottom. They are not round, drilled donut holes but more elongated hollows. An ugly round knothole says bad pruning job. Connect two knotholes or stretch down and carve the bottom part to make a more believable hollow.

The grain on a straight branch is straight, not curved. Carve with the grain because the grain will eventually show through. Most dead branches are cylindrical, irregularly shaped, and with irregularly split blunt ends. Branches shouldn't end up looking like knife-carved golf tees connected to the parent trunk with a perfectly shaped collar. Dead branches are long and narrow on junipers compared to short and stubby on pines.

Branch fissures and splits are narrow slits, not routed-out concave channels. Wedge a new slit slightly open to stay split until the wood dries. Cracks are different sizes and will develop by themselves as the wood shrinks. The smooth, weathered, bleached look has several different hues, tints, tones, and shades. If a bonsai has multiple tall, co-dominant trunks with little taper, snap one off where you want a deadwood feature to start. Rip it down part way and peel off all the bark down to the junction.

When rewiring a branch, make sure the new wiring spirals in the same direction as did the previous wiring. If you are wiring and twisting a couple juniper branches for a future spiraling deadwood feature, make sure all branches spiral in the same direction.

Long lengths of stub cuts on trees with hard wood like juniper or boxwood can be left on as a design feature. Bark is peeled off, and the branches are wired, bent, and carved as a deadwood design feature. Make it appear as if it was struck by lightning not struck by a grinder. You want the whole tree, not just part of it, to look aged. Don't copy someone's carving technique or practice for every tree. Get ideas from studying driftwood, not other bonsai.[*]

---

* The points in this section were inspired by "Deadwood Features," pp. 122–32 in *Principles of Bonsai Design*, by David Degroot (n.p.: American Bonsai Society, 2015).

■ Is bonsai healthy with so much deadwood and so few live branches and foliage? Are "large bark fissures harmful"?

Yes, deadwood is healthy, and no, large bark fissures are not unhealthy. You can verify that fact on mature trees in nature at any time. Those large fissures in the outer bark are a good sign of a healthy, mature tree. Jagged, dead snags can add an illusion of age to bonsai. Stripping some bark off dead branches emphasizes the effect of a few live branches clinging to an old, dying tree. Try to enhance the natural contours of existing wood fibers when stripping or carving the woody tissues of deadwood.

Sometimes we must remove bark from a dead, dried branch. Wrap the branch with a wet cloth and enclose with shrink wrap. The bark absorbs moisture in about a week and then becomes easier to rub off. Wire and shape green wood the same as live wood. Moisture and heat have been used since ancient times for some serious thick wood bending. To bend rigid deadwood, keep a soaked rag wrapped around the branch for a couple days. After removing the soaked rag, wrap with aluminum foil. Heat only the inside of the curve with a propane torch and bend while protecting the rest of the tree.

Rocky Mountain juniper.

■ *Lime sulfur is sometimes painted on juniper deadwood to give it a temporary whitish coloring. Does "lime sulfur prevent rotting and further decay when applied on deadwood"?*

No, it does not. Deadwood is best left alone if the objective is a natural look, as on Walter Pall's Rocky Mountain juniper.

Lime sulfur is neither an effective preservative nor an effective preventative treatment (#374). Lime sulfur does not penetrate wood more than one-quarter inch and does not prevent further rotting and decay. It's not a cure-all for killing insects, bacteria, or fungi either. No deadwood treatment prevents the decay process. Some species are more resistant to decay than others.

Wood hardeners are simply liquid plastic and trap moisture and pathogens when applied to wood. Consider using other, more effective products for coloring or preserving deadwood. If a preservative is necessary, use water-based instead of oil-based preservatives.

■ *What about using an "escape or sacrifice branch to thicken the trunk"?*

Supposedly, a lower branch on a pine tree is allowed to grow unhindered for some period of time. That temporary branch served a couple purposes: to "thicken the trunk while promoting shorter internodes in that area" and to "help heal a callusing wound right below it." An escape branch works if you want to let a major lower deciduous branch thicken. Later, cut that back to a stub closer to the trunk. Secondary branching will start from the cut end.

The main problem with that technique is the sacrifice of a lot of time for a huge, unwanted future gaping wound injury when that thick branch is finally removed years later. You've only relocated the problem to another gaping wound. Trees growing in the ground develop exceptionally rapid lower trunk growth without large lower sacrifice branches kept on close to the soil level.

■ **Hedge pruning on bonsai? Are you kidding?**

Allow unrestrained top growth to quick start and thicken the lower part for a few months. This technique can be used in late spring and repeated in early fall for most deciduous trees. As Walter Pall shows us below, allow the first flush to grow freely and harden off. Then you can hedge trim the longer but weaker upper branches back to the desired outline.

■ **Is it OK to heavily chop the trunk of a collected deciduous tree back to a large stump in order to get to an acceptable bonsai faster?**

There are pros and cons.

Contraindications first: Some leader-dominant trees have a natural conical crown, branching form. Trees with upright growth habit will look quite unnatural in a hard trunk chop with resulting multiple vertical trunks rising from that stump. It takes much less time to develop a believable tree if you allow several co-dominant (forked) branches to grow from that stub and take a more natural ascending rounded form. It takes more time, skill, and effort to bonsai a tree with one central leader.

More mature trees can't tolerate drastic reshaping. Plants have a way of slowing down growth when they need more resources after an injury. Usually, regular light pruning is better than a one-time dose of heavy pruning on older trees. Prune less but more often. Pruning in late spring rather than early spring results in better-quality bonsai.

Conifers easily compartmentalize cut branches. However, chopping a large conifer trunk down to a stump will kill it. All said, trunk chops begin the stepped trunk–shaping process for many of our bigger collected trees. A large deciduous tree with the ascending, rounded crown growth habit may be too tall to bonsai. So we chop it down to size.

Trunk chops eliminate the high auxin level. High cytokinin levels from any robust growing roots signal adventitious buds above to break out on the top of the cut with new shoots. Top growth then signals root growth, and so on. The stepped trunk process goes slowly.

Your first cut could be horizontally across the trunk. Saw to a stump. Wrap the trunk with sphagnum moss under burlap and keep it moist during the hot days. You'll be rewarded with many adventitious buds Allow several codominant ascending branches to grow up from that point.

By the next growing season, you'll find where the adventitious buds start to flush out

Stepped Trunk Taper System

THIS YEAR'S CUT

NEXT YEAR'S CUT

and where the tree decides to wall off that first cut. Include the bottom or top edge of that newly formed collar in a second diagonal cut. Or you can eliminate the second step by making the first cut diagonally down, keeping the preferred branch as the next leader.

◼ What is the notching technique to encourage the development of a latent bud or to bend a large branch?

Notching removes a small kerf or wedge-shaped piece above a latent bud to undo repression. Notching is also a useful technique when bending a trunk or large branch. That subject is covered in the section on wiring branches. Nicking is the opposite from notching. Nicking is making a small cut below a latent bud to temporarily inhibit that particular bud from forming. Or you can simply pinch off that particular unwanted bud. The preferred bud above it will then pop out. That new branch starts growing more horizontally than vertically because it is weakened from the nicking below the repressed buds.

Notching or nicking right below a deciduous branch will probably kill that branch because of its linear vascular system. Working with conifers is different. With a more lateral vascular system, the flow of water in cells of narrowleaf evergreens is both linear and lateral.

■ What are some other techniques used to manipulate branches?

Cutting wedge-shaped sections or sawing kerfs out of a thick trunk or large branch can facilitate bending prior to wiring. Junipers are one of the several exceptions. Slitting the bark underneath the junction of branch and trunk prior to wiring encourages wound callus. Callus formation soon helps the branch to hold its new position.

Channel or remove a small section lengthwise, parallel to the branch, prior to wiring and bending. The thinner branch is now more pliable and easier to shape. Split with the wood grain using a splitting tool even on the main trunk. Drill small holes through a thick branch, or even one larger hole with a forstner bit, to form an acute angle or to break up a long, straight section before bending. Splint to straighten a branch.

On a smaller branch, simply attach a weight to the branch tip or pull it down and tie it to its container, the trunk, or another lower branch. Try to avoid using clamps to bend branches because they tend to split the bark and do more harm than good. If left on too long, clamps leave permanent evidence with a flattened section on the branch. Use a guy wire to help

hold the new position of a wired branch. An alternate to guy wiring is to use catch-and-release fish hooks at both ends of a wire.

The clip-and-grow technique, or directional pruning, is commonly used on deciduous trees.

"Cutting roots means you must cut off branches to compensate for the root loss."
Explanation: Pruning equals stunting. Removing branch tips and root tips at the same time equals no growth signals, which equals no available resources, which results in no growth. The tree is losing at both ends for a net loss.

Think of a seesaw as an analogy. To work well, a seesaw must move up and down. Prune the roots at repotting and energy decreases in the roots. Don't prune the branches at the same time and let the energy stay in the branches. Now the tree is able to sort it out with its intact, healthy growth signals. If only a few areas of existing foliage wilt and die from increased water demand, the tree is sorting it out. Existing photosynthates go to new leaves and new roots. But prune both the branches and roots at the same time and energy is lost on both sides. The seesaw is now balanced. ***When nature is balanced, it's dead*** (#375). It's a paradox!

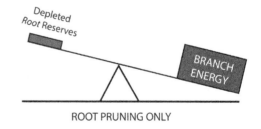

ROOT PRUNING ONLY

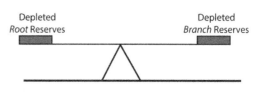

BRANCH PRUNING THE SAME TIME AS ROOT PRUNING

Continuing with the seesaw analogy, the seesaw can't easily go up and down if one side is overloaded (or overdosed). Overwatering and overfertilizing after pruning and potting is like adding a dead weight on top of depleted reserves. The poor tree can't function. Dosage is the key with pruning, watering, and fertilizing. *Fact*: ***Any extra pruning at transplanting or repotting has not been shown by science to promote survival or quicker establishment rate in plants*** (#376).

■ How can I spread forked branches apart or bring them closer together?

You can separate multiple branches or trunks by wedging them apart with a block or a straight piece of thick wire. Or pull them apart with a guy wire or a wire with two catch-and-release fish hooks. Hook the other end around another branch or around a root. Snug them closer together with insulated wire. Bend a hook at both ends of a thick wire to pull one branch against another or against a thick root.

WIRING, MAJOR BENDING, AND MINOR TREE SURGERY

■ Why do we wire bonsai?

To make bonsai look more natural, we do unnatural things such as wiring and bending branches. Here are a few more reasons we wire:

- To form the stem's basic initial shape and overall silhouette. Wiring can help shorten the branch length with bends, create foliage masses, give some movement or twisting to straight branches, straighten curved trunks, or even reposition small deadwood branches.
- To maintain and refine the lines and overall form on ramified branches.
- To produce more graceful lines and curves. The clip-and-grow method, on the other hand, is directional pruning on deciduous trees and produces more angular branching lines. Maybe you've seen pictures of what appears to be a snap-it-down-and-let-it-grow method.
- To reposition lower branches from the shading by upper foliage.

Wiring practices are used again and again on the same tree as a temporary tool in both the training and refinement phases to reposition branches. It is not "once and done."

■ Can wiring branches injure a plant?

Our branch-shaping process is usually much more gentle to the tree than any cruel, mutilating process caused by nature. Let's correct a few misconceptions:

- When we cut, break, bend, or wire a branch, we don't directly harm the rest of the tree.
- Phloem and xylem are dead cells. New callus tissue can develop into new cambium that can develop into new vascular tissue. New cambium, phloem, and xylem are able to bridge to any existing cambium, phloem, and xylem.
- Wire, by itself, doesn't injure a stem. The cells closest to the wire grow faster in a reaction to engulf and isolate the wire from the rest of the plant.
- Wires will not "freeze and kill the tree in the winter."
- Summer heat will not "cause wires to scorch a tree."
- Wires on a slow-growing conifer don't "need to be taken off every winter to give the branch a rest."
- Wires don't "grow into the branch."

> *Tip*: Remember that the vascular system is a series of stacked tubes. Those cylinders are composed of a series of woody straws of dead cells. Cylinders twist easier than they'll bend. Slightly twist a wired branch in the tightening direction while slowly bending it to reduce fracturing those woody cylinders.

- Crooked branches from wiring won't "become weaker than straight branches."
- Steel wire may rust but doesn't "cause black rot."
- Copper wire is not "extremely poisonous to azaleas."
- Weak branches can be injured from wiring and bending because branches low in growth regulators won't take the extra stress.
- Bending a branch back and forth in the same area may cause it to snap. Practitioners with years of experience have recommended "pre-flexing thick branches for several minutes before wiring." But that only causes the vascular system to fracture even more. Fractures are more likely to occur at a joint. It may not be such a big deal if a small wired branch does start to crack even halfway open while bending. Gently close back the incomplete fractured gap on the wired branch in order to hold it in place. Add more wire or tape if necessary to hold the bap shut. The tree's own repair system starts producing callus cells the very same day. Depending on the size of the injury and the health of the tree, layers of callus cells soon fill in the gap on the fractured site making that joint stronger than before the crack.

- Splitting injury can be minimized by holding the two small branches together with your fingers at the forked area when wiring or bending. Crotches are usually the weak part of a stem.
- Snaps, bends, and crooked branches are part of the natural development in some trees. Gnarls are not in any way structurally weaker than straight or forked branches.
- New, thicker tissue forms in new positions to adjust to a potential weakness soon after we wire and bend a branch. The tissue around acute angle bends should hold the final position better than any new tissue developing around a gentle curve.

■ How do I know when to remove training wires from shaped branches?

On some deciduous species with more than one growth spurt, you'll need to check the thinner wires on those smaller branches every few weeks. On some slow-growing conifer species in the refinement stage, you can check thicker wiring once a year on the new growth to see if the stem starts to grow into the wire. Cut off thicker wiring instead of unwinding so no more wood or bark is injured.

Cell elongation occurs soon after a branch is repositioned. Hardened tissue becomes irreversible growth. Swelling occurs because the water uptake backlogs in the xylem and the photosynthate down flow backlogs in the phloem.

> Tip: I occasionally wire thin-barked branches with ten-gauge insulated copper wire commonly used in low-voltage lawn sprinkler irrigation systems. It is inexpensive and cushioned. Use one wire insulation color for the winter wiring and another color for the summer wiring. Color coding helps me recall when the tree was wired and when it needs to be removed.

"Wet raffia wound around a branch tightens up and shrinks as it dries."

Sometimes we soak raffia and then wrap it around a hard-to-bend branch before wiring. Wound raffia gives it greater tensile strength so the branch experiences less pressure per unit area after wiring and bending. Raffia does not "expand when it's wet or shrink when it dries." Wrapping a stem with raffia, tape, or any other material does prevent photosynthesis in the green cortex of the stem, so don't "leave raffia on until it rots off."

"Let the branches and soil dry out before wiring or shaping bonsai."

Fact: Water the bonsai thoroughly before wiring because wet wood fibers are more flexible than dry fibers. Overwatering doesn't cause "excessive sap pressure or ugly callus formation."

Explanation: Dried-out branches contribute even more stress, making them more brittle and prone to snap. A more turgid branch is less brittle. Picture dry spaghetti snapping but wet spaghetti bending.

"Positioning a wired branch downward slows its growth and makes the tip dry out and die. Always position the ends of the branches back upward for best health."

Fact: **Auxin concentrates both in the apical tip and on the shady side of stems** (#377). **Branch repositioning can temporarily reduce or increase its supply of growth regulators** (#378).

Explanation: Changing the branch position from pointing up to pointing down can temporarily stress and further weaken that branch if it's already weak and low in auxin regulators. But as soon as the sunlight hits the repositioned branch, the bent part immediately goes into cell division and elongation mode.

Auxin wants to elongate cells and bend the tip of that same branch back up toward the light. New elongated plant tissue structure is irreversible. The wired and bent branch changes its auxin pathway to a more direct line down to the roots. Auxin reaches the root tip and then is destroyed by lack of sufficient oxygen. Basically, auxin has signaled the root tip to start new growth and produce more cytokinin. Cytokinin now travels up the new pathways to the stronger growing tips. Then, cytokinins are destroyed after signaling the adventitious buds to either open up or stand by.

The reason phloem doesn't always go downward is because it must first flow upward if the branch is repositioned horizontally or downward. The first response from a branch tip forcibly bent downward is more cell elongation on the upper side to repair stretch damage. This response is counteracted by the accumulation of the auxin growth regulator on the shaded lower side. Auxin wants the tip to grow and travel back upward after a branch is bent downward.

Rewiring, repositioning, or pruning is probably necessary again on younger, robust branches as the new tips want to continue growing upward. If pointing the tips of the branches upward is necessary to the bonsai design, then no problem. We won't confuse them.

Bent branches on some narrowleaf evergreens may indeed get minor but temporary tissue injury if wired and twisted around 180° and the leaf underside now faces up. The majority of the stomata used in gas exchange are located on the underside of the leaf.

When a tree limb gets bent downward, as in the Sabina juniper cascade, the new growth switches on the signal to grow toward the light. That branch is not going to "dry out and die if the tips point down." Some plants genetically grow into a low, horizontal-branching, procumbent habit.

Positioning stem tips downward can't "promote more flowering."

Sabina juniper.

Tools of the Trade

■ Why can't I seem to make smooth pruning cuts?

Cuts made with dull tools are more prone to squeezing, splitting, and crushing the wood or to peeling the bark. Good tools are worth it. Whether using double-cut hand pruners or knob or concave cutters, make a partial cut one way on thick branches and finish the cut with the cutters twisted to another angle. This ensures a smoother cut at the top edge of the parent stem flange.

Concave and bypass pruners seem more prone to pinching and splitting wood and tearing into living parent tissue. Knob cutters are useful to chew away and whittle down a thick, knobby branch stub. Cutting edges should slide over each other slightly on knob and concave cutters.

To use bypass pruners, put the good side of the pruner against the good side of the tree. When making a cut with a reciprocator saw, there may be a tendency for the blade to wander or for the branch to tear at the bottom of the cut. First make a hand saw kerf cut above or below the planned reciprocating saw cut to help prevent jagged or unplanned cuts. The blade alone from a good reciprocator saw makes a most useful saw tool for bonsai work.

Treat My Cuts!

■ How do I treat a partially girdled branch?

Sometimes we encounter a partially girdled trunk on an older bonsai. If you feel the urge to "treat the damage," enclose sphagnum moss under black plastic around the injured trunk like an air layer. Check for new bark formation after a few months. There's no need to apply fertilizer until after wound wood appears.

> *Tip*: Start a new air layer for propagation by carving deep cuts to girdle and promote new roots. Wrapping wire to girdle a stem is less effective for air layering.

■ I'm wiring a branch on my bonsai and the branch starts to fracture when bent. Must I "always apply sealing paste" and "wrap something hard around it"?

Skip the sealing paste part unless you apply it for looks. Continue wiring loosely (air wire) at that area to hold the shape.

"To prevent a swelling wound and promote faster healing, wrap with some hard material to bandage and put compression on that area."
Skip the bandage. Wrapping prevents bark photosynthesis, and compression hinders wound wood formation.

"Pruning cuts spread infectious diseases. Dip the pruning shears in bleach between cuts and apply a disinfectant to large cut ends."
We do not need to sterilize our cutting tools between one plant and another. Remember, disinfectants, such as concentrated bleach, not only corrode tools but also may be harmful to some plants. And to your skin, as well.
Fact: **No one has yet proven that pruning tools spread disease** (#379).

"Apply cut paste/wound sealant to the cut ends of all branches to keep the vulnerable tissue from shrinking and contracting; to stimulate callus formation; to shorten the healing time of wounds; to dress and keep the wound moist so the water doesn't escape and dehydrate the plant; to let the cambium roll over; to permit the scars to close; to keep infection from spreading; to protect it from excess bleeding and further injury; to keep the sap flow from harming the tree; to prevent branch withering; to seal off from the air, wind, insects, diseases, microbes; to prevent cracks; et cetera."

Fact: **The proper pruning cut is not a wound; it will callus if left unsealed** (#380). No benefit is provided by the use of wound sealants. Trees have no blood and no central nervous system, so they don't bleed, heal up, seal up, or feel pain. The best treatment for proper pruning cuts is none.

Explanation: In reality, field tests and university research prove that sealants are ineffective in preventing disease or in addressing any of the above claims. After pruning, grafting, or taking cuttings or air layers, the first response of the injured plant is to immediately produce undifferentiated cells of callus tissue. Soon, some of the new callus tissue specializes into new cambium. The callus tissue on cuttings and air layers eventually differentiates into roots. All callus tissue cell growth is an aerobic system requiring a continuous supply of oxygen. Sealant seals off the oxygen supply.

Putting a paste product on a wound seems to be a placebo for the person applying that product. The practice of wound dressing went out of favor years and years ago. "Natural healing" products only impede the tree's natural defenses, feed and house bad decay microorganisms, and eliminate good oxygen.

Trees do seem to have minds of their own and are quite capable of protecting and defending themselves. Healthy roots and stems are the prerequisite to wound closure.

And to address a couple more misunderstandings: Trees do not "carry their own protective wound dressings in their own bark." The generic word "bark" covers several distinct surface tissues on a tree. We can't refer to all those tissues as "bark." It can include live and dead phloem, periderm (corky outer layer), and other tissues. Bark is a jargon term for tissue outside the vascular cambium composed of many tissues, many origins, and many functions. The outer layer of a tree is the cork.

Trees have different protection systems to prevent injury, including:
- the waterproof, waxy cork.
- low-moisture older wood.
- extractions, or biological wood preservatives. Pine resin and turpentine are a couple examples. Some wood extractions protect humans—black cherry for coughs, witch hazel for sore throats, and taxine from yews for treating cancer.

After injury, trees have a couple defense systems in place: chemical changes to prevent the spread of pathogens and anatomical changes to wall off the tree from pathogens and to prevent injury from spreading.

The only live part of the cut area is on the inside edge of the parent stem collar (#381). That outer, cylindrical, parent ring is part of the tree's defense system. One of the tree's defense responses after a new injury is for the live cambium layer to form new callus tissue composed of protective chemicals. The majority of the wood in the middle of a concave cut wound is already dead. Wounds become walled off only in an area of an intact cambial zone that is part of the parent stem flange.

Wound wood tissue then forms and isolates the scar. The rest of the injured branch is forced to die and fall off. That new tissue used to isolate injury will remain with the tree until the tree dies. Once covered over, scars tissue keeps on growing around that scar. The healthy growing tree eventually engulfs proper pruning cuts. Unfortunately, any material used for "dressing the wound" actually slows the callusing process. A dressing inhibits the process of oxidation and slows the formation of wound wood.

Wound sealant can soon crack when exposed to the sun. Dark-colored sealant might put the wound site at risk for winter injury. Moisture entering behind the crack accumulates between the wound and wound dressings. Sealed between the wound and the wound dressing are pathogens lurking in that ideal moist, dark niche and causing serious decay.

"Pruning branches in early spring is dangerous if sap bleeds out of the cuts."

People put that stuff on pancakes! Have you ever seen a sugar maple tree dying in the springtime after being tapped for maple syrup? Did you know people also make syrup from birches? "Leaking sap" does not "limit spring growth or cause damage and kill the tree."

> *Tip*: Some conifer branches can be pruned to a short stub for a growing season. Wait until the stub starts to die back before cutting back to the branch or trunk. This procedure lessens the sap flow and produces less cellulose wood tissue. As an added benefit, it also lets you know exactly where the tree has decided to sort out where it wants to wall off that temporary stub. Eventually, the short stub is pruned to a scar. No damage will be evident, and the final surface will have a smoother finish. This practice for gradual preventative dieback is a good habit to form for most of your pruning.

"Prune roots first before pruning any branches to prevent weeping wounds."

No relationship exists between pruning the roots and the branches. It doesn't matter which one you prune first. Both exude sap, which is simply photosynthates, the product of photosynthesis.

Another possibility is to allow a longer, nice-looking stub to remain as a deadwood feature. Debark and carve it to create an illusion of strength and antiquity.

■ What can I do to prevent "bleeding"?

Not to worry, trees don't bleed. More sap does not mean bigger scars. Sap includes various deposits such as photosynthates, tannins, gums, resins, latex, or crystals. Those deposits will seep from some trees, including maple, birch, hop hornbeam (Ostrya), hornbeam (Carpinus), elm, birch, hackberry, willow, pine, and larch.

Pine resin is the best sealant for all pine wounds, maple syrup is the best sealant for maple wounds, birch sap is the best sealant for birch wounds, and larch sap is the best sealant for larch wounds.

Larch.

KEEPING FOLIAGE HEALTHY

Trees have three jobs:
1. Load up energy from sunlight and load up water and elements from wherever they can get them. A continuous supply of energy keeps all systems going.
2. Store energy in living cells as photosynthates, fats, or oils, especially in the roots. The accumulation period must end before the storage period begins—much as a battery must be charged before it stores energy. Accumulated energy from foliage is released for storage right before leaf drop.
3. Use that energy as needed. Stored starch must be changed back to glucose and become water soluble again before the plant can use it.

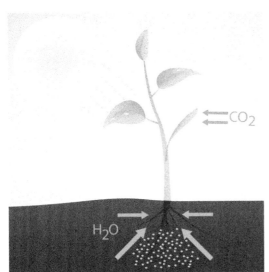

Sunlight and carbon dioxide from air give the green foliage energy to manufacture sugar and release oxygen. Respiration and roots are the water source for photosynthesis.

LEAF ANATOMY

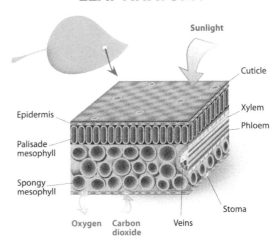

Sunlight

Cuticle

Xylem

Phloem

Epidermis

Palisade mesophyll

Spongy mesophyll

Stoma

Oxygen   Carbon dioxide   Veins

Trees use energy in one of three ways:

1. To grow up and out.
2. To invest in its protection system or to resist injury.
3. To develop a defense system to isolate pathogen injury.

SOLAR POWER

■ What powers a plant?

Bonsai are powered by sugar (#382). Without photosynthesis, there's no sugar. Without sugar, there's no respiration. Respiration produces water and carbon dioxide for photosynthesis. Foliage respiration also burns sugar to release energy (electrons, not food) to move that sugar up and down the sugar freeway to power all other living cells.

Energy is not exclusively about sugar and photosynthesis. Photosynthesis and respiration are two sides of the same coin. Photosynthesis is when the plant makes photosynthates with light. Respiration is when photosynthates are used to release energy. Photosynthates are food for animals and used to produce an energy source for plants.

"Fertilizer adds new food and energy to a plant."

Fact: ***New energy can come only from stored photosynthates or from fresh photosynthates produced by the leaf during photosynthesis and released by the leaf during respiration*** (#383). Only photosynthesis and respiration provide the energy for plants.

Explanation: Healthy living wood in both shoots and roots get their energy from the leaves. Fertilizer applications may promote an increase in the rate of a plant's natural processes that require and consume more

energy (electrons). If photosynthesis exceeds respiration, more energy is available to be used by the plant. If the sugar produced is not used immediately by the tree, then the sugars become linked together to produce starch. Not soluble in water, starch comes from glucose (a sugar), which is soluble in water. The difference between the two is a simple water molecule.

Photosynthate is the material of stored energy. Stressed bonsai are low in stored photosynthates. The amount of stored energy reserves is in direct proportion to the amount of living cells in the bonsai wood. ***Anything that weakens or injures a tree reduces the amount of living cells and depletes the levels of photosynthate reserves*** (#384).

"Plants convert carbon dioxide into oxygen at night for us to breath."

Fact: Green plants convert carbon dioxide from the air into sugars for themselves. Their oxygen comes from water, not from the air.

"Keep bonsai all day in direct sunlight for the most photosynthesis."

Fact: No bonsai requires full direct sunlight all day.

Explanation: Plants can detect any light present, including its direction, duration, intensity, and wavelength. The duration (amount of light exposure), quantity (intensity), and quality (wavelength) requirements are different for different plant species. Most plants tolerate and grow better in diffused, partial shade—especially during hot afternoons.

"A tree needs so many total square inches of leaf surface to produce the required energy to function as a healthy plant."

Fact: Deciduous trees with more leaf surface area have an average rate of photosynthesis seven times greater than a conifer has, with much less needle surface area. Conifers will retain most of their foliage all year in order to reach the maximum amount of photosynthesis. **Plants can allocate available energy produced by their foliage toward one function at the expense of another plant function** (#385).

Explanation: Both deciduous and evergreen trees produce all the required energy they need to function. The growth rate is different between young and mature trees. When they are young, energy goes toward more cell division, including foliage growth. When they're mature, a tree's resources go more toward maintenance and less toward new foliage growth. Minimal new foliage is produced on older trees, and they still function well. **The longer they live, the greater the percentage of the plant's energy goes toward maintaining existing woody stems and branches** (#386).

The same things that help grow a healthy plant can also stress a plant. In some cases, reducing the foliage can reduce total demand for energy. This is true only on trees with an established root system and only if a stressed plant has plenty of foliage to spare.

■ Does a deciduous tree store more photosynthates than an evergreen tree?

Yes. Sugars manufactured by the leaves are stored as photosynthates in deciduous trees to be available after leaf drop.

"Keep dormant evergreens in a dark basement with deciduous trees until spring thaw."
Fact: **Evergreen plants still need light to trap the sun's energy in wintertime or any stored reserves might be depleted** (#387). **With green needles on a conifer, or a green stem or bark on a dormant deciduous plant, active photosynthesis** can occur throughout the winter, assuming that light and temperature are sufficient (#388).

Explanation: Evergreens don't go "completely dormant," as in "inactive," even during a prolonged freeze. With substrate temperatures above freezing and with available light, evergreen plants are actively carrying on photosynthesis and respiration to keep their foliage functioning throughout the year. Roots grow year round on all trees, both deciduous and evergreen.

"Deciduous bonsai have no photosynthetic activity without leaves."
Fact: Green stems can photosynthesize even on resting deciduous trees. **Deciduous stems have chloroplast in cells of their chlorenchyma tissue and can still produce photosynthates (chemical energy) without leaves** (#389). The green color we get when we scratch a stem comes from the cortex, by the way, not the cambium. (Cortex can also be adapted as storage material in some plants. When we eat potatoes, carrots, or onions, we're eating cortex.)

Explanation: Total leaf loss does not hinder photosynthesis. As much as half of the light hitting the outer surface of one-year-old twigs can reach the chloroplast-containing inner tissues. The range is quite wide for different plants. With thick bark, less light can penetrate to the chlorenchyma. Some plants can photosynthesize in light even if the air temperature is below freezing. Roots grow all year. Similar to leaves, bark photosynthesis may be inhibited or even totally blocked in some cases.[*]

---

[*] H. Pranz, "Photosynthetic Performance of Twigs and Stems of Trees with and without Stress," *Plant Physiology* 30, no. 11 (1999).

HOW FOLIAGE RESPONDS

Can leaf injury stunt plant growth?

Surprisingly, a genetic and physiological basis does exist for stunting growth from injured leaves. The injured plant signals the growth inhibitor, called jasmonate, to slow down cell division, reduce future leaf size, and repress root growth in some species under stressful conditions.[*]

■ Why do some bonsai get their leaves scorched from simply moving the pot from one location to another?

The so-called sunburn comes from increased light energy.

Fact: **Deciduous foliage growing in shade tend to respond with thinner leaves, fewer cell layers, and less hairs and are usually larger** (#390). Leaves can twist on their petioles to fight for maximum exposure to sunlight and moisture. Thinner leaf tissue degrades, heats up, and then shrivels when moved from shade to sun.

Explanation: Those shade plants usually need more shelter and water but can adjust to lower light intensities. When moved to brighter light levels, their leaves can become scorched and look bleached out. **Foliage growth increases under shade stress. Root growth decreases when the foliage is under canopy shade stress** (#391).

During periods of harsh sun, drying wind, and rapid evapotranspiration, bonsai would appreciate their foliage being sprayed with water at the same time as their usual substrate watering.

---

[*] Sandra Noir, B. Moritz, et al., "Jasmonate Controls Leaf Growth by Repressing Cell Proliferation," *Plant Physiology* 161, no 4 (April 2013): 1930–51.

Tip: Roots also have a problem keeping up with hot summer days. Substrate gets cooked, the stomatas close on the foliage, and the plant can't keep up with increasing temperatures. It's time for shade cloth or for moving out of the afternoon sun. When going from a shadier to a sunnier spot, move pots progressively over a few weeks' period. Next time, new shade leaves will respond with thicker leaves.

What about evergreens? They have a waxy, waterproof, protective coating on their foliage. Broadleaf evergreens adapt to drought, sun, and wind with their waxy foliage. Narrowleaf evergreens also adapt to drought, sun, wind, and heavy layers of snow with their waxy and narrow needles. Those needles collect fog droplets. Some species have rough-textured leaves or fine hairs on their foliage to reduce the effect of drying winds.

■ What happens inside of a leaf when it starts to wilt?

Cell walls can't provide any water pressure when there is insufficient water inside the cell. Shrinking cells result in wilting leaves. Abscisic acid signals the stomata to close up, preventing further water loss. That action preserves water but at the sacrifice of no evaporative cooling. Even a well-watered plant wilts if it can't adapt to high rates of evapotranspiration. Transpiration helps evaporative cooling of a leaf but at the sacrifice of a possible water deficit. The tree has backup plans for heat and water stress, including the production of heat-shock proteins.

What is the first thing to do when I notice a plant wilting?

Determine and address which one of the many causes resulted in the foliage wilting:

- The plant gets too much or not enough water, fertilizer, or light.
- It's root bound.
- It's infested with disease pathogens.
- A winter injury is present.
- There are temperature extremes.
- There is root rot.
- There are insect problems, such as aphids or grubs, in the substrate.
- It has a mechanical injury.

■ How much light and heat do leaves tolerate?

Some plants tolerate more and deeper shade while other plants tolerate more and brighter light. Some sun-tolerating plants can reach their full maximum photosynthetic rate with a few continuous hours of low-filtered sunlight in the morning, then thrive the rest of the day growing in some shade. Other plants tolerate full sunlight intensity for several hours.

The same species thriving out in full sun in one microclimate may have a big problem in a different microclimate or different elevation. A major problem with full sun is the intensity of the heat along with the quick evaporation of moisture. *Plants can regulate transpiration but not evaporation* (#392).

When the temperature goes up past 100°F (38°C), the rate of photosynthesis decreases rapidly. Most of the plant's energy goes into transpiration. As much as 30 percent of the plant's energy is wasted during high temperatures. When the temperature goes up, the leaf's stomata close up to keep the moisture in.

In order to start the photosynthesis process, root cells must take up water and leaf guard cells must open up to take in carbon dioxide and release oxygen. If the guard cells open up for photosynthesis, the moisture goes out, causing that leaf to wilt during a hot day. Wilting leaves conserve water by exposing less total surface area to the sun.

> *Tip:* Notice if the leaves of a particular bonsai seem to wilt before nearby bonsai show any signs of stress. If the substrate holds water well and you know the sun's intensity is the stress factor, try moving that plant to a shadier location. If the foliage still wilts in a shadier spot with the same amount of watering, then try insulating the pot by partially burying it with mulch or placing the pot in a wider pot.

■ What are stomata?

Stomata (the plural of stoma) and lenticels control gas exchange and allow plants to breathe. They are minute, invisible openings found on any part of the foliage and stems but never on the roots. Stomata will close, even in bright sunlight, when the evapotranspiration rate is faster than the flow of water from the roots to the leaves.

Lenticel pores are the stomata for the aeration of stems and exposed surface roots. The leaves and roots can't supply air to the stems. Stems and leaves can't supply oxygen to the roots.

When foliage stomata are closed by darkness or lack of water or plugged by a spray of antitranspirants, then carbon dioxide can't enter the leaf for its work in photosynthesis. The process of respiration continues quite well even if stomata are closed or plugged. Willow and poplar species have a slight problem with constantly open stomata, so they require wetter environments. As with most other deciduous trees, most stomata are on the lower side of the leaf.

"Don't let pocket branches grow on the inner concave part of the curves of the bonsai trunk. They will die from lack of light."
Those branches might do quite well in spite of growing inside a curve. Diffused sun reaches all sides of a plant. Specialized shade leaves contribute resources to the shady side of a plant. If those pocket branches don't bother you, leave them. They're quite natural looking.

> *Tip*: Suppose you want to keep a "shaded branch" but you think that branch would look better slightly repositioned. Wire and reposition that branch. Or make a deadwood feature if it displays an attractive shape. Use any design flaw to your advantage. Turn flaws into features.

■ Does the water evaporating off a leaf cause a suction, making sap rise up from the roots?

That statement partially explains how water gets from the roots up to the top of the bonsai. Scientists still aren't entirely sure how water gets up to the top of the tallest tree. Most likely, it's a combination effect, including root pressure, vacuum pressure, evaporation, transpiration, diffusion, osmotic potential, cohesion, adhesion, solute concentration, and protein pumps.

■ Do evergreen plants require the same amount of water in the wintertime as at other times of the year?

No, you water both deciduous and evergreens considerably less in the wintertime. Keep the substrate barely moist and give it a drying-out period after heavy rainfall. Winter winds can dry out evergreen foliage with rapid water evaporation. Deciduous trees have adapted to winter desiccation by dropping their leaves since their roots can't take up water from frozen ground.

"Spray with antitranspirants in both the summer and winter to reduce stress."
Fact: **Antitranspirants merely increase plant stress and decrease the photosynthesis and transpiration rate** (#393). In reality, antitranspirants can't stay on the leaf long enough to do any measurable amount of good.

"During the summer, water collects on the leaves, reflects brilliant sunlight, magnifies it, scorches the leaves, causes sunburn, and scalds the roots. Saturate your bonsai every day during the summer."
Don't worry, leaves do not get "sunburn and heat stroke." If you set a magnifying glass directly on a leaf under the hottest rays, nothing happens. If you hold the magnifying glass at the right distance away from the leaf, you might be able to get the sun's rays concentrated enough to burn a hole in the leaf. Water droplets on the leaves can't "magnify the sun's heat." Not water reflection, heated water, or dehydration "can burn leaves."

A warm water hose left out in the hot sun quickly cools off as the water begins flowing through it. Water droplets on foliage usually evaporate before that water can become heated from the sun. The evaporation after watering on a hot day also reduces the soil temperature. Most parts of the substrate in the container get wet when it receives water slowly, thoroughly, and repeatedly. Still, you can't "saturate bonsai" unless you plug the drain holes or dunk the whole pot in water.

Chinese elm.

"Misting the leaves helps raise the humidity."

Leaf misting helps bonsai if the plant is in an enclosed greenhouse environment with consistent periodic misting. It would be impossible to raise the relative humidity in an outdoor environment from misting.

"Do not get water on the flowers. You will accelerate their drying out and dropping off and will hinder the initiation of fruit." "Do not water leaves with tap water. You will kill the cells on the leaf tips."

This is not the case in the real world of plants.

"Spray leaf polish on the leaves to make them shinier during exhibiting."

Don't do this unless you want to clog up the leaf's breathing capacity and energy production.

■ My tree has yellow leaves all of a sudden. Should I "fertilize immediately"?

In theory, we should be able to look at the color of the leaves and tell what's wrong with the plant. In actual practice, we can't. Yellowing leaves can represent many conditions. Don't worry if older deciduous leaves look yellowish. They'll soon fall off. Yellowing leaves could also be a sign of:

- Too dry or too wet.
- Too cold or too hot.
- Too windy.
- Not enough light.
- An insect or disease problem.
- Mechanical injury to roots or foliage.
- An essential element problem. You can determine what essential elements a tree has or lacks from a leaf tissue analysis. A yellowing leaf does not indicate that "it needs to be fed immediately" All too

often, minerals are available but tied up. Most micronutrients are partially mobile in a leaf. Spray iron or nitrogen on a leaf to see if chlorosis goes away. Over fertilizing an already stressed plant results in further stress.

■ Should I fertilize before or after flowering?

Before flowering is OK. After fruit starts to develop is OK. Applying fertilizer right before fruit develops might lead to fruit drop.

■ Are the darker-colored flowers dominant on trees with more than one flower color?

Yes. Try to protect the lighter-colored flowers because if a branch on a multicolored flowering tree ever mutates, then that branch will produce only darker-colored flowers. If you take a cutting from that same mutated branch, then the future flowers from the cuttings are the same darker color.

■ Should I disbud flowers and the fruit on a bonsai if I want to promote vegetative growth?

Yes, if your objective is primarily to encourage the development of branches and foliage. Disbud the future flowers and remove the drying flowers. Flower production doesn't take energy away from foliage production. Fruit and seed production is the energy waster. Fruit uses a high proportion of photosynthates that the foliage and branches could use in their own development. Woody growth decreases as fruiting begins.

■ *If my tree is full of blooms, does that mean it is healthy?*

Usually, flowers and fruit are produced on most healthy plants after a normal growing cycle. Stressed plants may attempt to flower and then go to seed production for self-preservation.

"Try to save the leaves as long as possible by bringing deciduous bonsai in the house during the wintertime and enjoy it all year."

Fact: **Insufficient light, humidity, temperature, carbon dioxide, and oxygen inside a house can prove too stressful and vulnerable in a hostile environment for any bonsai** (#394).

Explanation: True, trees can live on stored reserves for more than one growing season. A certain amount of resting is necessary to retain the photosynthates depleted from the leaves right before leaf drop and to conserve energy for further cell divisions. Most plants depend on seasonal transitions for this energy conservation. Deciduous plants use their stored photosynthate reserves until temperatures become warm enough for more active root cell divisions.

> *Tip*: Deciduous bonsai should be kept outside as long as possible even after the first fall freezes. Allow them to experience maximum decreasing day lengths and temperatures until winter solstice. The deeper and longer the resting stage, the more likely they'll survive the winter freezes.

An extended warm winter inside or when taking a plant back outside too soon confuses deciduous plants. Low winter temperatures, strong winter winds, and the sun's strong rays closer to the earth would desiccate any thin leaves. Either way, the normal metabolic activity declines in that outside bonsai if kept in the house during dormancy.

BUDDING BONSAI

■ **How do buds differ?**

Buds are either modified leaves, modified shoots, or modified flowers. All three types of leaf buds respond differently.

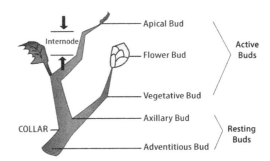

Active and Resting Buds

Leaf buds at the tips are called apical buds. The apical buds are the same size as the neighboring buds below them. At the joints, they're called axillary leaf buds, and if they randomly show up, they're called adventitious leaf buds. Some buds are full of actively dividing cells. Others are active but repressed and in between growth periods. Buds under repression are slowly elongating and resting while waiting. Buds never "stop and go dormant," but they may be resting while fully developed and ready to be called into action.

■ *Why don't more of the leaf buds on my tree flush out? How do back buds develop?*

Each developing latent bud has the potential to grow, but only if regulator switches located right above it turn on and allow it to flush out. Growth hormones are not turned on until starches stored at the base of that particular bud change back to glucose—and only if the bud has sufficient light and is fully developed. *Buds do not suddenly "appear on the stems in spring"; they are developing during the entire growing season and will be fully developed before fall* (#395).

Stem tip regulator switches tell the lower resting buds to wait until the existing foliage around them has been injured by insects or other things before they remove the chemical repression and allow the lower buds to pop out. Often you can remove the more active bud above and make a notch above the resting bud to encourage the bud below to grow. Removing terminal buds before winter can make a huge difference in allowing fall photosynthate storage to reach the base of lower buds. *Generated in the cambium zone, developing buds respond to stress coming from higher up the tree, farther out on the stem, or sometimes even below the bud* (#396).

When wiring and bending, point the branch tip straight out horizontally or down to try promoting back budding. This also weakens any auxin production at the tip bud. Pointing the branch tips up increases auxin production through geotropism.

The level of light the bud is exposed to as the bud swells helps determine the future leaf size (#397). If you leave the lower stems in deep shade, the development of back buds on those branches may be repressed. Lower shade leaves usually come out thinner and larger compared to sun leaves. But those shade leaves are also healthy and provide photosynthates to that area of the plant. Its growth regulators make future shade leaves larger to collect more light.

Adventitious buds are randomly available for back budding farther down from the stem tips. Water from the roots can't "open buds." "Inertia or frequent misting or extra cold temperatures" won't "bring out the back buds" either. Roots themselves have no buds, so we can't do anything to "bring out the back budding on roots."

■ Can a latent bud be found at the base of every leaf, ready to grow?

Indeed, a developing latent leaf bud already has formed several potential small leaves inside itself and is ready to expand when the conditions are right. A modified shoot bud grows away from the stem and can specialize into its own branch with its own meristem (growing tip). *New leaf formation includes a developing latent bud at the leaf petiole base* (#398). That petiole, basically a leaf stalk, is best left on during any pruning. Why? *Pulling the petiole off can injure the future buds in their axil* (#399).

On some species, the number and size of leaves that will form in the future is determined even before the buds start to open. Trees can produce leaves from buds continuously, in a single flush or in multiple flushes of growth throughout the whole growing season.

LEAVE OUR LEAVES

■ What are some types of leaf pruning?

- Defoliation, either whole-tree full defoliation or single-branch defoliation.
- Trimming the outer perimeter of leaves.
- "Decandling," or completely removing this year's new shoots on pines.
- Culling or picking off the big or bad leaves.
- Pinching or nipping.

■ Why do some bonsai hobbyists pinch off new foliage as it grows out?

Pinching with fingers or shearing with tools removes growing tips:

- to maintain the form and silhouette.
- to promote twig density.
- to affect the growth regulators.
- to attempt to reduce foliage size.

> *Tip*: Hedge shearing is a useful technique when first training for overall shape on deciduous plants. Wait for the flush of new growth to harden off after a good shearing, then head back redundant branches all the way to the junction or right above a node.

Continually pinching off evergreen foliage at the tips makes the tree weaker because it needs resources to repair the injury to each partial leaf. The vascular pathways are blocked. Pinching would be more appropriate for removing new aphid clusters as they appear near the tips of the new growth.

Seedlings, cuttings, and liners will be stronger if we allow them to complete a full growing season before any pruning. Slow growers especially need their maximum foliage.

■ Why do we remove new shoots on pines?

- To promote future branches in the proper place and length on some pine species.
- To keep new aggressive growth in proportion.
- To allow the tree to stimulate back budding.
- To decrease resources in one part of a pine.
- To build ramification.
- To promote short internodes.
- To promote short needles.

"Decandling" also works on cryptomeria and many other conifers. Pruning between nodes produces a whorl of juvenile needles, but in a couple years you probably won't be able to tell the difference. Over time, decandling can become a short-lived, temporary acclimation response. Be wary of a conifer with lighter green needles but no active growth. That tree is dead.

■ Is there a correct time to prune shoots on pines?

Yes, prune shoots, not candles. It's too early to prune shoots when new growth looks like whiskers on a candle. Wait until the needles start to mature. If pine shoots are pinched too early, they'll get fat buds at the new tip growth. Pines get skinny buds on older wood if they're pinched when they are almost mature—the optimal time for shoot pruning. We completely remove the shoots of double-flush pines, such as Japanese black pines, around July 4 in our hardiness zone 7 and 8.

Removing longer shoots at the right time and in the right climate can grow the next set of needles shorter on some pines. Not all pines benefit from shoot pruning. The touchier pines for us include Mugo, Japanese white, some Scots, and most of those with a single flush of growth.

Conifers have a longer feedback time for the signals between branches and roots than we find in deciduous trees. The Internet is loaded with opinions and advice on pine "decandling."

"Pinch all juniper tips regularly to slow down growth and maintain shape."

Pinching away all the tree's vitality one tip at a time is a time-consuming and rough way to weaken a developing juniper. Heading back to a node with scissors may be much more effective than pinching off the valuable growing tips of a juniper. The strength of junipers is in their growing tips.

Some of the newer or shaded juniper or Cryptomeria foliage is short and prickly feeling, called awl-like. That foliage often tends to mature into tiny, overlapping, softer-feeling flat scales, called scale-like. Awl-like new upper foliage allows moisture to flow down the plant to the lower, larger, longer, scale-like foliage that may be fighting for moisture and light.

SCALE-LIKE   AWL-LIKE

Mature and Juvenile Foliage

■ What are the disadvantages of defoliation and leaf pruning on deciduous bonsai?

We may need to rethink defoliation as a habitual practice when we're only hoping for smaller leaves. Some practices don't always work the way they're supposed to. Here's what they teach you in school:

Fruits, flowers, new growth, and new wounds demand the most energy from a plant and are the most immediately affected by defoliation (#400). Defoliation stops the solar panels and starts an immediate decline in plant functions. Fuel production for metabolic properties soon stops. Production of photosynthates for growth, root development, flowers, seeds, and defense against pests are all affected.

If the first foliage flush suffers from heavy insect damage or an early frost, the next group of leaves comes with depleted reserves. Defoliation creates competition for space with the resulting denser flush of weaker branches.

Cutting a leaf in half through the veins breaks its critical pathways. *No photosynthates can pass out through that cut leaf to the rest of the tree* (#401). Leaf veins are vascular bundles containing xylem and phloem that transport photosynthates, water, and other minerals. It's better to cut the petiole stalk in half than to cut its leaf in half.

Cutting a leaf in half immediately switches on a hypersensitive response in the branch. Similar to compartmentalization on an injured branch, an injured leaf is walled off from the rest of the tree to defend the tree from a possible pathogens attack. The tree destroys that partial leaf to the petiole base and allows it to drop off with the next strong wind.

Defoliation right after potting or transplanting rapidly depletes scarce stored reserves for several weeks. Any defoliation after the first day of summer deprives the tree of the preparation of photosynthate storage for next growing season.

Refoliation usually occurs a few weeks after defoliation, which in turn requires energy for bud break, further depleting valuable stored food reserves. Further branch growth is put on hold while it reallocates those resources for refoliation. It takes another two or three weeks after new foliage emerges to begin the full cycle of photosynthate production.

Complete defoliation at the wrong time can cause loss of vitality, weakness, stress, top and root dieback, stunted new growth, and a flush of aggressive twig growth, further resulting in random dieback (#402). Weakness from the stress of defoliation is usually associated with insect and disease problems and a decrease in winter hardiness. The new flush of thinner leaves tends to show a paler green color due to less photosynthates. *Total growth after defoliation is reduced, along with a significant reduction in caliper growth* (#403).

Valuable growth regulators accumulated in the axial of a leaf's petiole may be pulled off while being defoliated. Future buds are damaged. The capacity for evapotranspiration is gone from the leaf along with a fresh supply of water and essential elements. Researchers have discovered a tight correlation between the total water uptake and total leaf area. *Fewer leaves equals less water coming up to the leaves* (#404). New growth is usually weaker than the first previous flush of foliage.

When propagating by cuttings, then yes, cutting a leaf in half does slow down the evapotranspiration. But that outdated practice also stops photosynthate from getting to the rest of the cutting. Smaller leaves, twigs, and buds may look good for a show, but that means less cell division activity in the tree after the show. The defoliation process and the subsequent exhibition of bonsai indoors for several days is a doubly weakening process to any tree

Defoliation with the goal of making smaller leaves this year makes a much weaker tree for next year (#405). Smaller leaves this year doesn't mean leaves are automatically smaller next year. Defoliation may signal a second, more robust flush of growth with larger leaves and longer internodes instead of the smaller leaves and shorter internodes we were hoping for. Sometimes it works, sometimes it doesn't. Defoliation destroys future fruit or flowers.

Expect the death of some newer roots stemming from defoliation stress. Don't expect smaller leaf size after you apply fertilizer. One of the factors for the distribution of essential elements up from the roots depends on their demand coming down from the crown. Fewer leaves equal fewer elements coming up to the leaves from the roots.

One study implied that even a partial defoliation on only one side of a plant influences the capacity of the entire plant to adapt for lost leaf area. *Fewer leaves on one side of the tree equals fewer essential elements on both sides of the tree, even with full foliage on the other side* (#406).[*]

Some broadleaf evergreens and most narrowleaf evergreen trees can't tolerate defoliation. Defoliation of variegated plants can cause the future foliage to revert back to the original green color. *Early spring defoliation, along with heavy refoliation, weakens the tree by using up limited photosynthate reserves that can't be replenished by photosynthesis* (#407).

In the real world, not only insects and diseases, but also late spring frosts and environmental adversities can influence a tree to protect itself with an out-of-season leaf drop. If you defoliate when you already see woody tissue dieback, you've gone beyond the stress mode, and the tree might just give up. Pinching off the buds in early spring is far better for the tree. Why take a risk?

However, cutting off larger leaves at the petiole reduces the plant's moisture requirements. Selective defoliation removes unsightly leaves. Selective defoliation on a few of the larger upper leaves allows the sun to reach more of the inner leaves while restraining the immediate growth on upper branches. Partial canopy openings can also influence buds on the interior of some broadleaf evergreen trees. *Allowing higher light intensity into the crown helps ready those developed back buds on standby and also influences future smaller leaf size* (#408).

"Defoliation deceives the tree into thinking it's winter time, consequently decreasing leaf size."
In some cases, defoliating does temporarily lead to decreased future leaf size. For exhibiting in

---

[*] M. Coffelt and P. Schultz, "Impact of Late Season Insect Defoliation on Tree Growth," *SNA Research Conference Proceedings* 36 (1991).

an upcoming show, a grower living in the right climate might defoliate a healthy bonsai at the right time in hopes for newer, smaller leaves—and in hopes that it survives after the show. *Defoliation cannot induce dormancy or increase a plant's vigor* (#409). Vigor is genetics. Leaf size is genetics.

■ How many times a year can a healthy tree tolerate defoliation treatment?

Complete defoliations in the same or consecutive years on deciduous trees have killed even the healthiest of bonsai. One complete defoliation is all it takes to kill a conifer.

"Winter defoliation on evergreen trees helps to eliminate parasites and sunburn."
Yes—and helps eliminate evergreen trees!

"Early summer is the best time to defoliate."
That statement could be true if you are lucky enough to own a modern greenhouse facility. Or if you live in the right microclimate. Some areas have a more humid environment, which helps their plants adjust better to summer defoliation. The worst time to fully defoliate is early in the growing season, when the leaves first unfold. Buds take up a lot of the tree's energy when flushing out. Defoliating is too risky for practically all plants.

"Do not expose the tree to the sun's rays immediately after defoliation or the roots will burn."
If buried roots "burn," the cause is usually from excess fertilizer, not from the sun's rays.

"Defoliating the tree when also pruning the roots will correct root rot."
Those two activities aren't related. Root rot comes from a fungal infection and is usually associated with poorly aerated substrate. Defoliation at the same time as root pruning drastically delays fresh root growth. Prune and dispose of any affected roots, then ensure better substrate aeration to deter future root rot. Leave the leaves.

■ Will having the "leaves stripped off make the new internode length shorter"?

The exact opposite happens. *New growth after full defoliation usually produces a flush of longer internodes* (#410).

■ Since the tree has fewer leaves after defoliation, will it "need less watering and nutrients and more shade"?

Four strikes against it now: fewer leaves, less water, fewer essential elements, and less light. Watering during dry periods helps the process of refoliation. Fast-release water soluble fertilizer and shade can hinder the normal process of generating photosynthates again.

■ How long will it take a tree to recover from defoliation?

It could take a full growing season or could take a few years to recover. Why take a risk? Slow growers need their foliage. The effect on tree growth and survival after defoliation depends on:

- the health of the tree before defoliation.
- the severity of defoliation.
- whether it experienced total or partial defoliation.
- the time of year.
- the ability to photosynthesize effectively again.
- how often the tree is defoliated during the year.

- the presence of secondary insects and disease problems after defoliation.

If you must, remove only the larger upper leaves or individual larger leaves from a particular area. Save those petioles and save those buds.

"Thinning out old pine needles gives nourishment back to the shoots and encourages new adventitious back buds to form."
One problem with that practice could be that plucking off old pine needles decreases the available growth regulators in that area and thereby generally weakens the tree. Completely removing pine shoots will help release adventitious buds.

■ Do thick, broadleaf evergreen and conifer leaves last longer than thin deciduous leaves?

Yes. Thicker leaves do last longer because a thinner leaf has a higher rate of photosynthesis and cell division. A few leaves or needles fall off evergreens every growing season, and the previous year's foliage is replaced. Thin leaves of deciduous trees grow fast and die fast. Most animals prefer to eat leafy deciduous foliage rather than thin, prickly needles.

THEY SHRUNK MY LEAVES

■ What makes future leaves smaller?
Genetics, growth regulators, water, and light. *The outermost cell layer on each leaf responds to the environmental cues and consequently grows larger or smaller future cells* (#411). Then that outer layer (epidermis) tells the adjacent inner layers

of cells to divide more or to have fewer cell divisions. Leaf size is predetermined by the epidermis and dependent on the size and number of cells present.

Scientists have discovered that individual cells could even be larger in a bonsai leaf but with fewer and thinner cells than seen in a normal leaf. Established bonsai may eventually produce fewer cells over time as they mature. Complex environmental influences on leaf size often carry over from year to year. Trees adjust to fewer cells and fewer developing leaves over time.

The future leaf can become larger or smaller than the last set of leaves. One leaf can be of a much different size than an adjacent leaf on the same stem. *Future leaf size and internode length are influenced by water and light availability during the growing season* (#412).

The smaller size of future leaves can also be influenced by:
- spring pruning of the roots, branches, and foliage.
- fewer meristem (boss) cells.
- inhibiting hormonal responses.
- maturity of the tree.
- a restrictive substrate or container.
- restrictions in photosynthate production or other stressful environmental conditions causing a short-term acclimation response.

Sunlight is needed for leaf growth. Leaves in full sun on top of the canopy tend to become lighter in color, as well as smaller and thicker in size. The leaf is lighter green from less chlorophyl and more efficient use of light. In turn, smaller leaves require less water. Buds in full sun develop future sun leaves.

More sunlight requires more leaf surface and mass. More leaf mass requires all nineteen essential elements. *Shade leaves are larger, thinner, and darker green with more chlorophyll* (#413). They have adapted by taking less time to get all the sun's energy they need. Leggy interior stems and thinner leaves scorch and bleach out easier when they get intense, full sun—or the limited roots in a confining pot can't function well.

On the plus side, shade leaves are healthy, happy, and contribute vital resources to the interior canopy of any bonsai. Leave some of those healthy interior leaves. Large leaves collect a lot of energy.

"Nitrogen makes the leaf larger and greener."
Fact: **An application of nitrogen can't by itself make a leaf larger** (#414).
Explanation: The chloroplasts in the leaf make photosynthate energy. Nitrogen is merely a minuscule proportion of chlorophyll, only four nitrogens for every fifty-four carbons. It is only one out of the nineteen elements essential for making that leaf larger. Applying nitrogen fertilizer is not totally responsible for making leaves larger.

"Fertilizing in fall stimulates fall growth. Bigger leaves will die in the frost."
Fact: We don't want, nor can we expect, new growth from a fall fertilization program. Genetics tells the new growth to wait until next year. Container trees need fall supplements to assist in building up reserves and defenses for the next growing season.

"Small leaves this year ensure small leaves next year."
Fact: Some leaves and needles may be small for a short period. They can revert back. An acclimation response is short term. A genetic or adaptation response is long term.
Explanation: A plant may exhibit sparse small leaves this year due to water or nutrient starvation or due to barely surviving in a small pot. Repot this fall and notice how leaf size changes with next spring's new growth.

■ How does a smaller, confined root system lead to smaller-size leaves?
It's supply and demand. A recently root pruned bonsai in its confined space can promote fewer and smaller future leaves on its own. There's no need for any branch pruning or leaf defoliation. When the tree has fewer roots, it also adjusts with slower overall growth. This is a short-term acclimation response.

■ How can I make the bonsai fruit or flower size smaller?
The genetically predetermined size or shape of the fruit or flowers cannot be changed by any horticultural practices (#415).

"Reduce the length of the pine needles and deciduous leaves by watering and fertilizing less."
That's debatable and risky. Growers have several techniques for reducing needle length. One example may be to completely pinch off all the new shoots by early summer. The resulting newer buds produce a crop of shorter needles. Needle length can be trimmed back with scissors if you can tolerate the brown tips for a season or two. Less water equals less turgor pressure required for forcing the cell walls to expand. Small leaves will temporarily stay small because of drought stress.

LEAVES A' BLAZING

■ Why do some leaves flush out reddish to light green color and then turn darker green?

New leaf color is determined by the first pigments to form in that particular leaf. As light green chloroplasts form and trap more of the sun's energy, the leaf color appears deeper green. Foliage is every color but green. Chloroplasts absorb red and blue light (and some of the green light) but transmit and reflect the green light to our eyes. Green light is not used in photosynthesis.

The red color on juvenile or emerging foliage comes from anthocyanin. Anthocyanin, an antioxidant, seems to act like a red sunscreen in summer and antifreeze in winter. Interestingly, the amount of anthocyanin responds to the amount of photosynthates in a leaf or stem and has a role in transporting those resources to other parts of the plant. We see it in some new red foliage, in red-leafed cultivars, in red fall colors, and in plants grown in low pH or oxygen-starved substrate.

Red juvenile foliage contains less moisture and seems to react to drought stress by retaining more moisture than green foliage. It is said to assist in compartmentalizing pathogens in a leaf.

Tip: Reddish-colored foliage contains less moisture and photosynthates than green foliage. Placing a red-leafed plant in shade may cause that foliage to turn green. Don't overwater plants with red foliage because red leaves won't evaporate water as efficiently as green leaves. Overwatering those red plants may increase the concentration of toxic fertilizer salts in a leaf.

■ How can I get the maximum, the earliest, and the longest-lasting fall color on my bonsai?

Don't fertilize or repot after July and leave the plant in sufficient sunlight for better fall coloring. Fall color is contingent on many factors. The yellows and the orange colors are present in the leaf, masked by green chlorophyll. Anthocyanin, the reds, usually is created in the fall. Fall coloring is dependent on genetics, weather, temperature, light, and photosynthate. Fall foliage remains on the tree longer with higher concentrations of the cytokinin growth regulator.

■ What is the first day of fall for a deciduous tree? Why do some plants need to go dormant?

June solstice, when day length is longest. *The greatest factor causing trees to slow down or to increase growing again is daylight length* (#416). Dormancy doesn't mean part of the tree is inactive or dead. Latent growth still carries on during the resting stage of a deciduous plant. Besides daylight length, changes are due to temperature changes and simple genetics.

Tropical plants in natural environments have mild resting stages due to no drastic changes in light, temperature, or genetics. For other plants, shorter, milder, less obvious resting periods are interspersed throughout the growing season. *Resting periods let the plant conserve resources during harsh, stressful conditions* (#417). Leaf loss on deciduous trees is an adaption keeping them from drying out during colder temperatures when roots can't take up water from frozen ground. Plants drop their leaves to cut future losses. Roots are still carrying on cell divisions and pulling up water as usual all winter.

■ Is there also a fall color change in the foliage of narrowleaf evergreens?

Yes, but it takes much lower temperatures to slow down biological processes in narrowleaf evergreens than it does in deciduous plants. Pine needles take on more of a faded yellow tint and junipers turn more golden brown, while Chamaecyparis and Cryptomeria foliage take on a more bronze tinge throughout the wintertime. Most of that color comes from an accumulation of anthocyanin that lowers the freezing point of foliage. Some deciduous conifers, such as larch, bald cypress and dawn redwood, drop their needles for winter.

RESPONDING TO POTTING

The objective of repotting is to ensure the best-quality, newer, finer branching roots are growing in the best conditions in the limited available space for that particular bonsai. Our objective to repot should not be for "healing wounds" or for scheduled maintenance.

■ What is the difference between repotting and transplanting?

Repotting usually involves shaving away some of the old substrate and roots. Transplanting moves a plant from one pot to another pot or from one location to another with minimal or no root disturbance. Bonsai (as a verb) includes the practices of potting and transplanting when the roots indicate they are ready. When the roots are happy, the whole plant is happy.

Nature never planned for an uprooted tree to be planted again in the upright position (#418).

PLANTS GROW IN A TIGHTLY CONNECTED SYSTEM

■ Can bonsai float on water?

Sure can—if it's on a wooden board. Then the bonsai, the board, the substrate, and the pot are part of the whole system to keep it afloat. Take away the board and the plant drowns. Use a faulty substrate and the plant dies from too much or not enough air spaces. Using a wrong size pot negatively affects the root system.

A spider web can be considered a system. Disturbing one part of the web affects the whole web. Bonsai is a system. One changing condition in the pot can affect the dynamics of the whole system. We don't always see the changing conditions inside the pot. As one example, the percentage of organic matter dramatically increases as parts of the roots die and decay. Organic matter soon compacts.

Garden field soil is also one complicated, tightly connected system, but to a greater degree. ***Break one small connection, for example, eliminate the living organisms found in field soil and the entire soil system will also die*** (#419).

WHY AND WHEN TO REPOT

■ Why repot bonsai?

For several reasons:

- To increase the vitality of the plant. The rate of cell division slows down in the root cambial zone as the roots begin to age. In the confines of a pot, the growth rate of newer roots decreases. The uptake rate of water and essential elements decreases.
- To increase the available pore spaces and correct or maintain correct aeration. The physical properties of any substrate break down and compact over time. Water cannot easily penetrate a compacted substrate and will run off the surface. Aggressively growing roots become pot bound as they quickly fill the container, taking up the limited space. Limited pore space equals limited root growth.
- The roots accumulating in the bottom of the pot have no new pore spaces to fill, and they reach through the drain holes. They can push the entire root system up from the bottom into any wires tying the root system to the pot.
- To shift up to the next size pot for stressed roots or to accommodate aggressive growth.
- To gradually replace any clay field soil still clinging to roots of a collected tree. Any clay aggregates left on may extract too much moisture from an established root system.
- To replace a chemically aged substrate, especially if it contains an organic component. Excess chemicals tied up with organic matter or clay particles (including akadama) may become toxic to the roots.
- To control structural root growth by root pruning. This process makes room for new finer root growth. In other words, to replace bigger roots with smaller roots.
- To study the root system for any presence of pathogens. Sometimes stressed roots encourage the invasion of disease and insects.
- To reset the planting angle if needed.
- To reset and improve the cosmesis of the surface roots.
- To unplug the drain holes.
- To increase or decrease the size or quality of the pot.

A larger pot size promotes the conditions for growth and development. If that little bonsai in that little shallow pot isn't repotted up periodically to a larger container (or temporarily field planted), it'll be quite difficult for it to grow up and out.

Training and development can take decades before the plant is even ready for showing off in a smaller, higher-quality bonsai pot. If a temporary, smaller pot is necessary for exhibition time, it would be completely appropriate for the plant's health to slightly upsize the pot again after showing your bonsai.

Repotting is unnecessary:

- if a lot of fresh, white roots are growing uninhibited in the pore spaces.
- if substrate seems loose around the sides of the root system. When you poke around with your finger, the substrate crumbles away.
- if the trunk is unstable and can be wiggled around freely in the pot after it's been watered, even though securely fastened to the pot.
- when the branches have recently been drastically pruned to change the height and fullness. Let both the top and the bottom of the tree sort it out and catch up with each other.
- when a few stray roots start pushing out the drain holes. Cut or pull them out.

> *Tip*: Most plants grow best when moderately pot bound. Bonsai become stressed and weakened from enduring a repotting every single spring without fail.

The roots of pines and most other conifers require considerably more time to colonize a pot than the roots of **a deciduous tree** (#420). Deciduous trees require transplanting or repotting more often than evergreen trees. ***Mature, refined trees do not adjust well to big changes*** (#421). Well-established bonsai can tolerate being slightly pot bound.

> *Tip*: No need to disturb the whole tree every year. Some bonsai can be managed without ever going through a complete repotting. (Yes, you read that last sentence right.)

The repotting procedure is analogous to surgery It is the last resort and so many things could go wrong.

■ What's an alternative to complete repotting?

You might not want to slow down the growth rate of your bonsai by aggressive root pruning and complete repotting if neither one is indicated. You could shave or trim the outer edges and the bottom of the root ball. Some bonsai professionals poke a sturdy rod several places in old substrate and fill those voids with fresh substrate.

Cut out small, wedge-shaped sections from around the edge of the root ball while trying to avoid major roots. Replace those cut out areas with fresh substrate. Also while in the same pot, slightly scrape off the top, crusty layer of age-hardened substrate, weed seeds and all. Then top dress with fresh substrate.

Spray a solution of diluted liquid dishwashing detergent to soften age-hardened substrate surface. Repot if subsequent watering still flows off instead of into the container.

Tip: Match the same granular texture of the old material when repotting. A homogenous mixture promotes uniform roots in every part of the pot.

Any clay aggregates left retain moisture while extracting it from other parts of the substrate (#422).

■ What are some indications to repot?

Horticulturally, there's no general rules. It depends on various factors and indications:

- The growth rate.
- The environment.
- Health of the plant.
- Pathogens
- Size of the plant.
- Substrate quality.
- The size of the container relative to the size of the bonsai.
- The condition of the old pot
- Aesthetics. Changing the pot to better match the color, shape and style of the new pot to the tree's latest personality.

Most water usually flows down the space between the outside of the root system and the inside wall of the pot. When substrate doesn't soak in water as before, take the bonsai out of the pot and look for obvious dry areas and physical changes in the substrate.

Check for clogged or moved drain screens. Check for root rot and any other obvious pests or pathogens. Out of sight shouldn't be out of mind. A root system rising up into a mound and growing out of the pot could indicate the plant is pot bound and needs repotting.

When you know the roots have been fully established in an intact fibrous root ball but the bonsai seems to still be in decline, this might be a proper time to repot. Consider repotting into a slightly larger pot or slightly shaving the perimeter of the root ball to fit in the same size pot.

Other indications of decline or stress include:

- Growth has been noticeably slow over the past couple growing seasons. New shoots appear thinner and weaker.
- Vitality noticeably declines.
- Leaf size and quantity is noticeably reduced.
- Leaf color change and leaf drop comes earlier.
- Foliage is chlorotic or yellowish. The foliage seems to appear less glossy. Leaf margins look wrinkled.
- Newer foliage seems to stay wilted more than usual.
- Winter has left considerably more twig dieback.

"A tree gets all its vigor from its roots, so annual repotting is the basis of good bonsai cultivation. It then grows shorter internodes and thinner twigs."

Fact: Photosynthesis and respiration, along with its own growth regulators, are the basis of healthy bonsai. ***A tree gets most of its vigor from its genetics*** (#423). It does not get it from fertilizing, repotting, or its roots.

Explanation: No relationship exists between yearly repotting and the size of its twigs.

Example: Many famous large bonsai, root-over-rock plantings, and tray landscapes have flourished for years without any repotting.

■ Just because I prune branches and wire and shape my bonsai in one operation, does that mean I "then need to repot the tree at the same time to even things up"?

As brought up before, some plants may not adjust to all that stress in one sitting. During the potting operation, most of the existing tender roots are torn away and need some time to become well colonized again.

■ **Just because I prune branches, will "the pruning cuts weep copiously and lose important sap if the tree is not immediately repotted"?**

They won't. There's no relationship between sap and potting.

"If the branches are long and thin or yellow and twisted, and with leaves wilting and the roots dehydrated, this indicates the soil is bad and must be changed immediately."

This is not necessarily an appropriate indication to repot immediately. Take the plant out of the pot and examine for root rot. If the roots are good, set the plant back in the existing pot. Don't rush out to repot a struggling bonsai. Those symptoms may indicate too much or too little water, fertilizer, or light. First change the location of the pot and try to establish the cause of the plant's stress. Repotting under already stressed conditions would further add to the stress of the plant.

■ **What is the best time of year to repot or transplant?**

Unfortunately, nature did not plan for tree transplanting at any particular time of year. Fortunately, plants with a healthy fibrous root system can be successfully transplanted any season of the year. Spring seems to be the norm.

For us gardeners in mild winters of hardiness zones 7 to 8, one of the best times for repotting and transplanting is during fall. Why? ***Fall transplanting takes advantage of already established roots and ongoing rapid root growth occurring before spring budding out*** (#424).

- Environmental stresses are less.
- Water requirements are less.
- Temperatures are down.
- Evapotranspiration is reduced.

- Tops are going dormant while new roots are flushing out again and continuing to grow.
- More photosynthates are in both branches and roots.
- There are more good days to work and play outside.
- There's more time for plants to establish before bad weather or winter storage.
- There's more stable weather to promote rapid root development.

Most of the finer root hairs die when transplanted, and plant resources go to root generation in fall. In spring, resources first go to the branches and foliage, so the rate of root growth decreases. Summer's heat and drought stress follows spring potting.

The old guideline for "only planting in the spring or fall" seems to have come from the practice of using balled and burlapped plants that were common ages ago. Several outdated guidelines do not apply to bonsai repotting or to any other container planting. Transplanting during warm temperatures is not "going to cause root disease." With proper aftercare, container nursery stock can be field planted any time of the year.

> *Tip*: Some flowering trees bloom on new growth. You can repot those species after the first flowers begin to fade if you want flowering next year. You can remove remaining flowers or fruit prior to repotting.

Larger broadleaved evergreens are best transplanted in the spring in colder climates. ***Most deciduous and conifer trees are better equipped to deal with next summer's heat and drought with fall transplanting than with spring transplanting*** (#425). Whenever possible, repot in fall instead of the usual spring potting and transplanting.

BEFORE POTTING OR TRANSPLANTING

■ *Yesterday I bought a one-of-a-kind plant from the nursery that could be made into a striking bonsai. I also collected a nice plant from my backyard that I want to bonsai. What should I do first to both plants?*

The point here is that both nursery and collected plants require time and effort to train. In reality, the later refinement of both plants ought to be handled as a separate discussion. First, make any minor corrective pruning of the dead, dying, or diseased branches. You could prune off the top terminal bud to signal the roots to activate the lateral branch replacement buds. If the root collar is not evident, gently pull back the surface layer of soil to reveal it. Leave as many main surface roots as you can. Remove the surface adventitious roots, if any. Locate the main surface roots, or where the root collar starts, then transplant both plants into the ground or into a slightly larger container for a year or two. Let them stabilize and grow unhindered while you think about how you will train your new plants.

A few years of training come and go before either of those two new plants are finally ready for exhibition. It depends on the size, quality, and health of the plants you start with. Establishment comes first, then the early stages of development, then shaping, then refinement, and then final potting.

■ *What size pots do bonsai need?*

Ensure that the initial pot is large enough for the developing root system. You may or may not need to reduce the root system in later repottings. Keep small seedlings, cuttings, and liners in small pots. No top pruning is usually necessary until their roots completely colonize their pots. Then you can gradually upsize to the next pot for the next growth spurt.

During the plant's early stages, the dimensions of the container should be based on the quality and size of the root system more than on strict artistic design parameters. You'll know how big a pot to use when you try to fit the root system into it. Remember, some developing root systems will have two good growth spurts a year and prefer plenty of room. Mature bonsai can be repotted from a larger pot to a smaller show pot prior to exhibitions. After show time, allow them to grow again in slightly larger and deeper pots.

"First put the collected plant in a wooden box that lets the roots breathe better."
The texture of the substrate material, not the type of the container, determines whether roots get their air or water from available pore spaces. An old plastic nursery pot works great. Not the pot texture, the slickness, or the particular composition of any container is an important factor for optimal root growth.

■ *Is it better to dig a large plant from the ground in stages over time or should I transplant it all in one operation?*

Either way works well. Some growers first prune the crown, the roots, or both while the plant is still in the ground and then wait another growing season or so to collect it. Others say the plant is the healthiest it will ever be before you touch it, so transplant it all at once. During the past fifty years, I have personally proven many thousands of times that the latter case works well in my heat zone, even for digging up large caliper landscape trees during the heat of summer.

Tip: If you have the time and liberty, first heavily prune back large field stock. Then leave it alone for a complete growing season or so. Allow the tree to sort out the crown-to-root ratio. Its own defense system, along with a well-established root system, will readily work on dealing with the heavy pruning scars on the branches above.

■ Before repotting, what useful information can I learn from a substrate test?

- Essential elements present, toxic, or deficient.
- Electrical conductivity (soluble salts).
- Percent organic matter.
- Percent pore space/ density.
- pH.
- Water-holding capacity.
- Cation (nutrient) holding capacity

■ Can I reuse old substrate?

You can, if its disease free, pest free, clod free, dirt free, and trash free; with no crusty chemical accumulations; hasn't been watered with high mineral water; and the physical, chemical, and biological properties haven't changed. Then yes, substrate can be reused. Calcined (fired) clays can be reused over and over again. Prepare used substrate for reuse by discarding the old decaying matter, clumps, and clods because they'll break down over time. Additional coarse-textured inorganic material is usually mixed in with any good, reusable organic material. Sieving is a waste of time.

"Only buy sterilized soil or else sterilize it before repotting."
This is yet another outdated practice. Modern substrate usually starts out pathogen free, so sterilization is not an issue. Sterilized substrate is usually recommended for propagating seeds or cuttings in order to hinder the damping-off disease. Soil sterilization kills beneficial bacteria and any desirable good microorganisms. Organic fertilizer is ineffective in sterile soil. More good, beneficial microorganisms than harmful ones exist in field soil. Allow those beneficial ones to take care of the harmful pathogens.

"Sterilize an empty pot by leaving it outside for a full year."
Rinse out the old pot before using it again if you want. Leaving it outside for a year won't sterilize anything. The plant itself would more likely harbor a disease than would an old, unused pot.

"Let the plant and the substrate dry out prior to potting."
Soak the plant right before potting to ensure the roots are fully moistened and protected from any possible dehydration. The substrate itself should also be moist before and after potting. A dehydrated tree recently planted in dry substrate might decide to finally give it up.

During Potting

"Prevent root rot and ensure the pot has drainage by first putting some gravel at the bottom of the pot."
Please don't! The opposite effect occurs. A bottom "drain layer" or "air exchange level" consisting of coarser material keeps the bottom layer of roots waterlogged and vulnerable to root rot. *Substrate material*

should be of the same consistency throughout the pot for uniform aeration, drainage, and root health (#426).

■ What is the maximum amount I can trim off of a pot-bound root system during repotting?

Most robust, containerized nursery plants can survive without the bottom third to half of the root ball. Some nursery person once calculated that even a 95 percent root loss from large trees, transplanted with a mechanical tree spade, doesn't hinder their survival. During the repotting process, you can prune the excessively long, thick, and redundant roots. Thick or heavily matted roots can be shortened again during later repottings.

■ What about "raking out the roots"?

Raking out the roots is unnecessarily damaging and significantly stressful to the plant. There's no need to "pull all the roots free from one another and shake out all the soil." Shave or prune anything that doesn't quite fit into the initial training pot. Instead of trying to tease the roots out with a fork or stick, shave the edges of the exterior roots. Simply peel down the outer, thickened layer of roots on the bottom and sides with a knife, scissors, or saw. The shaving technique is much more effective than the traditional teasing-out technique. ***University studies have verified that shaving increases the finer new roots and reduces circling roots*** (#427).*

---

* E. Gilman, M. Paz, and C. Harchick, "Root Ball Shaving Improves Root Systems on Seven Tree Species in Containers," *Journal of Environmental Horticulture* 28, no. 1 (2010): 13–18.

"Always shake the old soil out, pressure wash, and clean the roots during transplanting."

This implies that roots are dirty. Roots don't ever "need to be cleaned." Washing the bare roots is not going to "rehydrate them." Any field soil clinging to the roots is not "going to weaken or kill the bonsai" or "choke or rot the roots." The roots of any plant that is already leafed out will suffer injury when the soil is pulled or washed off. Most likely, that delicate-looking white stuff you wash off is fresh, finer roots so vital to the plant—or beneficial mycorrhizae. Beneficial microorganisms in natural field soil may sometimes help smooth the transplanting process by reducing water stress.

Rotting or dead roots can be pruned prior to potting. Phytopthora-causing root rot is phytotoxic and will survive in field soil and inside roots for a long time. Even if all the Phytopthora was able to be pressure washed out with the field soil, it can't be washed out of the root tissue itself and must be cut off.

When transplanting established foliated trees from nature's field soil, we initially try to save a firm root ball with the original undisturbed soil. Gradually remove more and more of the original field soil with each consecutive repotting.

> *Tip:* You could wash out most of the heavy clay soil from the roots of a leafless dormant tree. The original clayish-type field soil is difficult to remove from a root system over time. Clay soil clumped around roots absorbs water away from substrate material.

Container-grown root systems eventually form a firm fibrous root ball. The healthiest bonsai root system is when the root ball mass stays firm, fibrous, and intact. Shaving the perimeter of the root system is the modern method for container repotting.

"Ramified branches will die back if any of the thick roots are not pruned and potted in coarse soil."
No cause and effect exists between thin twigs and thick roots. And no cause and effect exists between any type of substrate used during repotting and the thickness of roots. Pruning back thick roots and repotting can help influence future thinner, branching roots but has no effect on making thinner branches.

"Remove all the bottom roots and spread the side roots horizontally so the branches also spread horizontally rather than grow straight up."
Root arrangement does not affect branch arrangement, nor will it affect the tree's welfare. Any healthy root is going to take every opportunity to reach around and find available pore spaces. Any healthy branch is going to take every opportunity to reach up toward its energy source and fill in the spaces provided.

■ What happens if I prune the major roots and only prune the dead branches at repotting time?

The bonsai will thank you, not skip a beat, and grow on happier than ever. ***You're doing the plant a great favor any time you prune the weak, dying, diseased, or dead branches back to their base*** (#428). Otherwise, the newly pruned roots would have to send up valuable resources to wall off and isolate that weak branch at the base so it can die and fall off the way nature intended.

Scientific research tells us pruning the top after repotting does not enhance the survival or establishment of container-grown plants (#429). Supply and demand does not apply to top and bottom growth. Leave the leaves on until the roots are well on the way to occupying the pot. Leave the critical growth regulator switches in the branches that signal the new roots to waste no time in initiating new growth.

■ What happens if I do not prune the roots before transplanting to a bigger pot?

Transplanting to a slightly larger pot without root pruning would be an excellent idea if:
- the active roots still have plenty of room to colonize in the existing substrate.
- the entire root system fits into its new container.

Allowing a healthy root system to remain unpruned preserves its accumulated photosynthate reserves. The main reason we root prune when repotting is when we want finer root development. Remember, root pruning has no major effect on new branch growth. And a weak foliage system produces a weak root system.

"Always comb out and position the ends of the roots to face different positions so they will not get in one another's way."
Sometimes the exposed flexible surface roots on the root crown are repositioned for looks.

"Use chopsticks to pack in dry soil firmly around and in between all the roots."
Fact: ***Over compaction is usually due to excessive mechanical compression during repotting (#430). A compacted***

substrate is a far too common undiagnosed cause of plant stress and can negate the beneficial properties of the best mix (#431). Over mixing several different components of different sizes and densities is another factor that causes a packed substrate.

Over compaction first affects the root functions:

- Water and mineral uptake is impaired.
- Weakened or smashed roots from an overly compacted substrate are highly susceptible to pathogens.
- Roots become more swollen looking, with fewer finer roots and no mycorrhizae.
- Chlorosis is sometimes evident on the foliage.

Explanation: Packing the substrate into the pot with a blunt instrument to "eliminate air pockets" only eliminates valuable pore spaces and smashes roots. Less porosity leads to a poorly formed root system. There's no need to "stab the new soil and poke it around the roots." Ouch!

> *Tip*: Use your fingers to gently settle the substrate. Your fingers are more sensitive and closer to your hand than the ubiquitous chopstick. Modern substrate should still feel springy to the touch right after repotting.

Commercial nursery container growers take great care to not compact the substrate around the roots while repotting. Gently shaking or lightly tapping the pot on the table, or with the side of your fist, may be sufficient for us bonsai growers. **Under compaction, when potting or anytime, is better than over compaction** (#432).

"If a few air pockets are left between the roots, the plant will die from root rot or trunk rot."
Fungal root rot can become a concern after potting into a large container with a poorly aerated substrate. Modern substrates drain well. The first watering helps settle new loose substrate around the roots as it fills any voids.

AFTER POTTING

"Trees can get transplant shock."
The assaults made to the tree during transplanting or potting temporarily add to its stress. Transplanting kills much of the fine, delicate root hairs. Both new root and shoot growth seem temporarily on hold. Still, new root cells start dividing again soon after the transplanting. A few weeks later, the fresh new root tips at the apical meristem mature, die, and turn into root caps. Most transplants never skip a beat as the growing part of the root meristem continues pushing that root cap into new pore spaces.

> *Tip*: When you see new foliage or new stems appear in a few weeks, you'll know the photosynthate operation is working well. Keep the foliage and existing roots slightly moist so the evapotranspiration rate stays low. Plants do not need as much water until new roots form to take water up the plant. Allow sufficient sunlight for photosynthesis.

Collected trees may be transplanted at any time of the year from the unfrozen ground. Proper aftercare increases timely establishment after any planting procedure.

"Use a water soluble rooting compound, hormones, and vitamins to stimulate root recovery."

Don't we love quick and easy solutions to bonsai care? "Transplant aids" are usually expensive and pointless. **Plant additives during repotting are considered by university studies to be a total waste** (#433). A rooting compound applied to existing roots can inhibit root growth. Plants make all their own regulator switches and vitamins essential to root recovery. Biostimulants cannot stimulate any part of any plant.

"Always fasten bonsai to the pot."

This depends. Consider leaving it unfastened if the plant is safe and sturdy in its training pot. Then you can ease it out of the pot when you need to check what's going on inside. Most bonsai are usually top heavy when mature or when freshly planted in loose substrate. Unnecessary stress to new roots may be caused by wind or other factors shaking the tree or pot. Gently wire those plants to the pot so the more fragile roots are kept stable.

If the bonsai has multi trunks, prevent a permanent wire scar by not passing the wire between two trunks or on top of the thick surface roots. Wire over some lower roots if possible. A couple sticks placed over the thick surface roots makes a good root tie-down to the pot. Using string or insulated wire may be less scarring to the roots.

Once the roots firmly colonize a pot, tie-down wires may be unnecessary or even harmful. Remember the root system is going to grow and expand. It might lift itself up and grow into the fastening wire when pot bound. Container nurseries don't usually anchor their plants to their pots unless they are top heavy. Newly planted trees out in the landscape also grow better unstaked, according to university studies.

■ **Should I drench the top of the substrate or submerge the whole container in a tub of water right after potting?**

Either way works for that vital first watering to help settle loose substrate around the roots. Except for those real tiny pots, regular dunking isn't necessary. Regular immersing eventually breaks down clay aggregates (i.e. akadama), eventually leading to compacted, mushy substrate. Remember to leave a small depression around the pot's perimeter for a water reservoir.

■ **How long does it take for the roots of a recently potted bonsai to start taking up essential elements?**

From two weeks for small plants up to one year for some large collected plants. Once you see the top growth starting up again, you usually know you have fresh new root growth.

■ **Do roots grow faster in nighttime or daytime?**

At nighttime. It's cooler then.

"Plants in a shallow pot will dry out faster than plants in a deep pot."

For example, a one-gallon shallow pot and a one-gallon deep pot both have one gallon of the same type of substrate. Both have the same volume and are watered with one gallon of water. **The deeper pot dries out faster than the shallow pot because there is a greater effect of gravity and capillary action on the deeper pot** (#434).

"Shallow pots retain less water and nutrients than deep pots."

The qualities of the substrate, not the pot, determine if any water or water soluble salts (nutrients) will be retained inside the pot. Planting

Pots diameter make no difference in water level before drainage.

too low in a shallow pot spells trouble later from both overwatering and under watering.

"The wider the pot, the higher the water level."

For example, a two-, six- and twelve-inch pot are all two inches in height. The width of the pot is immaterial in this case. All are filled with the same type of substrate, watered, and allowed to drain. *The water level is the same before and after draining no matter how wide the pot because of the same effect of gravity and capillary action* (#435).

"Deep pots lead to root rot."

Over potting with constant overwatering is a leading cause of root rot. We tend to overwater the plants in bigger pots and under water small pots. A small bonsai, over potted, overly soaked, and under aerated, is in no condition to overcome possible fungal root rot. Bonsai appreciate the smallest-size pot possible and grow best when the roots have colonized the entire pot.

"Keep roots extra saturated with water for one month to help nurse them back after potting."

Initial soaking can help the substrate settle and allow water to reach into the whole root system. Ease off further soakings. Newly pruned roots can't take more water. If the substrate's top half inch is still moist to the touch, skip that plant's watering session.

"Misting the tree several times a day is essential for a week after transplanting."

Misting can't help a plant outside an enclosed greenhouse environment (#436). The mist will immediately evaporate outdoors. You might occasionally spray the foliage of a recent transplant at the same time you are watering the roots, especially on a hot, dusty day. Those are six examples of why we do not water every bonsai the same amount.

"Keep the bonsai in full shade for thirty days after potting for it to recuperate."

Some repotted plants will be slow to take off at first. Allow sufficient light to trap the sun's energy and keep the photosynthesis operation going. Plants need bright light in a warm (but not hot) spot to fuel cell division. In about three weeks after a new flush of foliage, the photosynthates operate at their maximum potential, and the new foliage is less susceptible to leaf scorch.

As soon as a new shoot senses sunlight, it begins to green up and produce chloroplasts (#437). By three weeks, the photosynthate operation is in full swing. Sun warms up the substrate, which is usually good for root growth. The respiration operation in every living cell takes place day and night. Higher temperatures increase the rate of energy used up by the plant. More energy is available for the newly potted bonsai when the rate of photosynthesis is greater than the rate of respiration—more light and less heat.

If the repotted plant has been growing in the shade, put it back in the same amount of shade. If it's been growing in the sun, put it back in the sun. Watch for any sign of leaf wilt. Temporarily relocate any wilting plant to a shadier spot if it's not tolerating that sunnier area.

"The legs on the pot allow air to flow underneath."

A pot's legs, if any, are a decorative feature and allow drainage. Air flow is vital in the pot, not outside the pot.

"Spray antitranspirants for foliage protection after transplanting."

Case studies have shown that antitranspirants decrease both photosynthesis and transpiration (#438). They clog the stomates, stopping evaporation from pulling up water, stopping carbon dioxide for the production of photosynthates, and stopping the ability of a leaf to cool off.

"Either defoliate or cut the leaves in half to conserve water after potting."

Don't. That stops the flow of photosynthates down the petiole to the rest of the plant. The plant needs all the extra reserves it has for establishing itself after potting.

"Placing moss on the new substrate up to the trunk encourages new surface roots, ages the bark, increases the humidity, and helps avoid dehydration."

Moss is best used for temporary cosmesis, not as "an aid for root growth and increased humidity." Rethink moss except for when you exhibit your bonsai. When scouting for moss, notice that it thrives with poor drainage, poor fertility, and poor light. Moss is an opportunist. If moss does not grow well after you place it on the bonsai substrate surface, take it off. *Being unable to grow any moss*

on your bonsai substrate could be a good indicator that you have correct aeration, correct fertility, correct moisture, and the correct amount of light for optimum growth for that bonsai (#439).

Let's look at some of the common limiting factors plants encounter.

Japanese yew as shown on front cover.

WATER, LIGHT, AND TEMPERATURE

WATER WISELY

Plants are dependent on water. Essential elements are brought next to the roots in water. They enter into the roots in water. They are carried throughout the entire plant in water. The process of photosynthesis depends on water.

Plants depend on internal water pressure for the cell walls to stretch and grow and to keep from collapsing. It requires at least five hundred kilograms of water to produce one kilogram of plant growth. Most of the water in the pot is for the purpose of cooling the plant down. ***Every chemical reaction taking place in the plant takes place in water*** (#440).

■ How does water move throughout the plant?

Through evapotranspiration. ***Approximately 99 percent of the water coming up through the roots is gone soon afterward out the leaves*** (#441). The combination of evaporation and transpiration (evapotranspiration) can siphon moisture up the tree if water is available to the roots. Xylem tissue is long, narrow pipelines of bottomless dead cells going from the roots up to the leaves.

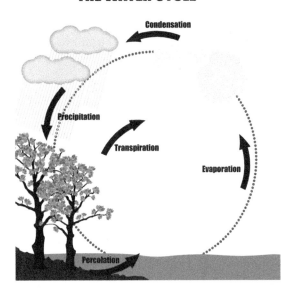

THE WATER CYCLE

Condensation

Precipitation

Transpiration

Evaporation

Percolation

Leaves must lose water before replacement water can get up to them through the xylem pathways (#442). On a long, hot, dry day, quite a bit of water is cycling throughout the atmosphere and moving in every part of a plant. Perhaps 3 percent of the water sucking up the xylem tubes stays in the plant. The rest of the water goes out the stomata. As water is lost from the substrate and roots, it absorbs heat energy when changing from a liquid to a gas. *Evapotranspiration cools the whole plant, roots and all* (#443). Increased evapotranspiration creates a larger demand for water but not for fertilizer.

■ How does water move throughout the pot?

Water channels down the inside edge of the pot and through any large pore spaces before leaching out of any unstopped drain holes. The bottom layer of water, the perched water table, becomes soggy and unable to drain more water. The water then starts to move back up the pot. Pots do not "need to be unglazed and of a breathable texture to help water movement."

■ How often and how much should I water my bonsai?

Watering protocol has no set rules. Correct watering takes a while to figure out. We soon learn to adjust both how often to water each individual plant and how much watering each plant demands. *Watering is the total of frequency times volume* (#444). Both the how often and the how much to water are balanced with many factors:

- Temperature and climate.
- Location of the plant.
- Species.
- Whether the plant has no leaves, few leaves, or has been recently defoliated.
- Relative size and age of the plant.
- Relative health of the tree.
- The last rainfall or watering and how much.
- Size of the container relative to the tree.
- Time of year.
- Evaporation due to sun and wind.
- Type of substrate material.

"Watering more frequently makes the roots elongate faster and the tree healthier."
If the substrate is waterlogged, roots can't "elongate faster." If watering is frequent but merely superficial, the unhealthy roots may not elongate at all.

■ Should I water every plant every day on schedule or as needed? Sparingly or generously? Am I supposed to "saturate the soil every time"?

Must one "always water bonsai every day and at the same time"? Of course not. Most plants have a wide feast-or-famine tolerance range. Nor should "all bonsai be watered at the same time." *Each individual bonsai requires a different amount of water and at different times* (#445).

Water only when the individual bonsai needs it. Apply both water and fertilizer on demand. The key is keeping the substrate moist but not totally wet. Skip the ones that don't need it. The word "saturate" is often misapplied to the practice of watering plants. *One cannot ever "saturate" a soil or substrate by soaking it* (#446). Multiple waterings brings the substrate to its full water capacity and completely soggy but never to the point where it can become saturated. To saturate a substrate requires plugged drainage holes and the complete submersion of the pot under water.

Tip: Segregate your bonsai by sunlight and water needs. You'll observe that plants with more sap flow, such as pines, ficus, succulents, and most tropicals, seem to prefer more sun and less moisture. In general, evergreen plants with thick, waxy, or fleshy leaves can be grouped together and watered much less often than deciduous plants with thin leaves.

You'll soon get a feel for how often and how much to water. Eventually, you'll look at the species, the surface substrate color, and the foliage condition. Then you'll spot water individual bonsai. The dense foliage canopy on some refined bonsai could act as an umbrella over the small pot and prevent rain from reaching the substrate surface. Double check those bonsai even after a good rain. They prefer one deep watering over several light waterings.

Water gently until you can see the water running out the drainage holes. Allow the water to soak into each substrate—even if you have to water one bonsai, water an adjacent plant, and then come back to fully wet the first plant's substrate again. Slow down the watering frequency in the wintertime, when the evapotranspiration slows down.

Tip: To compare the uniformity of your watering practices between different plants, place several similar-sized pots of bonsai on similar-sized saucers. Water as usual and then compare the differences in the amount of water collected out of each pot.

A good rain increases the substrate quality. A long period of rain can flush out potentially toxic chemicals accumulated from bad water.

◼ How do I tell when the substrate needs rewatering?

You can't look at the substrate to see if it's healthy. But you can look at wilting leaves and a drying surface of the substrate and know you need to water again. Water again when the bonsai needs water. You may notice the upper substrate profile seems paler in color and even seems to shrink. Lift up the whole pot to feel if it weighs less than normal.

Gently tap the (inexpensive) pot on the bench. If it sounds hollow or feels lighter, the plant needs to be rewatered. Most cheap moisture meters measure soil conductivity, not the actual water present. If you grow several different species in dissimilar substrates and in various locations, you may want to invest in a good moisture probe. After probing with a meter, double check with your finger. Another cheap monitor is allowing cheap weeds to grow in the pot. You'll find yourself looking at the weeds first to see if they're starting to wilt.

Pinch some of the substrate from the top profile with your fingers and notice if it is evenly moist. Push a pencil, chopstick, or similar probe down to the bottom corner of the pot to use as a water gauge. Probe down in the substrate with a fingertip to see if it needs rewatering. Your finger is a less-expensive probe than a moisture meter and just as accurate. Poke a pointing finger into the substrate. If your finger gets broken, your substrate is rock hard and your plant is dead!

◼ What are some symptoms of drought stress?

You may notice the newest top foliage starting to nod down and wilt. If the substrate dries out and the foliage wilts, then part of the plant temporarily slows the rate of cell division. Heat-check is the name of this condition, when the plant's defense mechanisms start to kick in.

Foliage loses the bright luster. Compare with a same species plant for a visible decline in overall color. Feel the difference with your hands. Leaf margins appear wavier, look scorched, curl under, and then turn brown. Crown dieback. Wind stress often shows up in the spring. We notice the substrate drying out faster and now allowing enough water to penetrate. Drooping leaves in the freezing winter or simmering summer may be a sun avoidance response rather than an indication of water stress.

■ Which is worse, under watering or overwatering?

Both. Under watering and overwatering can both make a plant more susceptible to disease infestations. Both practices make an existing disease worsen. Some external woes we see on a plant could be from internal woes years in the making. Another problem a long time in the making is the pot-bound plant. The dense center section of the root system may stay bone dry. Meanwhile, the outer section of the root system is wringing wet.

If you see the tips of the newer leaves starting to wilt or turn brown at the edges, that may be injury from under watering. The key is to keep the substrate barely moist and apply water before the plant wilts. Plan your watering around too much or too little rainfall. Substrates should hold enough moisture during the worst drought and yet drain enough water during the heaviest downpour.

If you smell a foul odor from the wet substrate, you may have root injury from overwatering. The wet-feet condition is more difficult to correct. Some plants, notably junipers, tolerate shade much better than they can tolerate wet feet. Smaller, finer roots can be injured or die in less than one day under overwatered conditions.

Injured root cell membranes can start to leak starches. That leakage attracts many pathogens already present in substrates containing organic matter. Pathogens will hinder the tree's ability to compartmentalize the smaller live root system from the dead roots. Chronically wet roots die. **Dead roots rot, and rot destroys plants** (#447).

■ What are some symptoms of overwatering?

Signs and symptoms of a waterlogged substrate are similar to the signs and symptoms of under watering. Leaves also wilt. Browning leaves feel soft and limp with overwatering but feel fried crispy and dry with under watering. White warty growth may be caused from leaf cells bursting secondary to the roots taking up more water than they can use. Foliage first seems to look dull or yellowish. Both the newer and older leaves start to fall off.

Growth is slow and stunted. The trunk stays darker colored around the root crown. Stems feel soft and mushy and break easily. Flowers look mushy and molded. Water may be trapped in the pot due to clogged drainage holes. Roots can't tolerate wet feet for long. They'll feel mushy and smell rotten. Harmless green algae grows on the substrate and root crown. Moss, mold, and mushrooms abound. These are all dead giveaways that the roots have more moisture than they need. Air is the most critically important element in a bonsai substrate. Your substrate is either a breathing apparatus for healthy root respiration or a prison cell for soggy roots.

■ Why do bonsai need less water during fall and winter than during summer?

One practice that drowns bonsai is "saturating bonsai every day at the same time, once a day." The correct watering practice relies on daylight and temperature changes. So what do daylight and temperature have to do with overwatering? From the second day of summer to the first day of fall, day length gradually becomes four hours shorter. If we are still "watering our bonsai everyday at the same time once a day," the plant needs considerably less water. Shorter fall days means less time for photosynthesis. And less time needed to replace the water lost to evapotranspiration from lower temperatures. No leaves left on a deciduous plant means less evapotranspiration. Decrease watering during any period of cool temperatures for more substrate oxygen and better conditions for root growth.

What's different about broadleafed evergreens during winter? They need more sun and more checking for low moisture than dormant deciduous plants because of a more active winter root growth.

Tip: Early morning temperatures can be 30° lower three months after our June summer solstice. Plants need less watering in the fall and winter. We can't afford to have root diseases emerge. Early fall is the season to remind yourself to dial down on the watering. And to remind yourself to double check those roots. Plants with a substrate that feels as hard as concrete will definitely get repotted that fall while it's still warm. Roots are still active even if the tops are slowing down. Dense roots get shaved down on both perimeter and bottom and shifted up into the next larger container. Fresh new substrate is then poured around the insides of the pot. By spring, plants in hardiness zone 7 and 8 have a strong, healthy root system.

"With reduced watering, the roots will spread out more in search of water, the leaves will be smaller, and the roots will grow stronger and healthier. The bonsai will become dwarfed and forced to produce more fruit and flowers."

That won't happen in a bonsai pot. A flowering plant requires more moisture during its flowering period.

"Mist indoor bonsai every day to increase the humidity."

Again, the effect of misting is only temporary or nonexistent. If you mist continually and the substrate surface is continually damp, how can you tell when the bonsai needs rewatering? An occasional misting can wash some dust off the leaves. Except in an enclosed greenhouse environment, misting cannot increase the relative humidity.

■ Does a "humidity tray create enough humidity" for my bonsai?

No, it can't possibly create any humidity. Some deeper saucers even create a bathtub effect by keeping the roots soggy. Clumping several bonsai closer together can possibly raise the micro-humidity.

"Do not water your bonsai midday on a hot summer day. It will scald the roots and parboil it. It will scorch the leaves and spoil the flowers."

Quite the contrary. Some of the water evaporates after watering, and evaporation reduces substrate temperatures. You can't "give a plant heatstroke or boil it" with irrigation water. "Heavy drops of water" can possibly affect the delicate flowers on annuals but won't harm the flowers on the woodies we use for bonsai. And there's no need to "water bonsai with ice cubes in the summer."

■ During summertime, should I water when it's hotter or cooler, in early morning or late evening?

It depends. During a heat wave, tiny bonsai require watering in the morning, in the evenings and maybe in between. The effects of heat and wind are less in the morning. When watering late in the evening, any fungal pathogens on the foliage are more active because they thrive in the dark and cool moisture. However, evening watering gives the plant the longest period without moisture stress.

Higher temperature ranges slow the rate of photosynthesis. High amounts of water lost from evapotranspiration for long periods have a negative effect on plant growth. The key is to keep the substrate slightly but continually moist in the summertime.

"Always use water on your bonsai at air temperature; otherwise, they won't absorb water and fertilizer and the plant might go into shock."

The roots take up water at a wide range of temperatures. Plants can't "go into shock."

"Dunking the pot is the best way to water bonsai."

Sometimes we submerge pots right after potting. Watering the substrate from above would be more efficient. Water with a watering can or with a hose. Tiny bonsai are best watered by dunking the little pot. Now we have true saturation.

"Water foliage with every watering."

You don't have to. Aim for the roots when you water. However, watering the foliage can wash off powdery mildew and a few soft-bodied insects. Bonsai appreciate the dust being washed off occasionally during a dry summer. Wet both the leaves and the root zone of azaleas because those species easily absorb water through their foliage. On the other hand, water deciduous foliage sparingly. Most diseases are encouraged and spread by water.

■ My tap water contains calcium and chlorine. Can "tap water be toxic to bonsai"? Should I "only use collected rainwater on bonsai because it provides both water and food"?

If it is good enough to drink, your water is good enough for bonsai (#448). Usually, the amount of minerals present in tap water is not enough to harm a plant. Chlorine is an essential element and required in relatively high amounts in the plant. Chlorine is needed in the first step of photosynthesis.

If you noticed a white crust forming on the top of the substrate, it could be lime deposits due to hard, alkaline water. That's harmless. If you notice crust accumulating after a "superfeeding" with liquid fertilizer, it could be fertilizer salts. If a leaf tissue test points to high chloride salts, it's from foliar fertilizer and not from your water source.

Fog water is the most beneficial water for bonsai—that is, if you could collect it. You'd find more oxygen and other good minerals in fog water than you would even in rain water. To "let tap water stand overnight to evaporate all harmful chemicals" offers no benefit. To "ban all harmful dihydrogen oxide" is futile.

"Aquarium or pond water contains the ideal plant food."

Certain ions, including sodium and phosphate, are common in some aquarium and pond water but toxic to a plant in relatively high concentrations. You know what essential elements you're getting when you see the ingredients written on a fertilizer bag.

▪ Can my bonsai survive by itself when I'm on vacation for a couple weeks this summer?

We can't answer that question for you. An automatic sprinkler irrigation drip system helps tremendously. So does a reliable friend or neighbor to check if the system is working while you're gone and to spot check if your plants need individual hose watering.

> *Tip*: One way to reduce plant moisture requirements is to place the bonsai pot inside a larger pot and add perlite to that empty space in between for insulation. The inner pot stays cooler, and available water lasts longer in summertime. An added benefit of the same pot-in-pot method is winter cold insulation.

Saucers may help temporarily, but don't leave your plants on saucers too long. Two weeks with wet feet and your bonsai may be a goner.

▪ Would drip irrigation be worth the time and water savings for only a few plants?

Not with a few plants, no. An automatic drip line irrigation system can prove valuable on larger groups of plants to apply fertilizer (fertigation), control pests, control pH, and reduce surge growth stress. *When fertilizer is randomly and infrequently applied, plants tend to grow in surges* (#449). The resulting stress from surge growth triggers pathogen activity, among other health problems. Healthy plants require less water and fertilizer and maintain a higher resistance to pathogens.

At one time, we operated a commercial ornamental and shade tree nursery with some trees under drip irrigation. Now, our personal bonsai collection is sectioned apart by light and moisture needs. Occasionally, I still use a soil moisture meter bought more than forty years ago. With this simple meter, I can spot check to verify if a container plant in our water-retentive substrate does not require watering. That probe has saved much needless watering and helps verify for me if the substrate changes density and the plant needs pulling out of the pot for further checking.

> *Tip*: Some of our younger, long-term developing plants are growing in large, shallow nursery pots. Those large plastic pots had the bottom half cut off and two slits cut on two opposite ends. A long soaker hose runs through those slits and connects the bottoms of the pots in several adjacent nursery rows on nursery fabric. Even during the worst of a recent dry, El Niño summer, those container plants on top of the soaker hose on a simple timer required irrigation only every other day.

"The only groundcover plant you should plant with bonsai is green moss. Any other plants but moss will compete with the bonsai for

fertilizer or water and will block the drainage holes."

Moss is not in competition for any available water in the substrate. Its small roots, called rhizoids, do not penetrate or disturb the substrate and compete with the roots of the tree as much as an aggressive groundcover planting. Even so, moss can do much more harm than good when it covers the substrate, pot surface, root crown, or trunk. Water can run off the surface before infiltrating and soaking in the substrate. Moss provides a perfect entrance for pathogens as it latches onto the lower trunk.

Don't expect moss to grow on modern bonsai substrate the same as it grows on field soil. Rhizoids grow on finer-textured clay particles or wet tree trunks. Moss is traditionally used as a temporary groundcover when displaying at shows. Green moss can turn brown in a hurry, but that's normal. It goes dormant when dehydrated.

■ What is a weed?

A weed is a plant in the wrong place. Weeds take up a lot of water and a lot of nitrogen. Some weeds are quite prolific. A few weeds complete a life cycle, from seed to seed, in less than one month.

"Moss growing on the side of a tree trunk causes rot."
Neither moss nor lichen will cause rot (#450). Moss can easily be brushed off the trunk in small patches. Lichens are a combination of a fungus and algae. They crust over and become difficult to scrape off, but lichens won't directly harm a tree because they don't go deep enough to cause a problem.

"Dwarf groundcover plants around bonsai help it transpire less and conserve evaporation moisture."

Since the total surface area of the plant increases with additional groundcover plants, more total evapotranspiration comes up from the foliage and substrate. Groundcover plants use moisture from the substrate for transpiration.

> *Tip*: Compatible dwarf groundcovers can look great with group plantings of bonsai. Try to keep the groundcovers away from the trunk to help prevent constantly wet bark and an easy entrance for pathogens.

LIGHTEN UP

■ How can I tell if my plant needs more light?

The tree does not seem to be growing in size while set in a shady spot. The older lower leaves seem to be dying. Any new growth has smaller leaves, longer internodes, and a lighter green leaf color. If photosynthesis is hindered by deep shade on lower, older foliage, the leaves may show blanching or yellowing.

Use a light meter. Some wavelengths of the sun's spectrum produce more energy than others. Morning sun is healthier for plants than afternoon sun because it contains more of the blue and red light spectrum.

"Bonsai do not need light in the winter and can be kept in a dark basement."
All woody plants require light all year. Any green plant can photosynthesize when exposed to sufficient light—even bare, dormant deciduous trees.

◼ Can I "keep bonsai in the refrigerator for six weeks to provide a dormancy period"?

No, they'll die.

◼ Do evergreens and leafless deciduous trees necessarily require as much photosynthesis during any resting periods?

Probably not. Low transpiration rates suggest the stomata are mostly closed on evergreens in winter. Evergreens go through prolonged high rates of evapotranspiration during winter. They can weaken in low light and dehydrate in low moisture. The chloroplast in the bark of deciduous plants also carries on some photosynthesis during the winter.

> *Tip*: Some trees can manufacture all the photosynthates they need with as little as three hours of good light a day. Some of your bonsai may need to kept in a dark building over the winter to protect them from constant low temperatures. Be sure to bring them back out into the sun for at least three hours a day when the temperatures stay above 45 degrees F so they won't starve.

◼ Is sufficient exposure to artificial light the same as exposure to sunlight?

Artificial light and sunshine are not equal. A big difference exists between intensity and duration. Excesses of both can be unhealthy. Proper lighting from artificial sources can be beneficial on tropical bonsai brought inside for the winter. Stems and foliage can detect the quantity and quality of light, any light present, and its direction, wavelength, and intensity.

Morning sunlight provides the best part of the light spectrum available for photosynthesis. *Longer duration of light also increases the opportunities for photosynthesis* (#451). The bending of light reaches those deciduous trees grown in full shade. Light lets plants know when to start their resting period.

Many plants root fairly well from air layers or cuttings, but those roots may have a difficult time surviving the next hard winter. Recently rooted cuttings stand a much better chance of making it through the winter if they don't run out of stored photosynthates. Their original reserves were allocated toward the rooting process. An increased photoperiod can help root establishment even with little or no foliage present.

> *Tip*: Take a flat of rooted cuttings or a recently potted air layer inside the garage for a couple more months after rooting and put under artificial lights. Keep the plants a few inches away from a fluorescent or LED shop light for at least ten to twelve hours per day every day to increase the critical duration of light. More energy equals more root growth.

◼ Full sun, part sun, full shade, or part shade—how much light do bonsai require?

That's a tough one to answer. Do all pines and junipers, for instance, "always require full direct sun from dawn to dusk" in your little niche? Most likely not. Conifers take a longer time to grow and replace their foliage, so intense sunlight may be even more detrimental to evergreens than to deciduous plants.

We can't follow someone's recommendation if he or she lives in a different microclimate from your own. Check with your state's horticultural university recommendation, not with someone across the globe. Three hours' duration of direct midday sun in the Deep South may equal six hours of the same sun in colder zones.

Growing instructions were likely copied down from one author to another without regard to your specific climate. Cultural information hardly ever tells you about a plant's natural habitat, ranges, or microclimates. Some plants can condition themselves to more sun or shade when other environmental factors do not limit that tolerance. Plants with variegated foliage don't live well in full sun, although some light is required to bring out the variegated color.

■ Do I have to "turn bonsai every few days"?

You don't want your bonsai to become two-dimensional like those images you get from the web, do you? Seriously, turning a different side of the tree toward the sun encourages the plant's phototropism. Light waves can bend somewhat to reach low–light intensity, shady spots. Diffused light reaches the other side of the plant.

> *Tip*: A good time to rotate the pot a half turn is right before you apply fertilizer and check for weeds. Twice yearly works well if you follow a twice-yearly CRF program.

Periodic turning a pot can:
- promote the softer, mature foliage on conifers.
- increase resistance to pests.

- help with more uniform growth.
- influence the auxin growth regulators migrating to the shaded side.

"Bonsai grow best in maximum sunlight for maximum photosynthesis."

Fact: Direct maximum sunlight creates maximum heat but not the maximum rate of photosynthesis. ***Plants will use diffused morning sunlight more efficiently than bright afternoon light*** (#452). About 25 percent of the total sunlight energy directly reaches the plant. An additional 18 percent of the total energy from the sun reaches the plant after being diffused or scattered.

Explanation: Think about why photographers prefer cloudy days to shoot their best outdoor pictures: because diffused sunlight is better light. The best and most productive light for plants is not visible to us. The total light transmitted to plants growing in full shade appears too dim for our eyes. Green plants utilize diffused sunlight to get the best wave lengths available for photosynthesis. By its unique properties, diffused light can bend around corners to reach lower leaves and produce energy even in shade plants.

> *Tip*: A light meter comes in handy to recognize where the most productive light is for our particular species of bonsai.

■ What's more harmful, moving bonsai from a shady to a sunny location or from a sunny position to a less sunny position?

A plant needs more time to adapt and acclimate to a sunny location when it's relocated from the shade. Shade leaves are usually thinner than sun leaves on the same tree. Moving a plant from the shade to a location against a sunny wall can also cause intolerable overheating.

When is shade cloth indicated?

Constantly drooping leaves on deciduous bonsai are telling you they can't take the hot sun. Some conifers may tolerate full sun. But the threshold for most deciduous plants is about 75 percent of unadulterated hot sunlight during the afternoon. Excess light generates considerable heat inside the substrate, cooking the substrate and shutting down microbial activity. Our zone 7 to 8 deciduous plants can thrive under afternoon shade netting of 30 to 50 percent in summer.

Why do my outdoor bonsai grow better than my indoor bonsai?

Some newbies see pictures of professionally grown bonsai inside an exhibit hall and assume that indoors is also a good place for growing them. Outdoor trees grow better outdoors. Even indoor tropical bonsai are not ordinary house plants. They are originally native to the outdoors and often can't tolerate inside light, temperature, humidity, and low carbon dioxide. Put your indoor bonsai outside for a season or so when you can. They grow better in more natural conditions.

Why won't my hardy bonsai live indoors?

Bonsai are outside plants (#453). Some tropicals adapt well to indoor conditions. Most plants are unable to tolerate less light and less humidity when suddenly brought indoors and can't adapt to the change. A day or two to show them off inside causes little setback to most bonsai.

THIS COLD, COLD POT

"Ease up on fall watering to coax bonsai into winter dormancy and reduce winter injury."
Trees are not like dry bulbs that stay dry until they are growing. Keep substrates moist. Less water does encourage fewer leaves, but fewer leaves equals fewer photosynthates. Hardy deciduous plants gradually ease into a semi resting period when most cell divisions temporarily slow down. Temperate plants begin preparing their own path toward a resting period the second day of summer as the days gradually become shorter.

Other local conditions such as elevation, topography, air flow, and proximity to large bodies of water influence temperature, light, moisture, and winter injury. Winter injury is typically due to freezing followed by warmer weather. It shows up later as dead buds or shoots, winter burn on evergreen, or frost cracks on the bark. *Desiccation, or drying out, is usually the result of lack of available moisture, not from freezing temperatures* (#454). The cells in the root collar and in most other roots on deciduous trees still slowly carry on cell divisions year round below frozen ground.

Water all year, but only if they need it. Reduced water increases drought stress and can kill the newer, finer roots. Roots don't go dormant. Not watering can ease them into permanent dormancy. Drought decreases a plant's natural ability to condition for dormancy and the substrate's ability to insulate the roots against freezing.

What is the temperature range for photosynthesis? How low does the temperature need to drop, and for how long, before initiating winter dormancy?

Photosynthesis stops when temperatures stay lower than 40°F for several days in a row; also when temperatures stay above 100°F for several straight days. The temperature initiating dormancy is usually around 40°F for at least forty days. The process leading to the initiation of foliage loss is not triggered by cold temperatures but by the gradual shortening of day length.

Dormancy can be shallow, deep, or both. A tree may have more than one resting period during one full growing season. Similar to animal hibernation, winter dormancy—or quiescence—is quiet cell growth.

■ Why do some plants go into dormancy?

- Because weather gets cold. Thin deciduous leaves and flowers can't survive freezing.
- To conserve energy until better weather.
- To prevent new tender growth.

To release dormancy, most trees have a certain chilling requirement. A certain amount of freezing time is required followed by a certain period of warming to end the winter resting period.

"Bonsai will die if the soil and roots are frozen."

Sap in stems and roots contain an antifreeze substance to allow photosynthate transport in below-freezing temperatures. Water bonds with cellulose (sap) and doesn't freeze the same way liquid water freezes. Wood can freeze, and the water in some substrate materials can freeze. The small amount of substrate in a small bonsai pot is not enough insulation against possible freezing moisture. Frozen substrate moisture is locked up and unavailable to the roots.

Familiarize yourself with your particular plant's cold zone requirements where you live. Both cold hardiness and heat hardiness are genetically predetermined in each species. A list of heat zone ranges for plants is also available online. Verify if your species can normally

tolerate the cold and heat of your climate and growing in the ground. Compensate a few degrees for roots in the pot. There's no reason to waste your time trying to grow trees way out of your particular zone. Concentrate on the many easy-to-grow plants available.

■ What are some average root-killing low temperatures for temperate plants?

Cryptomeria, Japanese maple, and boxwood roots can tolerate down to 15° F. For Junipers and azaleas, it can go down to 0°F. Spruce can handle temperatures down to minus 10°F. When moisture is scarce, unprotected broadleaf evergreens seem to be susceptible to prolonged freezing substrate temperatures below 20°F. Delicate tropical bonsai facing threats of temperatures much below 45°F should stay inside.

"Plant cells burst under freezing temperatures."

Fact: Living cell membranes can possible shred but cells cannot "burst."

Explanation: Cells can dehydrate from lack of water. Any freezing occurs to the moisture in those spaces outside of the living cells and in between the living cells. Ice forming outside the cells is able to draw out liquid sap from the living cells. Sap keeps the cells from freezing in the sapwood vessels. That liquid sap—for example, maple syrup—is simply dissolved sugars acting as antifreeze.

The temperature would have to fall super rapidly and become super cold almost instantly to be fast enough to freeze the sap inside a cell's membranes or plant tissues. Exposed roots or bark can crack in the winter. If you hear the sound of a small explosion in the forest in the bitter cold of winter, it could be from the dead xylem or phloem vessels popping. I've heard it!

"Cold weather kills off the bad bugs."
Bugs seem to have antifreeze in their systems. They burrow down deep for the duration and do well. Soil insects can supercool but not freeze.

◼ How do plants in a small bonsai pot respond to winter cold?

Cold is not the problem for the crown. Dehydration in the stems is the culprit. If the stem or foliage cells can't evaporate or transpire to pull up and get rid of the excess water sitting in the root cells, then any excess water around the root cells may freeze and become unavailable. Stems dry out.

Long periods of winter winds and low moisture, along with low temperatures, can cause water to evaporate quickly from evergreen foliage. This condition is usually called desiccation or winter burn and is noticeable by early spring. Any plant tissue destroyed by desiccation is dead tissue.

Even with no foliage, deciduous trees can transpire through the green bark and through the green buds in winter. The thin bark of younger bonsai often becomes injured both from reflected heat in the summer and from intense sunlight during winter when the sun is closer to the earth.

"Ice damage" doesn't occur on bonsai. Frozen thin bark can thaw out and then refreeze again. Cracks, winter sunburn, and any wounds make easy access for pathogens entering through living tissue. Cell membranes gradually start to store photosynthates and allow moisture to relocate out of the cells into the substrate during a coming cold spell. Roots subject to extremely dry conditions in the fall are weakened for the upcoming winter with reduced energy reserves. You'll notice reduced bud break and shoot expansion by spring if any roots have dried out during a freezing spell.

Tip: Bonsai still need occasional watering over the winter. Moist substrate is a better insulator than dry substrate. However, consider allowing the substrate to have a longer drying-out period after watering during constant freezing temperatures. Excess water inside root cells must be able to relocate back out into unfrozen substrate.

Don't overlook subtle signs of winter stress. A stressed tree is going to transpire less than a healthy tree. Substrate temperature in buried, mulched pots can be 20°F less than the temperature of the substrate in aboveground pots. Under consistent temperature of 40°F, tropical plants do better indoors

The lowering temperatures may be good for a hardy plant by triggering the life processes for the roots in an almost frozen substrate. Root respiration depends on oxygen in the pore spaces. When water starts to freeze in the substrate, the newly available pore spaces fill with beneficial oxygen.

Controlled-release fertilizer can be applied to deciduous plants after leaf drop, but only if needed. Those fertilized plants will not break dormancy or reduce their cold hardiness.

At least five easy options are available for overwintering hardy bonsai, depending on where you live:

- Leave them.
- Move them. That's when a garage, greenhouse, or cold frame comes in handy. Spring fruiting and flowering trees require certain chilling units of about 40°F during dormancy to release fruit or flower buds. This applies more to fruit and nut crops than to bonsai.
- Bury the pots.

- Snug them up on the ground. One successful way of overwintering temperate bonsai in hardiness zone 7 and below has been to consolidate the potted bonsai close together and then snug up bales of straw mulch in and around the outer edges of all the pots. Commercially available opaque insulating blankets can add a 20 to 30°F increase in ambient temperature when snugged around containers. The problem with those blankets is accumulated heat buildup during the day. Plastic bubble wrap will generate less heat while also functioning as a windbreak.

> *Tip:* Scrape away some of the bark with a fingernail at various places toward the top stems in order to see if they're still green or lighter in color below the bark. The upper, younger branches seem to be less winter hardy than the lower, older, thicker branches. Deal with it later on in the spring when the new foliage growth has emerged, thickened, and hardened off.

- Mulch them. Cover the pots but not the stems or foliage.

■ What can I do to a help a bonsai recover from winter injury?

Wait and see. Resting vegetative buds may still be quite alive and biding their time even if leaves are dead and branches look dead.

Prune back to the live wood in spring in order to preserve the plant's stored resources. Avoid fertilization and any further stress. Another choice is to transplant a winter-injured plant back in the field or into a larger nursery container if the plant has considerable dieback. Leave it alone for a growing season or so to recover. Only minimal moisture is necessary.

"All bonsai should be located against a solid fence background to protect them from the cold wind."

This depends. Pathogens prefer calm air, and bonsai respond well to touch. A little breeze can be good to bring in carbon dioxide for photosynthesis. A light-colored, south-facing fence could possibly reflect excessive heat back on the bonsai during the heat of summer. Besides heat, the bright light of the closer sun in winter also dries out twig and bud tissues.

■ Why do trees sunscald in winter?

Bark and leaf injury from sun and fluctuating temperatures can occur at any time of the year on young trees and certain species. Heavy pruning during summer can suddenly open up the top canopy for the sun to injure the thinner bark or leaves. Reflective surfaces contribute to the problem. Moving bonsai from shade to sun can also contribute to bark and leaf injury. Rapid temperature fluctuations injure active tissues because the plant needs several hours or even days to respond.

Someone has found winter temperatures on the sunny side of some trees to be as much as 77°F higher than the opposite, shady side. Injury on thin bark will eventually callus over. The only evidence on the trunk will be a slightly ribbed bulge.

Extreme Heat

■ What can I do to help bonsai endure a prolonged heat spell?

Temperature can be good or bad. Increased temperatures plus increased light plus increased moisture equals disaster for some deciduous bonsai. Scientific studies have indicated that root zone temperatures over 100°F in a substrate can kill tiny new roots. In some cases, the bonsai pot would be better off in a shadier place in the ground or mulched instead of sitting on an exposed bench. Gravelly substrates inside clay pots will usually measure higher temperatures than organic substrates inside plastic nursery pots.

Substrate temperatures of 130°F have been reduced down by 25°F when the pot was buried in mulch or in the ground. Buried pots have considerably less watering requirements. Those buried pots also measure a much faster rate of growth than you would measure in the same species in exposed pots.

Other techniques that work during summer's extreme heat:

- The pot-in-pot method. A slightly larger container is permanently placed in the ground, and then the bonsai pot is temporarily placed within the larger pot.
- Water deeply and more frequently. Evapotranspiration is the combination of total moisture lost from both the surface of the substrate and from the stomata under the leaf. The evapotranspiration effect itself cools the plant as the water absorbs heat while changing from a liquid to a gas.
- Water the foliage at the same time you water the roots.
- Provide shade protection. Taller plants can shade smaller plants. Reposition under a shade tree. Cover with shade cloth. Light color works better than dark color. Good shade cloth material does double duty with shiny foil on top to reflect the heat.
- Keep away from enclosed solid walls and a solid overhead to allow fresh air flow for cooling off and for carbon dioxide.
- Provide heat sinks. Heat sinks can be bricks placed in empty pots to draw heat away from adjacent potted bonsai.
- Transplant into a slightly larger pot of lighter color for more insulation and less heat absorption.
- Place pots on trays and bunch them closer together temporarily.
- Mulch around and over the pots. Over the years, I've observed the effect of mulching and seen various studies. More recently, I have heard lectures regarding the pros and cons. No significant difference has been scientifically proven in surface evaporation either with added mulch or without.
- Hope for the next cloudy day.

■ How can I assist my bonsai to cope with global warming?

Move them to a cooler spot!

What are some other horticultural challenges to growing bonsai?

Japanese maple as shown on back cover.

BONSAI CHALLENGES

Bonsai is 50% art, 50% horticulture, and 50% philosophy.
—*Julian R Adams, "Tips and Techniques—Persistence and Remembering,"* Journal of the American Bonsai Society *49, no. 4 (2015).*

Aftercare is where we spend most of our bonsai time. Trying to make them perfect. Caring for our bonsai does take a lot of time but should not take a lot of unnecessary money. Collector plants do demand constant monitoring, a little attention, and a lot of patience. A huge difference exists between having a lot of bonsai and having a lot of good, high-quality bonsai. High-quality bonsai is both attractive and healthy.

The challenge is to find out which plants are easy to grow in your particular niche. Which species appeal to you and work well in your area? Consider your elevation; the amount of sun, rain, and wind; and other limiting factors. Soon you find you're paying more attention to season changes, weather patterns, and nature's way of responding to surroundings. Focus more on why the tree is healthy in the first place than on any products you might use to "cure sickness." Bonsai are just plants, not something special with animal characteristics.

Somewhat like pets, our plants are so obedient and forgiving. Unlike pets, plants never complain, even when we get addicted to them and spend too much effort on them. Too often, we find it necessary to back off from our own human reactions to bonsai care. Instead, we could try to understand how bonsai react to our care for them. Plants can tell us what our eyes can't tell. Eventually, we learn to follow all the horticultural clues, both visual and unseen, that they give us.

Challenges come during every stage of the growing season for every tree. Scientists classify five phases during one growing season:
1. A calm beginning.
2. Foliage development and manufacturing photosynthates.
3. Growing up, then out, then thicker.
4. Storing photosynthates to jumpstart next growth cycle.
5. A calm resting.

CONTENT WITH OUR NATURAL BEAUTY

We bonsai to show off nature's special beauty. Don't expect instant beauty at the expense of optimal health of our bonsai. Appreciation of bonsai doesn't depend purely on ending up with a perfect, aesthetically pleasing plant. Everyone can notice and appreciate a healthy, well-cared-for plant.

Allow time for bonsai to self adjust each time you transplant, relocate it to a different site, apply fertilizer, prune, or wire. It would be easier on us if a plant began the growing season with exceptional vitality in the spring and kept on growing robustly until fall. But it doesn't.

Growth curves are different for different species (#455). Some plants have growth curves peaking in the summer, and other trees go through a couple small growth curves. Good horticulture is recognizing and supplying the plant with what it lacks at every stage of the growth cycle—and knowing when to back off. Focus on the roots one year and the branches the next growing season. Give it time. Take time to appreciate the natural beauty and good health.

Know your bonsai. The key is to become familiar with the natural tolerances and limitations of each species you cultivate. Some species tolerate a wide range of limitations, and some plants have a limited rate of growth. Optimal culture practices applying to me may be detrimental to the way you treat that same species in your own particular microclimate or in their habitat. The quality of air, water, and light varies considerably throughout the world. Not all air is equal. Not all water is equal. Not all light is equal. Learn when and how much you can push their limits.

WHY WE ARE SO SMALL

What makes a bonsai dwarf? Is there a genetic difference between dwarf and normal plants? Is there a genetic difference between large and small leaves on the same cultivar? Basically, there's no difference. Cell size doesn't usually change, but fewer total cells exist in a compact plant than in a normal plant. Bonsai can have even bigger leaf cells than leaves of normal trees similar to what was observed in dwarf plants from high altitudes.[*]

Short growing seasons also seem to contribute to a stunted tree. We can't alter the climate, but we can modify a harsh environment. Practically everything in a harsh environment triggers the plant's growth responses to activate one way or another.

Researchers have discovered no evidence of genetic differences between dwarf and normal plants (#456). The same species in a swamp or at high altitudes can be short and shrubby but in the nearby forests grow tall and straight. Every individual tree is amazingly genetically wired with a tremendous ability to survive and to condition itself to wherever it ends up since it can't relocate on its own.

The outer cell layer of every leaf, called the epidermal layer, controls what size the leaf is going to be (#457). That outermost cell layer senses and responds to the immediate environment and then produces either more cells or fewer cells. It then signals the adjacent inner layers of cells to produce either more or less cell divisions. Plants are only stimulated to grow when their own growth switches send them the signal to grow. Leaf size adaptations can be either short term or long term.

---

[*]arnoldia.arboretum.harvard.edu/pdf/articles/1993-53-1-why-are-bonsai-leaves-small.pdf.

Try not to confuse the horticultural practice of stunting bonsai by manipulating growth switches with the horticultural practice of dwarfing trees by manipulating genetics. To bonsai is to grow ordinary compact trees from normal plants or from normal seeds, not from "dwarf plants" or "bonsai seeds."

■ Will a "bonsai seed" grow into bonsai?

A seed only grows into a plant. We may find it appropriate to eventually shape and manipulate that plant into a miniaturized plant. Seed will never "grow into a bonsai." It would be completely wrong to term any seed a "bonsai seed."

■ Will a bonsai stop growing when it grows up?

Maybe, if it ever becomes permanently dormant. *Even through dormancy and throughout maturity, some cells continue to grow and divide every day* (#458). New tree skin grows over a tree every growing season. A young tree normally grows upward and outward to reach available light. At maturity, the tree canopy still spreads out to some extent. Foliage and roots of mature, established trees gradually undergo fewer cell divisions. The transpiration/photosynthetic rate gradually slows down.

Cell size depends mostly on its water content (#459). The mature tree eventually produces fewer cells. Senescence is when all the cells quit dividing. This happens to the best sometimes.

"Normal-sized trees live longer than bonsai trees."

Every life is subject to the laws of nature. Some domesticated miniature trees have been recorded as being over one thousand years old. Some bristlecone pines out in the ravages of nature are over five thousand years old. Impressive! *Even a five-thousand-year-old tree has foliage and roots less than one year old and cell divisions only one day old* (#460).

■ What environmental conditions keep growth stunted on a tree?

- Strong ultraviolet light waves from the sun—for example, at higher elevations—inactivate those switches normally causing stem elongation. Sunlight helps compact growth.
- Alternating periods of hot and cold.
- Heavy exposure to whipping winds also results in stockier branches, smaller leaves, and shorter internodes.
- Periods of drought followed by constant dampness.
- Pathogens.
- Ice crystals, sandstorms, termites.
- Altitude, topography, relative humidity, air drainage, frost pockets, shelter, and pollution also influence the local climate.
- Heavy animal grazing, a heavy snow load, and bush hogging can keep the branches pruned—similar to our pruning and wiring.
- Sandy, gravelly soil inhibits aggressive root growth.
- *Obstructions and a compact area for the roots to grow keep the roots compact (*#461).
- Plant litter and animal droppings provide only limited essential elements to the stunted tree.

Keeping a plant inside your home stunts the plant, but not in a healthy way. It is stunted not only from lack of enough light but also from lack of fresh breezes and reduced exposure to enough fresh carbon dioxide for photosynthesis. The roots may have too much carbon dioxide due to too much water. Plants can't endure inside conditions for long.

Some factors are in our control to keep a plant compact. Genetics are not so easy. A treatment with growth-retarding hormones wears off in a short time. Too much loving care may lead to the declining health of a plant.

"Applying growth regulators help keep bonsai compact."

Growth regulators inhibit the natural allocation of regulators and carbohydrates in a plant. In the past, container-growing nurseries have occasionally tried growth regulator treatments to decrease shoot elongation and reduce the labor costs of pruning.

Such treatments are effective on some plants with a strongly upright growing habit by preventing the main leader from elongating. Those inhibiting compounds tend to induce more aggressive sprout growth with longer internodes. Growth regulator products have inconsistent results and also may produce phytotoxic effects on a tree. At this time, chemical growth regulator products cannot be recommended for use in bonsai culture.

"Bonsai enthusiasts torture their trees."

If our bonsai get "cruel treatment," think about the poor lawn getting tortured every time we mow. Or fruit trees or roses being "punished" while they get pruned to "twist their arms to make them bear more fruit or flowers." Ouch!

It would be quite difficult to bonsai without pruning, potting, wiring, and bending. In their small pots, our domesticated compact trees seem to look better and live longer than their wild cousins. We treat them better. They get pampered, not tortured—usually too much pampering. *The fact that our bonsai survive attests more to the tree's genetic vigor and less to our bonsai talents* (#462).

■ Why do some people list the approximate age of their bonsai? Is age related to value in bonsai?

It would be difficult to know the exact age of older bonsai. Some older-looking bonsai are probably younger than they appear. Every time you notice an age listed for a particular bonsai, keep in mind that the plant more than likely might be overvalued and overestimated. Did someone physically plant the seed and keep records?

What if someone didn't start it from seed? The most honest answer to how old it is would be age indeterminate. Cut the main trunk in half or pull a plug out of the center. Count those rings to get a more accurate age.

HOW WE ADAPT

■ How does a plant respond to constantly changing conditions?

Plants respond to their environment with complex sensory and regulatory switch systems (#463). Plants have no brains and no nerves, so they can't ever feel pain. They're stuck and can't move to a better environment. They are excellent adaptors by conditioning themselves with survival strategies according to their circumstances. In hostile conditions, they'll grow within their means and exploit whatever they find to work with. Nature's way is defending itself when vulnerable and overcoming stress when injured.

Two principles of life exist in any tree: defense (health) and reserves (stored energy) (#464). Their defense is biochemistry. Their reserves are biochemistry. They will adapt to environmental insults by modifying their survival strategies. Trees generate their own defense system to isolate living parts against wounds or wound infections. They can form a boundary and adjust future growth when injured, infected, or threatened. With a weak, injured natural defense system, trees die young.

Individual trees can't "heal themselves." Intact forests can heal. Forests are one healthy interlocking system in a complex ecosystem. Plants make their own defense regulators and depend on their own high amount of readily available energy reserves. ***Our bonsai are fueled by their own brand of glucose*** (#465).

If the foliage of some plants is attacked by bacteria or bugs, the plant reacts by producing jasmonic acid, a signaling mechanism for a variety of conditions that includes plant defense. Their epidermis (skin) is their first line of defense. Once invaded by a pathogen, the plant stimulates a chemical attack to kill or prevent that pathogen from further injury. They can respond to touch by limiting or changing branch development.

Trees act as big solar cell batteries by trapping and storing the sun's energy until it's needed. ***Plants can increase their top growth to reach light in response to low light intensity*** (#466). A tree can even signal its lower, overly shaded but weaker branches to stop growing and drop off. They can increase or decrease their storage of photosynthates. ***A plant under moisture stress will stop photosynthesizing, which stops their energy supply and slows their overall growth*** (#467).

Plants can generate new cells in new places, generate more or fewer cells if needed, or incorporate dead cells into functional structures where needed. They cannot regenerate, replace, or rebuild injured cells or tissues. ***Trees use all available resources, including their own tree parts, when regulating their growth*** (#468). Plants run their own lives quite well with only a handful of plant growth regulator switches, which they produce on their own. Auxins, gibberellins, cytokinins, and ethylene work together to switch the plant's own growth on or off.

Trees cooperate with their many associates around them, both living and dead. They'll grow new tree parts in a new space and position if an old tree part departs. ***When exposed to sudden changes, plants condition themselves rather slowly*** (#469).

■ Why do some of my bonsai struggle so much to survive?

That's another tough question. Most likely, their stresses are related to all the limiting factors for survival in their particular niche. Different ranges and tolerances are built in to different species. Some will grow well in your area, and some will only languish. Concentrate more on the wide variety of easily available plants you know thrive where you are. Notice if that new deciduous species you're cultivating matches the local climate.

As always, plant growers have choices. Either select easy-to-grow plants for your microclimate or change your microclimate to fit your plant.

Do the buds break and the foliage turn color about the same time as the same native

Tip: Native plants don't necessarily survive any better then exotic imports or noxious weed trees from afar. Some plants do grow more robustly in your area when they have to make fewer adjustments for your environment . If it makes a good bonsai and if it's easy for you to grow, don't hesitate to try an exotic plant. Use plants that won't be too fussy about their substrate.

species? If the new buds on your plant are still tight while the buds have flushed out on similar varieties in your area, maybe your bonsai tolerates a colder climate or requires more 40°F chilling hours to break dormancy.

Many species tolerate more extreme ranges and conditions (#470). The bonsai struggles to survive when it reaches the extreme end of its tolerance range. All organisms eventually senesce (finish cell divisions). Some plants are tastier than others. Living things are eaten by other living things. And expect nature to occasionally play tricks on some of your bonsai.

■ Does a plant create and allocate energy?

Yes.

■ Can we manipulate the plant's energy?

Yes.

■ Can we give them energy or electrons?

No.

■ Do plants or plant parts share their energy (electrons)?

No.

■ Can we move the energy (electrons) around from one part of the plant to another?

No. *Through photosynthesis and respiration, green plants provide all the energy (electrons) for their own establishment, growth, defense, and reserves* (#471). Those electrons vibrate or hop around from one molecule to another within all plant cells. Electrons can't hop from one stem to another or from one leaf to another.

Through photosynthesis/respiration, the plant produces simple sugars (chemicals) delivered by fancy sugars (molecular compounds) as energy for its own use. Energy can be stored as starches (a fancy sugar biomolecule) for later use as simple electrons.

Only the tree itself can release energy (electrons) when its chemical bonds of carbon components break up. *This occurs through its own cellular respiration (the opposite reaction of photosynthesis)* (#472).

In its simplest form, photosynthesis gets sugar energy from light energy. That sugar (photosynthate) can be stored or transported along its pathways as long sugar molecules. Cell respiration gets energy from burning sugar when breaking down those bonds of molecules and releasing electrons. Trees live on their own electrons. *All the tree's energy is in the form of electrons, not food* (#473).

A tree loses electrons as it responds to external changes (#474). For example, when we prune a branch, the tree loses a few electrons. The response from the parent branch is to wall off that lost part and protect itself before it loses more electrons.

Three parts of the plant responding to electrons are the growing root tip meristems, the growing foliage tip meristems, and the growing cambium meristem (#475). *If one response component needs more electrons to respond to injury, the other two response components don't share their own electrons with that one injured component* (#476). If one thin lower branch is weak with few electrons, no other healthier tree part will give any electrons to that stem. No energy is ever shared or moved around in a plant. If you think about it, that's why properly pruning a branch, or even decapitating half of a stout sumo trunk, doesn't normally injure the whole tree.

The total amount of electrons can be allocated throughout a plant (#477). Root and stem growth regulator switches can send a signal to either the roots or the stems to allocate the production of future growth when part of a plant or the entire plant is under stressful injury or change. *Thick, healthy upper branches; healthy buds and foliage; healthy roots; and a healthy intact cambium always hold on to all of their own electrons* (#478).

Energy for root metabolism also starts with the sun. Electrons are created when the first flash of sun hits the leaves. Different parts of a plant can now use that energy after being converted to sugars by cellular respiration. *We can't add any amendment to the roots to feed them, to stimulate their growth, or to give them electrons* (#479). *Left alone, the weak stems, buds, and roots get weaker as they lose electrons, and the strong get stronger as they accumulate electrons* (#480).

We can repress or weaken a plant's vitality but not its vigor. Vigor stays the same because it's genetic. A tree's genetic code comes from way back in the good old days when its predecessors lived together in a forest. In the forest system, trees provide energy not only for themselves but also for neighboring organisms.

Vitality is the tree's ability to grow and adjust to where it ends up growing. We can't give plants anything to increase or revitalize energy. We can, however, improve on some of our horticultural practices that might allow the tree to stay strong and healthy.

LOOKING GOOD

■ What is a healthy plant?

The word "healthy" can be a controversial term. We can't correctly attribute any human characteristic to plants. For example, plants don't "have an immune system." Animals respond to electrical signals, while plants respond to chemical signals.

We can discuss plant health in terms of vigor, vitality, ability to adapt and survive, persistence and ability to flourish, rate of metabolic efficiency, tolerance to damage, resiliency in defending itself, lasting resources, and strength and resistance to environmental stresses. The word "healthy" is simple enough for us to use here.

The words "healthy" and "unhealthy," as they apply to both plants and animals, could relate to the ability to resist strain.

Strain is that point beyond stress. Stress is that point near the upper limits of where a plant is consuming valuable resources but barely surviving.

The same factors that help grow a healthy plant can stress the same plant. We can control the too much or too little water, light, temperature, and fertilizer supplements.

Plants survive when the plant cells in the stems and roots continue dividing. *Plants can be full of virus and bacterial infections and yet be completely healthy at the same time* (#481).

Researchers in Panama have identified more than four hundred different kinds of bacteria in one isolated, healthy tree. Another tree researcher, Dr. Shigo, has estimated that a healthy mature tree may have more than one thousand infections at one time and still be full of vitality.

The plant is able to endure those troublesome infections and still look completely healthy. A bonsai can endure the extreme stresses from pruning, bending, wiring, repotting, temperature fluctuations, fertilizing, watering, injury by insects and diseases, and numerous extreme mechanical assaults and yet continue growing vigorously. Remember, vigor is genetic.

■ Can you actually feel the difference between unhealthy and healthy foliage?

We can't always tell how healthy a tree is by looking at it. But we start to get a sense for it as we continue in this hobby. Interestingly, healthy foliage actually feels cooler and seems softer to the touch. Feel the difference when you grasp a clump of healthy leaves in your hand.

■ If I buy a plant sight unseen online or even in a bonsai nursery, how do I know the plant is healthy?

You don't. Many growers commonly overwater and over fertilize their plants to get them salable sooner. Those plants are destined to a short life. Unfortunately, some individuals do not understand insect or disease pathology. Well-meaning enthusiasts commonly exacerbate diseases by overwatering, over fertilizing, or over treating a disease. A worse disease can result, or one disease can be traded for another.

Before you receive the tree you purchased online, you probably won't be able to see the injured leaves picked off or the unseen injured roots recently tied down to the bonsai pot. Most state governments have plant nursery inspection requirements, pesticide applicator certification, and pesticide storage requirements. Restrictions don't usually apply for individuals raising bonsai as a hobby for themselves, not using restricted pesticides, or not selling their own bonsai from their own private collection to someone else in another state.

■ Why do my trees planted out in the field grow better and faster than the same type of trees kept in a pot?

One cause of the more robust plant growth out in field soil is that plant roots have access to readily available water and essential elements. Most of the genetic code in plants has been prewired for growing in a forest niche, not in a pot. The roots can grow unrestricted.

Field soil temperature fluctuates less, meaning garden field soil temperature is lower in the summer and higher in the winter than uninsulated substrate temperatures in a pot. *Potted plants sometimes cannot endure repeated cold injury caused by freezing and rapidly fluctuating temperatures*

(#482). One of the most limiting factors to bonsai is when they are placed at the extreme end range of low and high temperatures.

During a cold winter, the dormant potted bonsai usually copes with less available water. The water is frozen, but roots can't use ice. Higher substrate temperatures, along with higher evapotranspiration rates, will slow the growth of any potted plant during sweltering summer days.

Established field-planted trees eventually do not need any fertilizer applications after one complete growing season. ***Plants are much better able to prevent and fight off pathogens while growing in the ground*** (#483). Plants in the ground eventually become more self-sufficient. Their maintenance needs become fewer, and they are able to grow much faster and more robustly while in the ground than in the confinements of a pot. Plants are happier and more carefree in the ground.

Small bonsai never grow up to become large bonsai if forced to live under the many limitations of a small pot (#484). Especially on older, refined bonsai, the trunk seems to stay about the same thickness. Tissues have become so toughened to the point where the trunk can't expand and thicken up. Years of restrictions and trying to live in the same small pot can slowly sap the health from an old bonsai.

"You know a plant is healthy by looking at it. Pump it up with superfeeding and see the healthy, new, luscious green growth." Yes, it looks healthy—temporarily. But too soon after that, the poor plant declines and is unhealthily stressed by all sorts of insect and disease problems.

"To keep bonsai healthy and make them more resistant to disease, treat with a lot of water and fertilizer and keep in full sun to kill any pathogens."

Fact: ***We can't use water and fertilizer as a pesticide, a preventative treatment, or to keep a plant healthy looking*** (#485). Too much or too little of both have killed too many plants.

Explanation: Waterlogged trees emit ethanol. Then they smell vulnerable and sick, according to the hungry bugs. How wet is too wet? Maintain drier substrate moisture levels below 50 percent to inhibit ethanol production in the spring, when bugs are most attracted to host plants.

Adding fertilizer to a plant with infected roots benefits the pathogen, not the plant. Throwing on a "lot of water and fertilizer" is only a shotgun approach and may give only a shotgun effect. If a substrate test simply shows a lack of nitrogen, why waste money or risk toxicity on the phosphorus and potassium?

Leaving bonsai out in full sun can't kill pathogens because most pathogens require a minimum of 140°F for thirty minutes of exposure to die. Viruses aren't affected until they are in an extended exposure to over 200°F.

Fact: ***Conditions favorable to plant growth are the same conditions favorable to plant diseases*** (#486).

Tip: Once you recognize what plants are supposed to look like in their natural condition—for example, their natural leaf color and size—then you can more easily identify what is abnormal. Determine which local tree problems are prevalent in your area. Notice how much growth was produced every year on plant species. Compare growth among matching trees of the same plant species. You learn quite a bit about your tree when spending quality time with it.

Explanation: Disease opens the door for bugs with legs. Bugs open the door for more diseases without legs. Another common pathogen with legs is aptly called "human blight."

■ What contributes to the declining health of a bonsai?

We don't always know for sure. Poor environmental conditions, poor soil conditions, opportunistic pests, and pathogens (and people) are all related to plant stress and decline.

Before humanity came on the scene, not one pathogen existed. All organisms were good guys doing their job. We interfered by cultivating a few plants, declaring war on everything else, and decided to start eliminating some of those good guys.

Bonsai won't lie (#487). Learn why your trees decline and die. Take a dead one out of the pot and dissect the roots. See if the problem came from the top down or from something in the substrate or the roots. See if your state's University Horticulture Department can help you diagnose your plant's death. Some labs need only an image and description sent over the Internet. Jim Doyle's observation is that learning how, about, and why a plant died leads to knowledge of keeping the next similar species of plant alive—through death there is knowledge.

PESTERING PATHOGENS

■ What is a plant disease? How can I control a disease once my bonsai is injured?

When a plant is not functioning right, it may have a disease. When an abnormal process is going on that could injure or kill it, the plant is diseased. The definition depends on your perspective.

Pathogens cause diseases. We usually picture a pathogen as an organism such as bacteria, fungus, virus, nematode, or some other predator lurking on the perimeter of your property, waiting for you to water or fertilize your bonsai too much. It's not an ideal world out there.

Sometimes pathogens may not be an organism but something such as nutrient deficiencies or toxicities causing a particular plant to not function right. ***Pathogens may also be air pollution, poor-quality substrate, lack of oxygen, or any improper growing practice*** (#488).

We seem to recognize a pathogen attack but not the factor predisposing the potential for the attack. More often, a plant does not function right when the pathogen is from being either too hot or too cold or from having too much or not enough water, humidity, light, or essential elements. ***Disease is not caused by one single organism or agent*** (#489).

Plant disease occurs when the combination of all three factors are present:
1. A pathogen.
2. The right environmental conditions for the pathogen.
3. Favorable conditions in the plant for that pathogen.

A relatively weak pathogen on a weak plant with the right conditions can spread substantial disease. ***Usually, it's the moisture, light, fertilizer, and temperature dynamics upsetting a plant*** (#490). The good news is we can control all four of those limiting factors.

The five main methods for controlling a plant disease include:
1. Exclusion. Remove the diseased plant.
2. Eradication. Prune the infected part or kill the infection with chemicals.
3. Protection. Spray with a systemic chemical to help prevent future infection.

4. Don't put the tree at risk.
5. Use trees relatively free of diseases.

■ List a few trees relatively free of troublesome diseases.

Some trees may be resistant to common diseases and decay. Others lose resistance under relentless stress factors. Arborvitae, bald cypress, beech, black gum, burning bush, cedar, chaste tree, Chinese elm, Cryptomeria, Eleagnus, ginkgo, hackberry, hemlock, hop hornbeam, hornbeam, Katsura, Lantana, larch, trident maples, persimmon, privet, quince, silver bell, Sophora, star magnolia, Stewartia, sweet gum, witch hazel, yellowwood, yew, Zelkova, and many, many more.

Try a tough plant and not necessarily one listed here. Tough ones are well worth buying. Focus on those less-demanding plants at first. Some plants will grow on you.

Choose those genetically superior species or cultivars best for your area. Know your plants. Is it a slow, medium, or fast grower? Know its tolerances, limits, and possible symptoms of drought and neglect. Let it perform at its best.

"Bonsai have more pests than their wild counterparts."

If so, one can easily control those pests. Bonsai are so small and slow growing, it may not take long for a pathogen to cause considerable injury. Bonsai can't usually outgrow the pathogen as well as its bigger relatives can out in nature. Smaller plants do have less surface area for insects and diseases to bother with. *Pests would rather work on the weaker plant no matter what size* (#491).

Insects and disease microorganisms seem to detect the susceptible, defenseless new growth on plants. Some plants possess little disease resistance. All of the plant's resistance mechanisms can in some way be broken down.

In nature, the tree responds to pests by several defense mechanisms. One response is for the tree to produce more or smaller foliage. *Almost all plants grow more roots, branches, and foliage then they would need for survival* (#492). On some healthy deciduous trees, as much as half of their leaves can be sacrificed to pests (or to defoliation) before the tree starts to decline in health. Moderate insect damage is tolerable.

Our bonsai keep under our constant vigilance because we are accustomed to watering them often. As our observation skills improve, we are more aware of what's normal for our bonsai, and we can catch any unusual problem early.

No such thing exists as 100 percent control of pathogens; nature never deals in absolutes (#493). In theory, pathogens won't bother a healthy plant. In actual practice, they will. Sometimes if you ignore pests, they might eventually go away with minimal injury to a plant.

■ Which is worse for the plant, diseases or insects?

Disease spreads quickly, so that may become a plant's worst enemy. Bacteria and fungi are microorganisms infecting living plants. Insects, mites, and nematodes infest.

> *Tip*: Disease and insect clinics are sometimes available at state universities to help identify disease and insect pests on your bonsai. Guess which disease or insect pathogen the North Carolina Plant Disease Clinic most often diagnoses as the cause of plant death in all the dead plant samples it gets? Excess fertilizer toxicity—one of the many human pathogens.

Momentary, acute damage to a plant, such as deer feeding on plants, is injury. Not all infections, infestations, injuries, damages, and wounds are unhealthy.

GOOD AND BAD

■ What are the different classes of plant diseases?

Fungi, bacteria, and viruses infect plants. Fungal spores come around with too wet, too hot, or too cold conditions or poor air circulation. They can proliferate in the stagnant air between crowded plants. Applying fungicides rarely completely kills off all fungal diseases. Spraying with fungicides might affect fungi but probably won't affect the other two diseases.

Are all fungi bad? Of course not—consider bread, wine, and cheese. *Most fungi are beneficial to the plant* (#494).

Bacteria are much harder to control than fungi. A virus is the most difficult pest to control because it has the ability to mutate. But viruses rarely kill a tree. They may detract from the aesthetics and possibly add some stress, but you can cut off any infected part if you want. *No generic solution exists to control all plant diseases* (#495).

■ What do I do if the leaves look like they're starting to get some kind of spots or blemishes.

First, get rid of infected leaves. Once you have spots or blemishes on the leaves, you can't spray with anything to make those spots disappear.

"Cankers and lesions forming on the branches will stop the water from going up the plant to the foliage."
Canker disease is a common symptom of an infected open wound. That disease blocks the transport of photosynthates but can't block water movement in a plant. Those infected sunken parts on a stem can be gouged out.

■ Should I be concerned about slime, mold, fungi, mushrooms, fairy rings, moss, or lichens? Are those plants or plant diseases?

They're all organisms, but not all are plants. Not one of those common organisms will automatically cause a bonsai to malfunction. Have you ever noticed any rocks harmed by lichens? In fact, the presence of lichens indicates clean air. If you buy a bag of lichens for mulch on substrate, you don't have pure lichens. Lichens are both algae and fungi.

"Any bug or bacteria living on bonsai or in the soil can be potentially harmful."
There are more beneficial insects and bacteria than harmful that live on, in, or around a tree. Some attack those dead parts of a plant that don't have a defense system. In the process, those good organisms break down dead tree organisms. Also in that breaking-down process, essential elements are released or recycled.

A lot of living things also move around in natural field soil. Because something moves around doesn't mean it's dangerous. Some examples of the good guys are beneficial mycorrhizae, nitrogen-fixating nodules, and fungi growing at the base of a branch stub.

■ I'm starting to notice some swollen places on the roots. Would that be nematodes? Am I supposed to "submerge the remaining roots in a nematicide solution for about ten minutes and repot"?

Those swollen places could be good mycorrhizae, or it could be good nitrogen fixators. And then it could be good nematodes or bad nematodes. You can't tell the difference between good and bad nematodes just by looking. Nematicides kill both the good and bad nematodes.

■ Which witches broom make good bonsai?

Witches broom are abnormal stem galls with smaller leaves from the tree's reaction to damage from pathogens or chemicals. Sometimes witches brooms can be propagated as dwarf-looking trees. Sometimes bonsai recall their genetics and revert back to normal.

CRAWLING CRITTERS

■ What should I do about insects on my bonsai?

We tend to notice insects before we notice other pests because they move around so much. Sometimes we panic at the sight of an insect that can't cause much harm to our plants. Their worst insult is if they transmit plant diseases, not if they chew or suck on a few leaves. Occasionally, we're lucky enough to find a good insect feeding on a few bad bugs.

Instead of the spray-and-pray method, try this: First use the don't-do-anything method on them for a while. If the creepy crawlies are big enough, use the two-finger-squish or else the two-block-pop method. Next, you could try blasting them off with water, or try a water and dish soap (not detergent) combo spray.

If they still bug you after they've eaten through more than a third of the available foliage, then try insecticidal soaps or horticultural oils. Total coverage with tiny droplets is essential for controlling insects or eggs with horticultural oils. The best time to spray oils is during February, while the plant is coming out of the resting stage. Oil bleaches out the blue color from blue spruce. Besides Picea, other oil-sensitive plants include Acer, Cryptomeria, Cotinus, Cercis, Cedrus, and Juniperus.

If you go the commercial spray method to control a bad infestation, several relatively safe and effective insecticides are available.

■ Would mycorrhizae move around? What is that fluffy white fuzz crawling around on the roots on my new bonsai?

It's probably sap-sucking root aphids. Mycorrhizae do not crawl around. Fluffy white stuff on the foliage could be a problem with mealy bugs, wooly aphids, or plant hoppers. This example is mentioned to emphasize a few points:

• Loosen up on the idea that your young, developing plants "must be tightly wired down" to their temporary containers. Bonsai get substrate and root issues, and you may occasionally need to take a quick look at their roots to check for root problems.

- Younger, developing plants are usually less resistant to pathogens than mature, refined ones.
- Containers kept on the ground during insect season will get insect and disease issues. Disease issues also come with wind or water.
- We tend to blame much of our bonsai decline on under watering. But if a plant dies during disease season, it may have been weakened by constant overwatering and by insects during insect season. Finally, it gets killed by overwatering and diseases during disease season.

TIME TO RECOVER

■ **One of my bonsai is starting to look miserable. What can I give it to keep it from looking worse?**

No chemical or generic solutions exist that you could possibly use to help a declining tree improve its vigor or its health (#496).

"If you can't figure out what is wrong with your bonsai, give it the emergency repotting treatment. First defoliate, and then jet-spray all the soil from the roots. Thoroughly soak the entire plant in a systemic fungicide with vitamin B-1 for a couple hours and then try repotting in a sterilized pot."

Things do go wrong. Why panic? After a while, we tend to get pretty good at recognizing and troubleshooting plant problems. Look for abnormalities, patterns, and sudden signs of trouble. If after giving your bonsai a once over you're still unsure what the problem is, then you might take it out of the pot. Carefully examine the condition of the root ball and substrate.

Consider planting it in the ground or place the whole root system in a slightly larger and deeper container, then move it to a better location. Leave it for as long as it takes to see some improvement. Refrain from putting any products on it.

Plantings out in the garden in field soil win every time over potted plants in the finest substrate mix. How do you know if your field soil is good enough to grow your bonsai? What's good enough for your vegetable garden is good enough for your expensive bonsai. A soil test will prove it.

Constant, unnecessary repotting, defoliating, bare rooting, and chemical drenching are stressful setbacks to any bonsai (#497).

"All bonsai showing insect or disease damage must immediately be quarantined so the pests can't spread damage from one plant to another."

That premise seems reasonable at first. Insects do move around, and disease spreads. But the fact is, once treated, bonsai need not be quarantined. One particular pathogen discovered on only one plant species rarely spreads to injure another species. Living things can get injured but not damaged. This phenomenon helps explain why no universal products exist to treat all pathogens.

"Repeat an insecticide treatment every five days for maximum prevention and effectiveness."

Spray insecticides only as needed, not as a precautionary measure. Each insect species has a proven insecticide, with rates and timing for controlling that insect group. Complete plant coverage and dosage matters more than the brand of insecticide, assuming that the product lists the insect species needing control. If one product fails to control an infestation, try another product also listing that particular species. Insects can develop immunity.

An insecticide doesn't usually work on mites even if spider mites act more as spiders than mites. Mites, spiders, and ticks have eight legs, so they are not insects. Usually you can first try to spray some of the aphids, mites, or mealy bugs off the foliage with a strong jet stream of water. Mealy bugs are those cottony masses noticeable in the branch crotches and are the easiest insect to control. All it takes to dislodge them is one strong jet stream from the water hose.

The spray-every-five-day treatment does apply to mites. Spider mites breed often and prolifically, but they're easy to control. A heavy infestation of mites can be controlled with a miticide. Follow the rates and timing given on the miticide container. Spray under the foliage to catch the hatching eggs, which mature to adults in five days. Repeat the treatment every seven to ten days until controlled.

For scale infestations, you might have to reapply contact or systemic insecticides. Or scrape them off with your fingernail.

■ Do any biological, natural, or non-chemical controls of plant diseases and insect pests exist for bonsai?

Yes, quite a few, but most natural pesticides have been proven to have little effect on controlling plant pathogens. Try not to divide pesticides into natural or synthetic in the way we divide types of fertilizers. Divide pesticides in terms of their safety and their effectiveness.

Both chemical and non-chemical pesticides have been tested for safety in the environment but have not necessarily been tested for their effectiveness for controlling pests compared with other pesticides. In order to be effective, more and larger amounts of organic pesticides need to be applied compared to synthetic pesticides. High dosages are the real poisons.

The larger amounts of organic pesticides needed to kill a pest may be more harmful to the environment than using more effective but much smaller doses of synthetic pesticides (#498). Unfortunately, the science of biological control of plant pathogens is not as far along as research on effective insect control.

■ Does sprinkling some borax "do away with pests"?

No, but borax (a salt of boric acid) may help eliminate some weeds or even some decent bonsai. Borax contains boron, an essential element toxic to plants when applied in large doses. Before purchasing any pesticide, first find out if it is both safe to the plant and effective against the specific insect you want to kill.

"Lime sulfur prevents any insect or pathogen infestation over the winter."

Bonsai won't overreact and die because of a few overwintering insects or diseases (#499). Winter pests are fairly scarce.

Lime sulfur was popular against scale insects until the early 1900s. It's no longer recommended as a safe and effective long-term pesticide. The sulfur part was considered a decent contact pesticide. Considerably better pesticides have been available since that time.

The reason lime was mixed with sulfur was because the lime was thought to counteract the sulfur acidity part that lowered the soil pH. It turns out that sulfates do not lower pH, and the calcium in lime does not raise pH. Another problem was lime sulfur washed off the tree with the next watering and into the soil, where it built up to toxic levels.

Fact: Applied above 80°F, in large doses, or used with horticultural oils, lime sulfur is highly phytotoxic (poisonous) to a plant. Lime sulfur also can injure buds and foliage. And it smells.

Lime sulfur is quite easy to make. You need not "stock up on lime sulfur." The EPA has not "banned it."

◼ Does "baking soda kill pathogens"?

It does not.

"Use fungicides and insecticides once a month as a preventative for future disease or insect problems."

Forget the schedule. You water and fertilize when the plant needs it. You feel comfortable leaving your plants alone for a few days if the substrate stays moist.

Sometimes we do need to rehabilitate a weakened tree. Wait until it becomes sick first. ***Don't spray poisons if you don't see any pathogens; the prevention of pathogens often is worse than the cure*** (#500). Spraying synthetic pesticides as a preventive measure or on a preset schedule may lead to resistant pests. ***Even "natural" pesticides may harm people, pets, plants, and beneficial insects*** (#501).

Watering foliage does not "cause fungus on pine needles." An occasional strong stream of water on the foliage can do wonders against almost any insect infestation.

Aphids, fungal diseases, and spider mites love the combination of higher temperatures and increased plant stress. To control insects, diseases, and mites when all three appear, there are several safe and effective all-purpose, three-in-one, ready-to-spray products. Follow the product instructions.

Cultivate healthy habits. Sanitation is usually the first line of defense. Dead leaves left on the substrate attract live insects and diseases.

◼ Is pruning, wiring, or transplanting safe and healthy for bonsai at any time of the year?

Yes, indeed. As the old-timers say, you can prune or wire anytime you have sharp pruners or wire in your hand. You can collect plants from the field anytime you have a shovel in your hand—generally speaking.

◼ What is a good care schedule to follow so I can know exactly what to do and when?

Trees, as weeds, won't follow a rigid schedule according to the calendar. Different activities occur at different times even within the same cultivars.

It's formidable for one person to come up with a comprehensive schedule for everyone because each bonsai has its own special niche. Conflicting information is often given, even for the same species. It would be so frustrating to try to follow seasonal care checklists. All plants have their own growth schedules according to the areas in which they're grown.

Birds don't go to their flight training workshop, get a flight schedule, and then walk home. Birds fly on their own schedule. Bonsai grow on their own schedule. Robots, however, operate on someone else's schedule.

Be skeptical of the abundant bonsai misinformation compiled from various sources by people living in other microclimates. Good bonsai people go by their bonsai, not by yours or anyone else's. My simple but effective bonsai maintenance may not work for you. That is why I try not to mention too many specific plants in *Modern Bonsai Practice*.

Every effort has been made to keep the scientific principles listed here as simplified and useful as possible. Actual implementation is not so simple. There is no magic or any green thumb necessary. Only limited experience is necessary in order to be successful.

Hundreds of years of bonsai-ology cannot be ignored. If something works for you and you have good bonsai, keep on doing good bonsai. Try new or different types of trees. Be willing to lose some and start anew. Use your new science-based knowledge and start trusting in what you can't see.

No quiz today, good folks. Happy bonsai-ing! May all your bonsai live to a ripe old age and never senesce. Embrace bonsai!

WALTER PALL uses good horticultural principles in his practice of bonsai. Good bonsai is the result of both common sense and modern bonsai practice. On the next pages, enjoy more of his bonsai in his Gallery.

WALTER PALL
GALLERY

Linden.

Linden in winter.

Euonymus in fall.

Euonymus in winter.

Euonymus.

Cornelian cherry.

Above and opposite: Cherry plum.

Cherry plum.

Cherry plum.

Cherry plum.

Plum.

European larch.

Larch.

Larch.

American larch.

Japanese maple.

Japanese maple.

Japanese maple.

Japanese maple in winter.

Japanese maple.

Japanese maple in spring

227

Japanese maples.

Japanese maple.

Japanese maple.

European spruce.

Japanese maples.

Japanese white pine.

Spruce.

European spruce.

Spruce.

Spruce.

European spruce.

Beech.

Beech in fall.

Beech in winter.

Beech.

240

European beech in fall.

European beech in winter.

Japanese beech.

European beech.

Crabapples.

Crabapple.

Crabapple.

Hawthorn.

249

Hawthorns.

Hawthorn.

Field maple.

Maple in fall.

Maple in winter.

Mountain maple.

Mountain maple.

Opposite: Maple in fall.

Birch.

Birch in fall.

Trident maple.

Trident maples.

Trident maples.

Trident maples.

Junipers.

Mugo pines.

Mugo pines.

Hornbeam forest.

Korean hornbeam.

European hornbeam.

Hornbeam in fall.

Hornbeam in winter.

Hornbeams.

Oriental hornbeam.

Sabina juniper.

Sabina juniper.

Sabina juniper.

Honeysuckle.

281

Honeysuckles.

Needle juniper.

Rocky Mountain juniper.

Rocky Mountain juniper.

Rocky Mountain junipers.

Japanese yew.

Opposite: Lilac.

Japanese black pine.

Japanese black pine.

Japanese black pine.

Scots pine.

Scots pines.

Scots pines.

European ashes.

Ash in winter.

Boston ivy.

Boston ivy.

Cork bark elm.

Elm in winter.

300

Hillier elms.

303

Oak.

Oak forest.

Oaks.

Chinese juniper.

Oak in winter.

Chinese juniper.

Chinese elms.

Chinese elm.

Apple.

Magnolia.

Chinese quinces.

Chinese quince in winter.

Chinese quince.

Deutzia.

317

Deutzia.

Japanese maples.

Japanese maple in fall.

Japanese maple in winter.

Japanese maples.

Japanese maples.

Japanese maple.

Thyme.

Azaleas.

Azaleas.

Dogwood in winter.

Juniper.

Spirea.

INDEX

Y

Z

ABOUT THE AUTHOR

Author Larry Morton, BS Ornamental Horticulture, is the former owner of Landscape Consultants, Inc., and Preferred Trees Nursery. He provides seasoned, proven, professional advice on how you can care for your miniature trees.

Cover and internal design by Word Mule
www.wordmule.com

CPSIA information can be obtained
at www.ICGtesting.com
Printed in the USA
BVOW05*0006011216

469396BV00005B/6/P